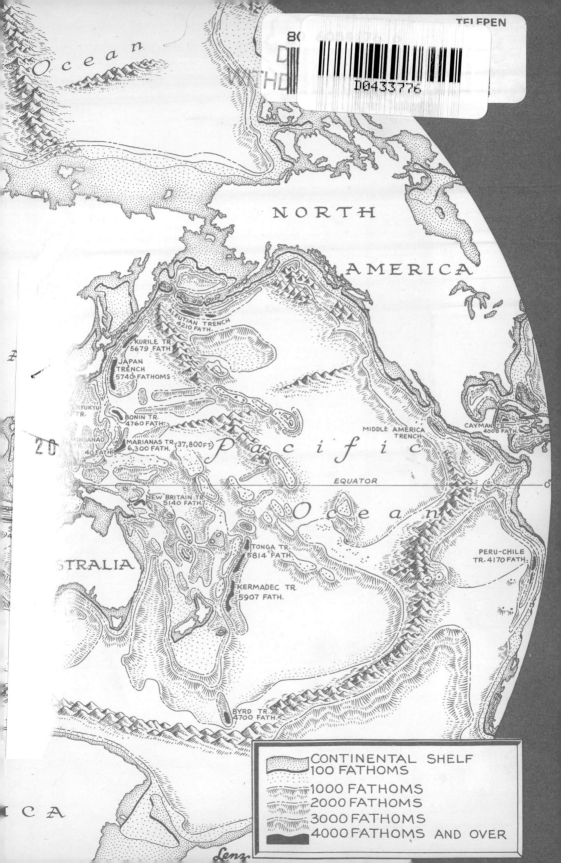

Frontiers of the Sea

FRONTIERS OF THE SEA

The Story of
Oceanographic Exploration

by

ROBERT C. COWEN

Introduction by
ROGER R. REVELLE

Drawings by Mary S. Cowen

LONDON
VICTOR GOLLANCZ LTD.
1960

Printed in Great Britain by
Lowe & Brydone (Printers) Ltd., London, N.W.10

To ANNA *and* MARY COWEN

ACKNOWLEDGMENTS

The author and publishers, are grateful to the following authors, magazines, and publishers for permission to use material contained in this book:

A Century of Darwin, edited by S. A. Barnett. Cambridge, Mass.: Harvard University Press, Copyright 1958 by William Heinemann, Ltd. Used with permission of the publishers.

The Earth and its Atmosphere, edited by D. R. Bates, Basic Books, Inc., Publishers. Used with permission of the publishers.

The Galathea Deep Sea Expedition, edited by Anton F. Bruun. Used with permission of Allen and Unwin, Ltd., and The Macmillan Company.

"To the Depths of the Sea by Bathyscaphe," by Jacques-Yves Cousteau, *National Geographic Magazine*, July 1954. Used with permission of *National Geographic Magazine*.

Larval Forms, by Walter Garstang, Introduction by Sir Alister Hardy. Special acknowledgment is made to Sir Alister Hardy for permission to use extracts from the Introduction.

The Open Sea, by Sir Alister Hardy. Used with permission of William Collins and Sons, Ltd., London, and Houghton Mifflin Company, Inc., Boston.

Founders of Oceanography and Their Work, by Sir William Herdman. Used with permission of Edward Arnold Publishers, Ltd.

Earth, Sky, and Sea, by Auguste Piccard. Used with permission of Oxford University Press, Inc. Published in Great Britain under the title *In Balloon and Bathyscaphe* by Cassell and Co. Ltd.

Climatic Change: Evidence, Causes, and Effects, edited by Harlow Shapley. Cambridge, Mass.: Harvard University Press, Copyright 1953, by The President and Fellows of Harvard College. Reprinted by permission of the publishers.

The Earth Beneath the Sea, by Francis P. Shepard. Used with permission of The Johns Hopkins Press. Published in Great Britain by the Oxford University Press.

The Search Beneath the Sea, by J. L. B. Smith. Used with permission of Henry Holt and Company, Inc., and Longmans, Green and Co. Ltd., the British publishers of the book (under the title of *Old Fourlegs:*).

"The Circulation of the Abyss," by Henry Stommel, *Scientific American*, July 1958. Used with permission of *Scientific American*.

The Planets: their Origin and Development, by Harold C. Urey. Copyright 1952 by Yale University Press, New Haven. Used with permission of the publishers.

Living Resources of the Sea, by Lionel A. Walford. Copyright 1958 by The Ronald Press Company. Used with permission of the publishers.

Introduction

BY ROGER R. REVELLE

Director, Scripps Institution of Oceanography

IT IS an ironic fact that we are learning to leave this planet just when we are beginning to think about it as a whole, as our planetary home. With our Sputniks and Explorers, our deep space probes and Project Mercuries, we shall soon soar beyond all horizons. But men were never as aware as they are today that their survival depends on careful husbanding of every resource of Earth. This realization has led to a great surge of interest in the largest and least-known feature of the Earth's surface, the ocean. Mr. Cowen's book, with its clear exposition of what we know and what we hope to find out about the ocean, is thus completely timely.

Men like ourselves have lived on Earth for perhaps five hundred thousand years, yet through all but a tiny fraction of that time our ancestors might have been bacteria proliferating on the skin of an orange, for all they knew about their world. Only within the last few centuries have men had sufficient understanding to be able to think of the Earth as a whole, as a sphere unsupported in space, isolated and complete in itself, yet held in its appointed place by describable though invisible forces. This sphere did not always exist and will someday die; it has changed and will change continuously throughout its lifetime— in short, it has a long history that is part of the universe's history. Only within the last few decades have we developed the tools to decipher that history.

This is not to say that our remote ancestors did not ask meaningful questions about the earth. They were hunters and farmers; to survive they had to be good observers. More important, they were men; they could not help being filled with wonder at the world of wonders they saw about them.

Consider, for example, Chapter 38 of the Book of Job. The unknown

A*

poet who wrote this chapter imagined the Lord appearing out of a whirlwind to give Job an oral examination about the Earth. Some of the oceanographic and meteorological questions He asked were these:

"Hast thou entered into the springs of the sea, or hast thou walked in the search of the depth?

"Who shut up the sea with doors?". . . saying 'Hitherto shalt thou come but no further; and here shall thy proud waves be stayed?'

"Hath the rain a father? . . . and Out of whose womb came the ice?

"Canst thou lift up thy voice to the clouds, that abundance of waters may cover thee?

"Who can number the clouds in wisdom, or who can pour out the bottles of heaven?"

These are difficult questions. No wonder Job failed to answer them, for we can give only partial answers today. We don't yet know from whence the ocean waters sprang, although we have searched for some of the depths. We know why the sea's proud waves do not cover the earth—the waters are enclosed in deep basins, underlain by heavy rock, above which the comparatively light rocks of the continents float like giant rafts. But no man knows how the continental rafts rose from the seas or why areas that were once dry land are now deeply covered by the ocean.

We know the ocean is the parent of the rain and the ice, in the sense that all the water falling on the land was originally sucked up by evaporation from the surface of the sea. With our Earth satellites we are beginning to count all the clouds of the air. But we are far from being able to ensure abundant rainfall when we need it, for we cannot as yet pour out the bottles of heaven. Our hopes for such weather control rest on gaining more understanding than we now possess about the great interlinked heat engines of the sea and the air.

The questions asked by the unknown poet were natural ones in a semi-desert country bordering the sea. They must have been asked many times by the watchful shepherds and the keen-eyed merchants of Israel. Today we know that to answer them we must formulate and answer more wide-ranging questions—questions about the ocean and the atmosphere as a whole, how they interact under the sun and with the solid Earth. These questions are the subject of this book. With skill and insight Mr. Cowen has shown how far we have come in answering them, how the questions are related to each other, and what we still need to know. It remains to say something about the basic objectives of oceanography, and why men become oceanographers.

As men's knowledge has increased, their attitudes have changed. The ends of the Earth were once a terrifying distance away. Now it is fashionable to speak of the Earth as a small planet chained to a second-rate star, an insignificant cinder circling through the splendid Galaxy. By an inverted humility, we are thus enabled to feel superior to our ancestors, who thought of the Earth as the center of all things, and of the stars as a kind of indirect lighting arranged in musical spheres above their heads. This is all very well, provided we keep in mind two things.

First, although our planet is small, it is inconceivably old; its age, in fact, appears to be a very respectable fraction of the age of the Galaxy. Because the Earth is so old, its history must reflect much of the history of the Galaxy. The records of that history still exist. They are locked in the rocks laid down in ancient seas, in the mud and rocks under the present ocean, in the chemical composition of the waters and the air, and in the bodies of living plants and animals. One of the prime objectives of oceanography is to learn to read these historical records.

Second, life as we know it is nearly impossible except on a little, old planet like our Earth, revolving around a star like our Sun. If the Sun were much bigger, it would have existed for such a short time that life could not have evolved on any of its planets; if the Earth were much bigger, its gravitational force would be too great for creatures like ourselves. But the most important biological characteristic of our planet is the presence on its surface of liquid water in large quantities, for water is the pre-eminent substance of our kind of life. It is hard to think of life beginning except in the sea, and we know that most of the evolution of living things took place there.

No other planet of our solar system has an ocean, with the possible exception of cloud-covered Venus, and planets with oceans may be few and far between in our Galaxy. Thus the old idea of the Earth as the mother of life has gained new meaning in recent years; we now believe the ocean was the placental fluid which nourished and protected Earth's children. Consequently a second objective of oceanography is to discover the many ways in which the existence of oceans on the Earth has affected the nature of living things.

Why should we study the ocean? There are several so-called practical reasons: to learn how to increase our use of marine resources; to be able to use the ocean more effectively in defending this great island, the North American continent; hopefully to learn how to fit our earthly environment more closely to men's needs through controlling climate, which depends on both the ocean and the atmosphere. But it seems to me that the really practical reason was given by the poet of the Book of Job. Not the questions but the admonitions of the poet's dialogue are important to us today, for they state the most profound justification for studying our Earth, and indeed for all scientific work. The Voice out of the whirlwind said: "Gird up now thy loins like a man, for I will demand of thee and answer thou Me. Declare, if thou hast understanding." Man is challenged by the voice within him, the voice out of the whirlwind of consciousness, to seek and to know all he can. Knowledge of the air and the sea and the solid Earth, and of our fellow creatures who share this planet, increases our ability to use the Earth wisely and well. But the challenge out of the whirlwind is not this; it is to gain understanding simply for its own sake, because we are that one among God's creatures who is capable of understanding.

However, oceanographers are not such a serious-minded lot that they keep asking themselves why they are doing their job. The spiritual ancestor of most of them was Ulysses. He was called the Wanderer, because he was the first to venture into the River Ocean, out of the salt and fishy Sea-between-the-Land, the wine-dark Mediterranean. Perhaps he disliked administration, hated farming, and was bored by Penelope. In any case, Ulysses managed to spend a great deal of time away from home. He never stated his reasons very clearly, but he still lives in the hearts of oceanographers, the scientists who go to sea:

> There lies the port; the vessel puffs her sail:
> There gloom the dark, broad seas. My mariners . . .
> That ever with a frolic welcome took
> The thunder and the sunshine . . . Come, my friends . . .
> Push off, and sitting well in order smite
> The sounding furrows; for my purpose holds
> To sail beyond the sunset, and the baths
> Of all the western stars . . .
> Some work of noble note, may yet be done . . .

Contents

PREFACE

Earth is a water world.

If you could look back at our planet from the moon, through the obscuring haze of the atmosphere, its most striking characteristic would be the dark cast of the oceans. The continents and islands on which so much human history has been lived account for less than a third of the planet's surface. Indeed, half of that surface is under 10,000 feet or more of water.

The sea, spreading as an irregular but unbroken envelope, dominates our world. It regulates the weather. It is the ultimate source of all our water. It provides a habitat for plants and animals far greater in area and volume than the life zone of the land, so that marine organisms can be thought of as the most broadly representative life forms of the earth. Moreover, billions of years in the past the sea is believed to have been the birthplace of all terrestrial life. Yet in spite of their importance, we have scarcely begun to learn about our oceans. Oceanography is a relatively young science. Its efforts so far have raised more questions than they have answered. But it is a fast-growing science that today is tackling problems of importance to all mankind.

Can men look to the seas to meet their ever growing needs for food and minerals? Can they learn to farm the waters as they do the land and take advantage of the teeming oceans? Can they extract the mineral wealth that lies in dilute form at every seacoast? And, in another vein, can men use the sea as a vast dump to solve the problem of what to do with the radioactive wastes that may become the greatest liability of the atomic age? These are the kinds of questions that now are helping to shape the research concerned with the sea. They are not strictly "scientific" questions, although it will take a good deal of basic scientific research to answer them. They have a practical flavor that is foreign to the pure search for knowledge for its own sake that has characterized oceanographic work until recent times. After millennia of neglect, the oceans are beginning to command the attention of land-based men as something more than a hunting ground for fishermen or a highway for ships. The fact that such questions have begun to share a place in the thinking of ocean scientists along with the traditional questions of the biology, chemistry, and physics of the sea indicates that, in terms of its broad perspective, oceanography is emerging from the academies and institutes and the restricted circles of its maritime applications. It is tackling problems of immediate and long-range significance for men everywhere. Its emergence is the theme of this book.

It has been impossible to cover comprehensively so large a subject. Some aspects of it are treated in detail. Other aspects which might be judged equally important are mentioned only briefly if they are referred to at all. However, it is hoped that in balance and emphasis this book will give the reader a layman's understanding of this important field of scientific exploration and a background against which to evaluate the new developments it generates.

I should like to express thanks individually to each one of the many specialists who gave generously of their time and knowledge to guide a reporter through the complexities of their fields, but the list is too long to be included here. However, I should like to thank, at least collectively, the directors and staffs of the Scripps Institution of Oceanography at La Jolla, California, and of the Woods Hole Oceanographic Institution in Massachusetts. I am especially grateful to Dr. Harold Edgerton of the Massachusetts Institute of Technology and to the National Geographic Society for permission to reproduce a selection of his striking deep-sea photographs, and to Dr. Robert R. Guillard of the Woods Hole Oceanographic Institution for permitting reproduction of several of his beautiful electron microscope photographs of diatoms. Grateful acknowledgment is owed as well to the U. S. Navy and to R. G. Munns, William S. von Arx, and Claude Rönne, all of Woods Hole Oceanographic Institution, for other photographs used in this book. I also wish to thank the Board of Trustees and manager of The Christian Science Publishing Society for permission to make use of material that has appeared in *The Christian Science Monitor*. Finally, there are two others who deserve special mention— Erwin D. Canham and Saville R. Davis, who are, respectively, the editor and managing editor of *The Christian Science Monitor*. I shall always be grateful for the example they have set as journalists and for the encouragement they have given me as a science writer.

ROBERT C. COWEN

Concord, Mass.
October 1, 1959

Frontiers of the Sea

ONE

Exploring the Hinterland

THERE are two ways you might look at the oceans.

On a planetary scale, they are the thinnest of liquid films, irregularly wetting the global surface. Their average depth of 2.4 miles is an insignificant fraction of the earth's 3,957-mile average radius. Together, continents and ocean basins form a surface relatively smoother than a polished billiard ball, albeit a slippery billiard ball since there is over twice as much water as land.

But on a human scale, the oceans are incredibly vast. Their 139,400,000 square miles of surface cover a volume of water so great that if the earth had an absolutely level crust the sea would form an envelope over 8,800 feet deep. These waters, in turn, cover a bottom scenery more rugged and grander than anything the land can boast. Mountain ranges tower above their surroundings, sometimes to heights greater than those reached by land elevations, while the deepest ocean trenches could swallow Mount Everest with several thousand feet to spare.

Here is the great hinterland of humanity, a virgin territory as challenging and more promising of economic reward than the forbidding regions of outer space. Men are becoming aware of its potential at a time when their technical powers and scientific capabilities are becoming equal to its challenge. They are becoming aware of it at a time when the pressing needs of mankind for food and materials have given them a mandate to take up this challenge, to learn to know and begin to exploit the 70.8 per cent of our planet's surface that lies in and under the seas.

The effort to learn is what specialists call the science of oceanography. The exploitation, on a small scale today and a bigger scale tomorrow, is the province of a number of technical fields. Its prospects shine with the promise of a virtually inexhaustible supply of minerals and metals, and of a significant increase in the world's food supply. But since first things must come first, more basic knowledge about the oceans has to be gained in many cases before exploitation can begin. The immediate task is to get to know our oceans better.

Actually, oceanographers already know a good deal about the oceans. After a century of modern oceanographic research they are able to chart the major surface currents. They have measured the general physical characteristics of the world's waters. They can map the ocean basins in broad outline and tell something of the history of the earth itself from the accumulated sediments on the bottom. And they have

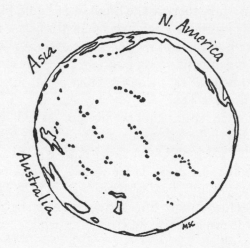

FIG. 1: *The water hemisphere of the Pacific illustrates the prominence of the earth's oceans.*

learned many things about life in the seas, although biological surprises continually appear.

There is also much that the scientists don't know. A recent report from the National Academy of Sciences in the United States, which surveyed the needs and problems facing oceanographers today, has outlined some of the research questions to be answered. Prepared by a special committee on oceanography headed by Dr. Harrison Brown of the California Institute of Technology, it summarized some of these questions as follows:

The seas present a challenge to man which in magnitude approaches that of space . . . We know less about many regions of the oceans today than we know about the lunar surface. Yet we have learned enough to know that major features of the ocean floor—35,000 foot deep trenches; 2,000 mile long fracture zones; flat-topped undersea mountains; broad ocean-long ridges; abyssal plains as flat as a calm sea—are uniquely different from anything either on the surface of the moon or the land surfaces of the earth. How and when were these features formed and why are they so different? An answer to these questions is essential if we are to decipher the history of our planet and its sister planets. Part of the answer lies in the records of ancient history locked in deep sea sediments; part will come from an intensive study of the rocks under the ocean. These studies, combined with studies of the waters and the living creatures of the sea, will also tell us much about the origin and evolution of life on earth.

During the last few years . . . great subsurface ocean currents—rivers in the depths of the sea one thousand times greater in flow than the Mississippi—have been discovered using newly developed current measuring techniques. We suspect that others exist and we need to know where the waters come from and where they go.

On the subject of weather and climate, the report explained that climate is influenced by the oceans in profound but as yet unknown ways. If scientists are ever to understand the mechanism of the weather, to predict or control its action, they must first understand the role played by the oceans.

Considering possible exploitation of ocean food resources, the report noted that "on the practical side, the problems to be solved concerning the oceans are at least as urgent as those of space. How many fish are in the sea? No man knows, nor do we know what determines the numbers of fishes in different regions, the quantities of plant and animal material on which they feed, or what could be done to increase these numbers. We must learn these things if we are to help solve the increasingly acute problems of providing animal protein food for the growing numbers of underfed people in the world. Given more study, man can economically harvest considerably more food from the seas than is now possible."

Here, then, is the challenge of the ocean hinterland. It is both a challenge to know and a challenge to put the knowledge gained to practical use. Oceanographers have learned much during the decades in which they have studied the sea. But today's knowledge has only begotten larger questions.

Birth of a Science

Modern oceanography can be said to have begun about a hundred years ago. However, men have been interested in the sea for millennia and there was a scattering of scientific ocean studies before the mid-nineteenth century. Aristotle, for example, was the first, and an expert, marine biologist. He made remarkable observations of many marine animals, both anatomically and in their natural habitats.

Blessed with brilliant sunshine and clear Mediterranean waters, the ancient Greek philosopher-scientist spent hours peering over the side of a boat, studying marine life in relatively shallow depths. His perceptive observations were translated into detailed descriptions of the habits and life cycles of marine creatures. He also recognized important distinctions between animal groups which enabled him to classify them in a hierarchical system of categories, some of which are considered valid today. He correctly separated vertebrates from invertebrates. He also was the first to note that dolphins, porpoises, and whales are mammals rather than some sort of fish, as was generally believed.

Aristotle, who took all knowledge as his province, tried to arrange what he saw into a universal scheme. Many of his generalizations have since proved to be erroneous. Nevertheless, he based his biological thinking on objective study. As applied to marine biology, this meant extensive field observations and careful dissections. If these procedures had been followed since the fourth century B.C., marine biology would be immeasurably more advanced than it is today. Aristotle founded a school and influenced many thinkers in his own and subsequent periods. But his scientific methods died with him, and there was no significant progress in marine biology for over two thousand years.

With the advent of open ocean sailing voyages, navigators began to take an interest in the physical side of oceanography, at least as far as major ocean currents were concerned, although the old sailing records produced little that could be called scientific studies of currents. Benjamin Franklin, however, was able to draw up a tolerable chart of the Gulf Stream, based partly on reports of Yankee sailing captains, which he eventually published in the *Transactions of the American Philosophical Society* in 1786. He also made his own observations of water temperatures on several Atlantic crossings by picking up buckets of surface water and measuring their contents. This technique he then recommended to sailing captains as a guide to when they entered or left the relatively warm waters of the Gulf Stream. The British explorer Captain James Cook also gathered scattered oceanographic information during his three celebrated voyages of exploration which occupied the latter part of his life (1768–79) and included circumnavigation of the Pacific.

In spite of such early sporadic interest, oceanography as an organized research effort is a young science. It grew up in the latter part of the nineteenth century partly because of the rapid spread of science in general and partly because the basic sciences that lie behind it—physics, chemistry, geology, biology—and the technology of research had reached a point where scientific exploration of the deep oceans became possible.

One of the pioneers who helped turn men's curiosity about the sea into a science was Matthew Fontaine Maury (1806–73), an American naval officer of notable vision and perseverance. Maury's interests were those of a practical sailor. But his intensive study of currents helped lay the foundation for the modern science of physical oceanography. Before Maury, men sailed without accurate knowledge of currents, winds, or storm patterns. When his lifework was finished, charts of major currents, prevailing winds, and storm tracks were part of every navigator's equipment.

Maury early set himself an ambitious program. The rigors and uncertainties of life at sea, often with only a sailor's instincts to guide him, made him acutely aware of the potential value of charts showing the average direction and strength of winds and currents. He once described his goal as "nothing less than to blaze way through the winds of the sea by which the navigator may find the best paths at all seasons."

His first book—*New Theoretical and Practical Treatise on Navigation*, published in 1836—was received with a degree of interest at the time. Then in 1839 Maury began extracting from ships' logs the data on winds, currents, temperatures, and the like, that were to be the raw material for his principal lifework. His appointment in 1842 as superintendent of the Navy's Depot of Charts and Instruments, including the Naval Observatory, gave him the opportunity to collect information on the ocean-spanning scale he needed. He began at once to search the files of old logbooks now at his disposal for data pertinent to the charts he envisioned. Five years later he published his first chart of winds and currents.

The oceans are vast and the data at Maury's personal disposal were limited. He overcame these difficulties by enlisting the aid of navigators the world over. They apparently were glad to co-operate, for Maury's charts were cutting their sailing times drastically. The average voyage between London and San Francisco, for example, was shortened by 180 days.

By 1851, log abstracts from a thousand ships had poured into Maury's office. These and subsequent reports enabled him to draw up charts on many aspects of marine climatology, including a guide to the principal whaling grounds, and to write the world's first textbook of oceanographic physics—*Physical Geography of the Sea*, published in 1855. The American Navy still pays tribute to this pioneering work in the monthly "Pilot Charts" of the Hydrographic Office that carry the legend: "Founded upon the researches made by Matthew Fontaine Maury, while serving as a Lieutenant in the U. S. Navy."

Maury's work led directly to one of the first international scientific conferences. It met at Brussels in 1853 to consider setting up a uniform marine weather observing system. Maury played a leading role in the conference and would have thrown it open to consider land as well as ocean weather observing if others had not wanted to restrict it to the sea. Nevertheless, he is credited with inspiring the establishment of the official meteorological offices in both Great Britian and Germany. Because of the demonstrated value of Maury's charts and partly as a result of this conference, other maritime nations began establishing hydrological services, which often co-operated with one another and with Maury in charting the seas. Thus Maury was something of a pioneer in stimulating international co-operation in ocean research as well as the first to chart the great currents.

Maury was essentially a climatologist, a statistician who extracted an average picture of what went on in and above the oceans from the mass of spot reports sent in from ships' logbooks. He was not a scientist, in that his chief aim was to aid navigation rather than to build a fundamental understanding of the sea. His contribution lay in the practical realm, demonstrating how a jumble of observations taken at widely scattered times and places could be analyzed to give a meaningful picture of average conditions in the oceans.

Meanwhile, in Britain, that other great branch of ocean science, marine biology, was being shaped in its modern form by a Manxman named Edward Forbes (1815–54). In a real sense, Forbes was the nine-

teenth-century heir of Aristotle in this field. He lived in the heyday of
the field naturalists and collectors, some of whom were turning to the
shallow waters of the sea for their specimens. While these naturalists
often were amateurs, Forbes was a life-long professional scientist and
teacher who, like Aristotle before him, saw his subject in large perspective and was widely recognized as the intellectual leader in his
field.

He made extensive surveys himself and encouraged others to take up
this line of research. In analyzing biological collections, he made full
use of the geological knowledge of the day, relating the succession of
fossils in rock strata to living marine plants and animals and tracing
the effect of the past history of land and sea on the present distribution of these organisms.

Among other things, he pointed out that the shape of the sea bottom
is an important environmental factor. Ridges and other obstacles, for
example, can isolate adjacent but quite different animal populations
from each other. He also noted that the chemistry and physics of the
sea—the concentrations and interactions of nutrients and minerals
held in the water and the play of currents—were important influences
in the lives of marine animals. By urging investigation of such factors,
he encouraged the development of other phases of ocean science in
addition to his own, although he may not himself have realized he was
helping to open up such a wide-ranging research field.

By the 1850's the universities of Scotland, where Forbes had been
educated at Edinburgh, had produced a school of marine biologists
that was familiar with and had written monographs on all important
groups of marine organisms. Forbes was the leader of that school. He
was also a contemporary of such famous marine naturalists as the Nor-
wegian Michael Sars and the Frenchman Henri Milne-Edwards.
He shares with them the distinction of developing the handling
techniques that stimulated wide use of the naturalist's dredge and thus
greatly facilitated the collection of bottom-dwelling creatures. The

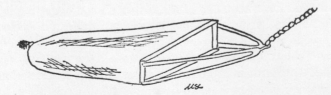

FIG. 2: *Nineteenth-century naturalist's dredge.*

dredge is a coarse netting bag on a rectangular frame that is dragged along the sea bottom and willy-nilly picks up hapless animals in its path. It can be handled easily by one or two men and was first introduced in the mid-eighteenth century by the Italian zoologists Marsigli and Donati. But it did not find wide use until effective techniques for handling it, especially in relatively deep water, had been worked out.

Forbes's contribution to oceanography, for which he is considered to be the founder of modern marine biology and for which he is remembered above his predecessors and contemporaries, lay as much in the inspiration he gave as in his own sizable output of research. That inspiration now is recognized as one of the main driving forces that got the budding science of oceanography going.

One of his biographers describes him as "a genial and lively genius, with a free and independent spirit that roamed over a wide range in quest of knowledge and occupation." He adds that "Forbes was certainly the most brilliant and inspiring naturalist of his day—a day when it was still possible to make original contributions to knowledge in several departments of nature." An indication of the breadth of Forbes's talents is seen in the fact that he held with distinction the posts of professor of botany at King's College in London (1842); paleontologist to the Geological Survey (1844); and finally professor of natural history at Edinburgh (1854). The first two posts, moreover, were held simultaneously for a time.

Besides his brilliance as a naturalist, Forbes had a sparkling sense of humor and a dash of literary talent which he combined with scholarship in a way that raised his scientific writing several cuts above the drab style of a laboratory report. His first important large work, entitled *British Starfishes* and published in 1840 at the age of twenty-six, is a classic illustration. Take, for example, the following description of his struggles with a disconcertingly self-destructive starfish aptly named *Luidia fragilissima* (page 138):

The first time I ever took one of these I succeeded in getting it into the boat entire. Never having seen one before, and quite unconscious of its suicidal powers, I spread it out on a rowing bench, the better to admire its form and colors. On attempting to remove it for preservation, to my horror and disappointment I found only an assemblage of rejected members. My conservative endeavors were all neutralized by its destructive exertions, and it is now badly represented in my cabinet by an armless disk and a diskless arm. Next time I went to dredge on the same spot, determined not to be cheated out of a specimen in such a way a second time, I brought with me a bucket of cold fresh water, to which article Starfishes have a great antipathy. As I expected, a Luidia came up in the dredge, a most gorgeous specimen. As it does not generally break up before it is raised above the surface of the sea, cautiously and anxiously I sunk my bucket to a level with the dredge's mouth, and proceeded in the most gentle manner to introduce Luidia to the purer element. Whether the cold air was too much for him, or the sight of the bucket too terrific, I know not, but in a moment he proceeded to dissolve his corporation, and at every mesh of the dredge his fragments were seen escaping. In despair I grasped at the largest, and brought up the extremity of an arm with its terminating eye, the spinous eyelid of which opened and closed with something exceedingly like a wink of derision.

Although Forbes is justly honored for his many positive contributions, the history of science will never forget his celebrated and erroneous theory of the azoic zone. In this, he set a hypothetical depth limit on marine life, which sea animals themselves quite regularly ignore. As doubts about the theory grew, they stimulated deep dredging activities that opened a new phase of oceanographic research.

The theory sprang from Forbes's researches in the Mediterranean. In 1841 he sailed as naturalist on H.M. Surveying Ship *Beacon*. The principal mission was hydrographical surveying in the eastern Mediterranean. But as far as Forbes was concerned, it was his first opportunity to study sea life away from Britain and he made the most of it, collecting and studying marine organisms in the same waters Aristotle once had explored.

He dredged the Aegean bottom more deeply than anyone before, to a limit of 1,380 feet. To his own surprise, he brought up living starfishes and other invertebrates from 1,200 feet, in those days an astonishing depth at which to find living animals. He noted that shellfish from the deeper hauls were types hitherto known only as fossils. He was the first biologist to see them alive.

As a result of his eastern Mediterranean studies Forbes distinguished eight major zones of depth, each characterized by a particular array of organisms. He further suggested the then plausible theory that marine life would fade out with increasing depth. Plants, which depend on sunlight, would disappear first, then the animals which feed on the plants and on each other. Below 1,800 feet, he speculated, there would be no animal life. He assigned all waters deeper than that to what he called the "azoic zone."

Forbes's theory reflected prevailing scientific opinion at the time. But disturbing evidence to the contrary was not long in coming. In 1860 a cable broke in the Mediterranean at a depth of 7,200 feet. When it was hauled up for repairs, a deep-sea coral was found firmly attached at the place where the break had occurred. Mollusks, worms, and other sessile animals—animals that lead sedentary lives firmly anchored to some kind of base—were adhering to parts of the cable that had lain at shallower but still unexpectedly great depths.

Prior to this, animals had been found in abundance as deep as 2,400 feet during the 1839–43 Antarctic expedition of H.M.S. *Erebus* and *Terror* under command of Sir James Ross. There is an even earlier instance on record in which a single deep-sea animal was found. During Sir John Ross's expedition to Baffin Bay in 1818, a starfish-like animal came up entangled around a sounding line from a depth of 4,800 feet. Also, in the decades of 1850–70, Michael Sars and his son George Ossian Sars were dredging organisms from depths as great as 2,700 feet. But skeptics either overlooked or discounted such dredge hauls partly on the grounds that the animals might have been caught in intermediate waters above the azoic zone as the dredge was brought back to the surface. The sessile animals that had grown in place at depths below 1,800 feet on a cable could not be so easily dismissed.

For a while some biologists clung to the prevailing azoic concept. As one of Forbes's students (C. Wyville Thomson, of whom more in a moment) subsequently wrote, "It was almost as difficult to believe that creatures comparable with those of which we have experience in the upper world could live at the bottom of the sea, as that they could live in a vacuum or in the fire." Water pressure in the sea increases at a rate of about .442 pounds per square inch per foot of depth, or nearly one and a third tons per square inch for every thousand fathoms (6,000 feet) of depth. It seemed incredible that life could exist in the crushing pressures and cold blackness of great depths. But we ourselves live under an atmospheric pressure of about 15 pounds per square inch and take no notice of it because the pressure is equal within and without our bodies. Likewise, delicate deep-sea animals, whose tissues are permeated by fluids under pressure equal to that of the surrounding water, can easily withstand pressures of tons per square inch in the abyss. It was gradually realized that, while Forbes had believed his Mediterranean observations were sufficient to support his azoic theory, he had based his reasoning on exceptional conditions that did not correspond to those of the major oceans or, for that matter, to other parts of the Mediterranean.

One of the younger biologists whose imagination was fired by the new discoveries was Charles Wyville Thomson (1830–82), later Sir Wyville, a student of Forbes who was destined to lead the most celebrated oceanographic expedition in history, the voyage of the *Challenger*. Like Forbes, Thomson brought a broad knowledge of the sciences to his study of marine life. Also like Forbes, he ended his career in the natural history chair at Edinburgh. It was he more than any other scientist who proved the azoic theory wrong, and it was he, through his leadership of the *Challenger* expedition, who brought Forbes's oceanographic pioneering to fruition as a full-fledged science.

Inspired by the catches being made in relatively deep water by George and Michael Sars, Thomson was eager to begin deep-sea dredging himself. Through the help of friends and the good offices of the Royal Society, the British Admiralty was persuaded to furnish the means for several research cruises. For two months in the fall of 1868, Thomson and his colleague, Dr. W. B. Carpenter, had the use of a small gunboat, H.M.S. *Lightning*. Another gunboat, H.M.S. *Porcupine*, was placed at their disposal in 1869 and 1870. These various cruises explored deep waters from the Faeroe Islands to south of Gibraltar. One of the results was the first general textbook on oceanography, Thomson's *The Depths of the Sea*, which drew heavily on his cruise researches and was published in 1872.

Thomson describes the *Lightning* as "a cranky little vessel . . . which had the somewhat doubtful title to respect of being perhaps the very oldest paddle-steamer in Her Majesty's Navy." But although Thomson and his shipmates "had not good times in the Lightning," they were able to dredge animals from as deep as 3,600 feet. With the *Porcupine*, a more comfortable and seaworthy ship, they hauled specimens from depths of nearly three miles.

The dredging showed abundant life at all the depths they probed. Some of the creatures brought up seemed closely related to extinct forms of remote geological periods. Thomson was especially pleased with the remarkable discovery of a flexible sea urchin, a living "fossil" whose kind had been known only from remains in chalk formations. His description of this discovery in his book conveys something of the excitement such finds were causing in his day:

As the dredge was coming in, we got a glimpse from time to time of a large scarlet urchin in the bag . . . as it was blowing fresh and there was some little difficulty in getting the dredge capsized, we gave little heed to what seemed to be an inevitable necessity—that it should be crushed to pieces. We were somewhat surprised, therefore, when it rolled out of the bag uninjured; and our surprise increased, and was certainly in my case mingled with a certain amount of nervousness, when it settled down quietly in the form of a round cake, and began to pant—a line of conduct, to say the least of it, very unusual in its rigid, undemonstrative order. Yet there it was with all the ordinary characters of a sea-urchin . . . and curious undulations were passing through its perfectly flexible leather-like test. I had to summon up some resolution before taking the weird little monster in my hand, and congratulating myself on the most interesting addition to my favorite family which had been made for many a day.

The dredge hauls from the deep settled the question of whether or not life could exist in the abyss. But they only whetted the scientists' curiosity. Moreover, the rise of transoceanic telegraphy had aroused a practical interest in sea-bottom conditions that might affect the cables. Because of this, a certain amount of abyssal exploring had been done by several countries, including Great Britian and the United States. But the results were indifferent and only served to underscore the lack of general oceanographic knowledge. The time was ripe for a thorough-going scientific exploration of the sea.

Professor W. B. Carpenter, who had successfully interceded on behalf of oceanographic research in the past, wrote to the Admiralty urging dispatch of an expedition around the world. The successes of the *Lightning* and *Porcupine* spoke for themselves and the request was granted, provided the Royal Society concurred and drew up a feasible plan for the voyage. The Royal Society at once appointed a special committee which wrote out a comprehensive program for the project. In due course a navy ship, the H.M.S. *Challenger*, was made available to the scientists and the expedition was soon under way. It marked the beginning of oceanography as an integrated science.

It has been said that those who objected to spending government funds for such a purpose were mollified by being shown that the expedition would cost little more than keeping the ship in commission. But the fortunes of the voyage gave the government a better bargain than even this cost estimate implied. During the subsequent study of rock samples collected by the expedition, a naval commander sent some rock samples from Christmas Island to John Murray, a naturalist on board the *Challenger*, who had been collecting rocks as part of his coral-reef studies. Murray saw that this particular rock had come from a rich phosphate deposit. He persuaded the government to annex the island and obtained a concession to mine the deposits. The British Government subsequently received far more money in royalties and taxes from Murray's company than the entire cost of the *Challenger's* explorations.

The Great Voyage

On December 7, 1872, H.M.S. *Challenger*, a full-rigged spar-decked corvette of 2,306 tons with auxiliary steam power and a penchant for rolling like a barrel (46° one way and 52° the other), sailed out of the mouth of the Thames. From then until May 24, 1876, she sailed around the globe, logging 68,890 nautical miles in the major oceans and gathering data and biological specimens from waters of all depths and at almost all latitudes. The end product was a vast collection of

FIG. 3: *H.M.S.* Challenger.

marine organisms such as the world had never seen and fifty fat quarto volumes of new knowledge, some of which are still useful as reference works today.

The three-and-a-half-year voyage of the *Challenger* still holds the record as the longest continuous scientific expedition. It also has been unsurpassed in the scope and intensity of its oceanographic probing. Wyville Thomson headed the *Challenger's* civilian scientific staff, while Captain George S. Nares commanded the ship and the navy crew. Nares was transferred halfway through the voyage, with Captain Frank Thomson taking his place.

Wyville Thomson had been appointed professor of natural history at Edinburgh in 1870. When he recruited his small scientific staff, he included two others from the university—the naturalist John Murray, later Sir John, who eventually saw the *Challenger* results through long years of analysis to final publication, and the chemist J. Y. Buchanan. The rest of the staff included three other naturalists, H. N. Moseley, Dr. Rudolf von Willemoes-Suhm, who died during the voyage, and J. J. Wild, who, among other duties, acted as Thomson's secretary and helped illustrate some of the expedition's publications.

As a naval vessel, the *Challenger* usually mounted eighteen 68-pounders. All but two of these guns were removed, and the main deck was set aside entirely for scientific work. There were two compact laboratories, one for biological work and one for chemistry, a small but select reference library, and cramped private rooms for each of the civilian scientists.

Equipment for the voyage was the best that nineteenth-century technology could provide. In addition to a well-stocked chartroom and ample navigational equipment, the ship carried an assortment of hydrographic, magnetic, and meteorological instruments. There were water-sampling bottles adapted specially for deep-sea work, dredges and trawls for catching specimens on the bottom and at intermediate depths, and miles of sounding line and heavier rope for handling the dredges.

Lord Kelvin had contributed a system for taking depth soundings with wire, which he thought would be easier to handle than the customary rope. But the wire snarled so badly, all the official *Challenger* soundings were made with fine hemp rope. To make a sounding, a 200-pound lead weight was dropped over the side on the end of a line that lay coiled on a ten-foot-diameter drum. The weight of the lead was enough to unwind the rope. But by the time it hit bottom it had carried down so much rope that the line kept unwinding of its own weight. The only way to tell when the lead hit bottom was to time the rope, which was marked in hundred-fathom lengths, with a stop watch and estimate when the speed of the running line slackened off. The whole operation—to make one sounding and wind in the line—took several hours. How amazingly easy, by contrast, are modern techniques of echo sounding, in which a sound pulse sent out by a ship returns an echo

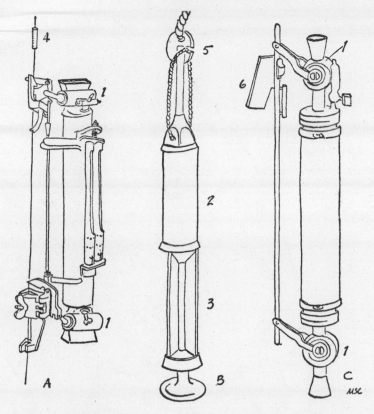

FIG. 4: *Water-sampling bottles: A—modern Nansen bottle with thermometers; B and C—Challenger bottles. A bottle is sent down open, allowing water to flow through it freely until it is closed at sampling depth. In A, a "messenger" weight (4) slides down the wire releasing the top of the bottle, which then turns upside down, pivoting about the lower fastening and closing valves (1). In B, the cylindrical sheath (2) slides down over the chambered shank (3) trapping water within the compartments. In C, valves (1) are closed at the desired depth by stopping the descent of the instrument and pulling it up slightly. The resistance of the water against the plate (6) forces the valves closed. A similar arrangement (not shown) releases the rope (5) in B to drop the cylindrical sheath.*

from the bottom to give an immediate and continuous measurement of depth.

The *Challenger* technically was the first steamship to cross the Antarctic Circle. But as a practical matter she generally traveled under sail and reserved her 1,234-horsepower steam engine for holding a position on station and for running the winches that hauled in the deep

B

FIG. 5: *Route of the Challenger expedition.*

MSC

sounding and dredging lines. It is doubtful that the expedition would
have been possible without steam power; much of the deep sampling
equipment was too heavy to handle by hand. Moreover, it would have
been virtually impossible to make a sailing ship stay put long enough
to occupy what oceanographers call a "station." This means occupying
a spot in the ocean whose latitude and longitude are carefully calculated and remaining there as stationary as possible while various measurements and samplings are taken.

The *Challenger* made 362 such stations in all. At each of them the
exact depth was determined, a bottom sample weighing anywhere from
an ounce to a pound was brought up, water samples were taken near
the bottom, and the temperature of the bottom was measured with a
registering thermometer. At many of the stations, bottom animals
were also dredged up, water samples and temperatures taken at various
points between the surface and the bottom, and animals were sometimes taken at intermediate depths with tow nets.

All in all, the *Challenger* team was given everything needed to do its
job, and its mission was an unqualified success. When the expedition
left Sheerness at the mouth of the Thames, knowledge of the deep sea
was almost a total blank. When it returned home and all the subsequent
reports were published, the ocean was still a largely unknown wilderness, but its gross measurements had at last been taken. New and
often bizarre-looking animals were found by the hundreds. Naturalists
eventually identified 4,717 new species and 715 new genera from the
specimens brought back. All of these were related to known contemporary forms, however, and scientists and laymen alike were somewhat
disappointed that the *Challenger* had dredged up no "living fossils."

The expedition also disposed of a rather grotesque scientific myth.
Careful examination of samples from some of the early deep-sea dredgings uncovered a gray gelatinous material that many biologists thought
to be the remains of some kind of living protoplasmic slime. Ernst
Haeckel, the great German zoologist, and the English naturalist
Thomas Huxley named the "creature" Bathybius. It was generally
supposed to cover much if not all of the sea floor, providing food for
more highly organized animals. In *The Depths of the Sea*, Thomson
described this material as "capable of a certain amount of movement,
and there can be no doubt that it manifests the phenomena of a very
simple form of life." He added that "the circumstance which gives its
special interest to Bathybius is its enormous extent: whether it be
continuous in one vast sheet, or broken up into circumscribed individ-

ual particles, it appears to extend over a large part of the ocean." The *Challenger* dredgings brought up bits of Bathybius too. But Buchanan was skeptical. He noted that, when the strong alcohol used to pickle specimens was mixed with sea water, sulphate of lime was precipitated as a slimy deposit. His analyses soon proved that this was what the biologists had supposed to be the remains of protoplasm. "Bathybius," Huxley later observed, "has not fulfilled the promise of its youth."

The expedition had a strong interest in biology, but it did not neglect other aspects of the sea. Its small team of scientists, most of whom were naturalists, made many physical, chemical, and geological observations. Thus when the *Challenger* data were analyzed there were so many deep soundings that the main contours of the ocean basins were well established. The deepest spot sounded was 26,850 feet in the vicinity of the Marianas Islands in the North Pacific. This region still holds the record for depth. During the recent International Geophysical Year the Soviet ship *Vitiaz* plumbed the deepest spot yet found—36,056 feet in the Marianas Trench. More recently Moscow Radio has reported that a subsequent sounding by the *Vitiaz* in this trench reached 36,173 feet.

The *Challenger* data also marked out major current systems and water-temperature patterns. Some of the latter are so persistent that there are areas where measurements taken today give the same temperature readings at the same locations as those found by the *Challenger*. The data also highlighted the cold bottom temperatures that prevail throughout most of the oceans—temperatures everywhere close to the freezing point.

In one sense, the work of the *Challenger* expedition was just beginning when the gallant ship reached home at Spithead in 1876. Some preliminary reports had been prepared during the voyage, but the bulk of the analytical work and writing lay ahead. Fortunately the small scientific team did not have to bear the whole burden. A "Challenger Office" was established at Edinburgh. Wyville Thomson was appointed director of the Challenger Commission and charged with seeing to the distribution of the data and collections and the publishing of results. For the next two decades, until the last volume was published and the Challenger Office closed down, the Scottish capital was the mecca of marine biologists and the leading center of oceanographic research.

Thomson and Murray asked specialists in several countries to share in examining the findings and preparing the *Challenger* reports. Thus the fifty volumes eventually published include the work of the most distinguished naturalists of the day. When Thomson was no longer able to carry on, Murray succeeded him and saw the work of publication to a successful conclusion. He even paid some of the costs out of his own pocket. In the end, the *Challenger* reports stood as a solid foundation for the science of oceanography.

After the return of the *Challenger*, two small subsidiary expeditions were undertaken to the Faeroe Channel north of Scotland. These had their roots in the old investigations of the *Lightning* and *Porcupine*. On those cruises Thomson and others had noticed that the Faeroe Channel was divided by temperature into two distinct regions—one relatively cold, the other warm. In comparing these early temperature observations with those taken in the same area by the *Challenger*, there seemed to be a sizable and unsuspected submarine ridge rising to within 1,200 to 1,800 feet of the surface. In the summer of 1880, John Murray conducted the "Knight-Errant" expedition under Thomson's direction to investigate this. He made four traverses over the area, which revealed a ridge rising to within 1,800 feet of the surface. It ran from the northwest of Scotland to the southern end of the Faeroe fishing bank.

Encouraged by this, Murray conducted a second expedition in H.M.S. *Triton* in the summer of 1882. He found distinctly different arrays of animals on either side of the ridge, which was named posthumously for Thomson. There were Arctic animals on the north side, and Atlantic animals to the south. The Wyville Thomson Ridge rising between the two groups was an insurmountable barrier to fishes and bottom animals that could not withstand the change of water conditions and pressure they would have to endure in rising high enough to pass over it. Here was a remarkable phenomenon whose discovery capped the explorations of the *Challenger* scientists, and it was found in their own Scottish waters.

The Glorious Amateurs

The success of the *Challenger* set off a spate of national oceanographic expeditions from a number of other countries throughout the remaining quarter of the nineteenth century. These were important in further extending man's scant knowledge of the oceans, but their chief importance was in supplementing in one way or another the fundamental discoveries of the British explorations, and there is no need to detail them here. There are, however, two post-*Challenger* oceanographers who deserve special mention. Each of them explored the seas as an avocation, yet each in his contribution to the field out-shines many of the professional marine scientists of the day. One was Alexander Agassiz (1835–1910), a wealthy Swiss-born American mining engineer and son of the famous naturalist Professor Louis Agassiz of Harvard. The other was His Serene Highness Prince Albert Honoré Charles (1848–1922), sovereign ruler of Monaco from 1889 to 1922.

Unlike his father, who reputedly was unable to manage practical money matters, the younger Agassiz was a successful businessman. He was educated as a mining engineer and early in his career he and his brother-in-law, Quincy Shaw, took over control of the then unsuccessful Calumet and Hecla copper mines on Lake Superior. Under Agassiz' management the company prospered. He made a considerable personal fortune and remained president of the company throughout his life.

But Agassiz' first love was scientific exploration of the sea, and his financial success gave him the means to pursue this end. He made a number of cruises in United States Coast Survey ships, principally the U.S.S. *Blake* and *Albatross*, as well as in chartered vessels. As in the case of his father, the United States Government seemed happy to co-operate in the marine research. The elder Agassiz had made several marine biological expeditions that resulted in important collections for the Museum of Comparative Zoology which he founded at Harvard and for which a special building was erected. But Alexander was the oceanographer of the family. All told, he traveled over 100,000 miles in tropical seas, notably in the Caribbean, the Indian Ocean, and the tropical Pacific. And for many years after his work was finished, it was accurate to say that his expeditions had mapped more lines across deep-sea basins and made more deep soundings than had all other scientific expeditions combined.

Agassiz' skill as an engineer enabled him to make a number of contributions to the purely practical business of collecting specimens and taking data at sea. For example, sounding wire, which was tried out experimentally on the *Challenger*, soon came into general use in one form or another. But the use of rope for hauling dredges and other heavy apparatus remained the bane of deep-sea research. The ropes were cumbersome to handle and susceptible to rot. Agassiz replaced hemp with steel cable and devised mechanisms to facilitate handling it.

The *Challenger* had employed a system of huge rubber bands that stretched from three to seventeen feet to absorb sudden tensions or slacking in the rope. Agassiz invented mechanical systems that did the job more satisfactorily and made it easier to bring apparatus aboard. If he had never done anything else, he would be remembered by oceanographers for doing away with the old system of rope and rubber. He also improved on some of the sampling devices then in use. He helped design a new type of double-edged bottom trawl that would work whatever way it happened to hit bottom. And he invented a tow net that could be lowered to any desired depth, then opened and towed and closed again before being hauled back up. This helped eliminate the uncertainty about the depth at which a net's contents had been caught, an uncertainty which had plagued marine biologists for years.

After his father's death in 1873, Agassiz took over direction of the museum at Harvard. He gave it devoted service throughout his life and spent something like $1.5 million of his own money for endowment purposes and various operating costs. But he remained primarily a seagoing oceanographer. His voyages took place mainly from 1877 to 1905 and embraced all phases of oceanography. Among other things, he made extensive studies of Pacific bottom deposits, of submarine topography and marine life in the Caribbean, and visited every important coral reef, atoll, and island. In fact, he devoted the last thirty years of his life to coral-reef problems and became a leading expert on the subject.

As a result of his explorations in West Indian waters, Agassiz noticed that Caribbean deep-water animals seemed to be more closely related to those of the Gulf of Panama than to those of the deep Atlantic. He then reasoned that the Caribbean Sea had once been directly connected with the Pacific Ocean and had since been cut off by the uplifting that made the Isthmus of Panama. Later investigations by geologists have supported Agassiz' conclusion.

He also made a close study of the Gulf Stream. This enabled him to relate the distribution of plankton—tiny plants and animals that drift in the surface waters—to the flow of currents. These planktonic organisms are the primary food supply of the sea. The microscopic plants are akin to grass and other land vegetation that form the basic food supply for animals. Tiny planktonic animals that feed on the ocean plants are the grazers of the sea. They convert the vegetable material into flesh that is in turn eaten by other animals. Thus the abundance of marine life in the surface waters is obviously related to the abundance of plankton. Agassiz showed that the occurrence of bottom-dwelling animals, which in one way or another feed on material drifting down from upper waters, was directly related to the distribution of this surface plankton too.

Sir John Murray summed up Agassiz' contribution to science by saying, "If we can say that we now know the physical and biological conditions of the great ocean basins in their broad general outlines— and I believe we can do so—the present state of our knowledge is due to the combined work and observations of a great many men belonging to many nationalities, but most probably more to the work and inspiration of Alexander Agassiz than to any other single man."

Prince Albert, descendant of the ancient family of Grimaldi and hereditary ruler of Monaco, had a far different background from Agassiz, the millionaire son of an impecunious scholar. Yet he shared Agassiz' passion for exploring the sea and, like him, had ample independent means to finance his avocation.

In his youth the prince had served as a lieutenant in the Spanish Navy. He was an accomplished navigator and quite competent to command his own ship. Thus he was a double rarity among oceanographers, for he owned his research vessels and served as both captain and chief scientist. It is a striking coincidence that the modern oceanographic successor of Prince Albert is another such sailor-scientist—Captain Jacques-Yves Cousteau, recently appointed director of the Oceanographic Museum at Monaco. Cousteau is also a naval officer turned oceanographer. He has not had a royal fortune to work with, but he has managed to own and command his own ship—the *Calypso*. His contributions to oceanography have already been substantial, for his invention of the Aqualung and development of its use in scientific diving have opened a new phase of ocean research. Like the prince before him, he is an energetic scientific leader in a period when oceanography is in the midst of vigorous growth.

Prince Albert carried out his numerous expeditions in a succession of yachts. Starting with the 200-ton schooner *Hirondelle* and ending with the 1,420-ton, 240-foot steamship *Princesse Alice II* acquired in 1898, each was fully equipped for deep-sea research and was larger than its predecessor. The prince's companions on his cruises often included such scientists as Baron Jules de Guerne, one-time president of the Zoological Society of France; Dr. Jules Renard, later director of the museum Albert established at Monaco; J. Y. Buchanan, who had sailed with the *Challenger*; and the British Antarctic explorer, Dr. W. S. Bruce.

Like Agassiz, Prince Albert had a practical skill at engineering which helped him improve the apparatus and techniques of ocean research. Among his inventions were huge baited traps, new types of nets and trawls for use at various depths, and a system of underwater electric lights to attract fish and other animals.

His most famous innovation was the mass use of drifting floats to track major currents in the Atlantic, beginning around 1885. At first he used bottles or wooden blocks. These were later replaced by copper floats adjusted to drift just below the surface and out of the direct influence of wind. Each float contained instructions in nine languages asking the finder to fill in certain information and return it to Monaco.

In all, he released some 2,000 floats. Enough of these were returned to enable him to draw up a fairly comprehensive chart of the Atlantic surface circulation. He became the leading authority on this subject and, after World War I, was able to give navigators valuable advice on where leftover mines were likely to have drifted.

The prince engaged in all phases of ocean research. Over the years he contributed much useful data on water conditions and bottom topography in the Atlantic and Mediterranean. But his most sensational investigations concerned the giant squid. Here, certainly, is the king of the invertebrates, the only one of them able to give the great-toothed sperm whale a stiff fight even though the latter feeds upon it. In fact, these huge mollusks seem to be part of the regular diet of this whale, the "cachalot," which averages 60 feet in length. That is why the best place to find a giant squid has been the cachalot's stomach.

The giant squid are among the most powerful animals in the sea. They are strong swimmers, probably living in deep intermediate water, neither close to the bottom nor near the surface. Their great muscular arms, thick as those of a man, are covered with powerful suckers. No one knows how big these animals can become. By actual measurement they can at least grow larger than the basking and whale sharks, the largest of the fishes. Measurements reconstructed from fragments of one squid indicate that its main body was 4.6 feet in diameter and 24 feet long, with an over-all length, including outstretched arms, of 66 feet. It probably weighed about 42½ tons.

One can imagine the prince's astonishment when he first saw the remains of such a beast in 1895. He and Buchanan had been taking oceanographic data near the Azores when a native whaling crew killed a sperm whale nearby. The whale charged the Monegasque yacht and expired as it passed under the keel. When it floated to the surface on the other side of the ship, it gave up fragments of its last meal. They were parts of giant squid, in good enough condition for zoological studies to confirm the existence of a hitherto unknown species of deep-sea monster.

The prince returned home from the Azores and equipped his yacht for whale fishing. The squid were too big and fast to be taken by net, but if he could catch the whale that caught the squid he might be able to get some good specimens. He hired a Scottish whaler named Wedderburn, and the two of them organized a number of highly successful whale hunts. At one point the beautiful beach at Monaco was virtually turned into a whaling station to prepare specimens for the museum, but in this way the prince learned a good deal about the occurrence and structure of both whales and giant squid.

Although the existence of giant squid has been known for centuries, relatively little is known about the natural history of these animals. The only specimens are those that have been washed ashore or taken from the cachalot. However, the giant mollusks may have been encountered at sea without being recognized. Their powerful arms may have occasionally been seen above the surface, giving rise to at least some of the stories of sea serpents. Perhaps, also, these squid are brought to the surface by whales before being eaten, which would account for stories of fierce battles between cachalot and squid that have figured in sailors' yarns. Whales have been found with wounds and scars apparently caused by huge arms and suckers and indicating a violent struggle. The prince caught one specimen with sucker marks around its lips, showing that its prey had resisted to the last.

In 1882, a Professor A. E. Verrill published an appendix to the 1879 "Report of the United States Commission of Fish and Fisheries" in which he summed up the knowledge of giant squid based largely on strandings investigated in the Newfoundland area by an amateur naturalist, the Reverend M. Harvey. Apart from this, about the only scientific information available today on these mysterious monsters is based on the researches of Prince Albert of Monaco.

Before he died, the prince gave oceanography an enduring legacy in the form of two endowed institutions—an institute for marine studies at the Sorbonne in Paris and the famous museum at Monaco. The establishment at Paris started as a lecture series in 1903. Three years later Prince Albert gave the university a building to be devoted to teaching oceanography and three endowed chairs—one in physical oceanography, one in biological oceanography, and one in the physiology of marine life. Four years later, in 1910, he dedicated the Oceanographic Museum.

There is a legend that Hercules once came upon the ancient port that lay between the rock of Monaco and the present site of Monte Carlo. The harbor is still called the "Port of Hercules." Struck by its beauty, he overcame the savage natives, took possession of the rock, and dedicated it to the advancement of knowledge, naming it after his own title of Monoechos. This is the rock on which the prince built his museum. It is an imposing structure, built into the cliff on the ocean side of the rock and rising steeply from the sea. It has been a modern fulfillment of Hercules' legendary purpose.

Growth and Challenge

By the turn of the century, oceanography was firmly established as a vigorous, albeit slowly growing science. Many countries had at least a small group of researchers interested in the sea, and the numerous government, university, and private institutions active in the field today were beginning to spring up in various places. There are too many to list here, but the Stazione Zoologica at Naples must be mentioned. Founded by Dr. Anton Dohrn, a wealthy German biologist, the year the *Challenger* sailed, it has been the progenitor and, to some extent, the prototype of the many marine biological laboratories that have been established since then.

Even while the marine naturalists of Dohrn's and Thomson's day were excitedly dredging up strange animals, the need for something more than simply collecting and classifying had become apparent. Dohrn saw this need, and the station at Naples supplied the answer. In this and subsequent seaside laboratories the biologist can study many sea creatures at leisure as they live and grow in tanks. He can study development and behavior and to some extent conduct experiments. Also, he has full facilities to run all types of analyses he may care to make. These things are impossible at sea or with preserved specimens, which usually lose all hint of having once been living creatures by the time they reach shore.

The station at Naples was and is an international enterprise. Dohrn contributed generously from his own funds and saw that the institution was successfully established as a permanent undertaking. He fostered and directed its growth and activities for three decades.

A number of countries have shared in its support. Dohrn had help from both the German and the Italian governments in founding the station, and soon other countries were participating in a unique system of annual subsidy. The station provides a number of working places, called "tables," although they may in fact be rooms or segregated parts of rooms. A government or an institution may rent one or more of these tables annually and assign it to a scientist of its own choosing. Such visiting scientists have to bring some equipment of their own, but the institution provides many facilities—for example, assistants, an ample aquarium, chemical facilities, a library, and a permanent scientific staff. It is an international institute for advanced marine studies that remains unique even today.

But while oceanographic institutions for biological and general ocean research have proliferated, the growth of the science as a whole has been relatively slow after its portentous nineteenth-century beginning. There are several reasons for this. In the first place, sea research is expensive and, except for an Agassiz or a Monegasque prince, oceanographers have been chronically poor. Physics and some other sciences have burgeoned in the last half century, but for many years it took relatively little money to enable physicists to produce significant results. Only recently have the research tools of physics become expensive behemoths that only governments can afford. The research tools of the oceanographer have always fallen in that category for, however simple his instruments may be, they have to be operated from a ship. Ships, usually government-owned, have been made available from time to time, but massive government investment in research is a post-World War II phenomenon, and even then oceanography has been far down the list of support. In 1958, for example, the United States Government, which has been as generous in this regard as most others, allotted only about eight million dollars for ocean research, and this was during the International Geophysical Year, when oceanographers were unusually active.

Thus a chronic shortage of funds has been a severe limitation to the growth of oceanography. So, too, has a lack of first-rate researchers. Dr. Roger Revelle, director of the University of California's Scripps Institution of Oceanography at La Jolla, sometimes defines an oceanographer as "a sailor that uses big words." That is a hard kind of sailor to find. Quite apart from the amount of money available to support them, scientists who can stand the rigors of sea life are fairly rare. Professor Alister Hardy of Oxford University, a leading British marine biologist and fisheries expert, says that finding competent research workers who don't get seasick to fill posts in the relatively well supported fisheries and marine biological research laboratories of Britain is his single most difficult problem with graduate students. And an oceanographer who doesn't go to sea would be an anomaly at best. The lack of first-rate sailor-scientists has hampered oceanography in the past. It could be an even more serious bottleneck in the future when, if present indications are borne out, there will be considerably more money available for ocean research.

The third factor that has held back oceanography is the sheer magnitude of its subject matter and the inadequacy of the research tools to cope with it. Oceanography is not so much a science in itself as it is the application of other sciences—physics, chemistry, biology, mathematics, geology—in trying to understand the oceans. But these sciences need data to work with, and the collection of the data is an awesome task.

In *Challenger* days and for several decades thereafter, the immediate task was to try to determine the gross characteristics of the seas and what lived in them. The scattered soundings, samplings, and dredgings then taken were adequate to delimit the ocean basins and the major characteristics of their waters, to give rough indications of what was on the bottom and a broad look at what lived in the seas. But even this strained the technology of the times. Once it had been accomplished, further significant progress could be made only by extensive detailed studies which were difficult, expensive, and sometimes physically impossible.

Maury's charts and those worked up by the early oceanographers showed average current and water conditions over broad areas. But to find out what really is going on in the sea, later oceanographers needed closer networks of observations. Moreover, these observations needed to be taken repeatedly so that sequences of charts could be compared and changes in currents and water characteristics followed over time. But this kind of surveying has seemed an overwhelming job, for it requires a number of ships working together or a very intensive effort by one ship in a limited area. The German ship *Meteor* conducted such a survey in the South Atlantic during a cruise in 1925–27. This remained the only one of its kind until the IGY, when one of the important projects was the reoccupation of the old *Meteor* stations so that today's measurements can be compared with those taken three decades ago.

Another source of difficulty is the fact that water, often miles of it, overlies many things oceanographers want to study. To map the ocean bottom, they needed many more soundings than it was possible to take with a weighted line dropped from a ship. To study submarine geology, they needed to poke and probe extensively into the bottom and to examine rocks in many places. But the best they could do for a long time was to send down a dredge and hope it would snag a meaningful sample. Then too, marine biologists learned a good deal by studying specimens and watching such animals as could be housed in aquaria. But they all realized they would never really understand plant and animal life in the sea until they could study it in its own environment, and that, for the most part, seemed impossible.

Thus the technology of research was a severe handicap to oceanographers. Until recently this technology had changed little from that of the late nineteenth century. There were modifications in water-sampling bottles, dredges, winches, tow nets, and the like, which made them easier to handle, but no fundamental advance. There were, however, a few notable exceptions to this.

During the 1920's, for example, the Scandinavian meteorologists, V. Bjerknes and B. Helland-Hansen, developed mathematical theories that, applied to the sea, enabled oceanographers to translate data on water temperatures and salinities into the speed and direction of currents, allowing them for the first time to trace water movements beneath the surface. They still could not observe deep currents directly, which remained a great disadvantage, but something of the nature of such currents now could be inferred from the kind of water-sampling observations oceanographers could make.

The development of the depth-ranging echo sounder in the 1920's was another major advance. It was a forerunner of the electronic age, whose technology is beginning to make many of the oceanographer's old obstacles look surmountable. The principle of echo sounding is simple. It consists of measuring the time it takes a sound "ping" to reach the bottom and echo back. Since the speed of sound through water is known, the distance to the bottom can be determined. Corrections have to be made for varying temperature conditions which affect the transmission of sound through water, but these have been reduced to a simple routine.

The general idea of using sound for depth measurement was first suggested by the French physicist Arago in 1807, but little serious work was done along this line until the early 1900's, when a number of people in Germany, France, and the United States began evolving practical echo sounders. The first series of echo-sounder depth measurements at sea was made in 1920 by the Centre d'Etudes of Toulon. Three years later the survey ship U.S.S. *Guide* of the United States Coast and Geodetic Survey was fitted with an echo-sounding depth probe. From that time on, the echo sounder was gradually developed into a precision instrument that today can plumb any ocean depth with an accuracy of about six feet.

One of the most useful improvements was made during World War II, when instruments were developed that converted the echo-sounder readings into a continuous record that traced out the profile of the bottom over which the ship passed. Before this, the instruments merely gave numerical depth figures and the profile had to be drawn manually from plotted charts of these individual depth measurements.

The biggest limitation of echo sounding is the spread of the sound beam. If this were a narrow pencil, one could trace out the bottom in precise detail. But the sound spreads out in a cone, so that there is always an area of uncertainty in making a detailed chart of the bottom. This is particularly disturbing in probing deep trenches or close to underwater cliffs. The sound cone sometimes echoes off the cliff face or canyon wall, giving a false reading. Nevertheless, even allowing for this inaccuracy, echo sounding has removed one of the historic frustrations of oceanography.

Echo-sounding records sometimes showed a weak second reflection coming from the harder bottom underlying loose sediments. Recently this phenomenon has been put to work by the development of the Sonoprobe, which uses low-frequency sound to penetrate as much as 200 to 300 feet of sediment. Developed primarily by the Magnolia Petroleum Company, the Sonoprobe is based on the difference between the speed of sound through water-saturated sediments and its speed through sea water. Studies of these various sound velocities have been carried out at Cambridge University, at the Lamont Geological Observatory of Columbia University, and at the U. S. Naval Electronics Laboratory at San Diego, California. Using their results, Sonoprobes can be calibrated to give a kind of "X-ray picture" that shows the outline of both soft muds and sediments and of the underlying rocky "skeleton." (See Plate 2.)

Another sonic technique that has enabled marine geologists to probe what they cannot see is deep-sea seismology. Explosions of dynamite or TNT in the ocean generate sound waves that penetrate deeply into the crust of the earth. The speed of sound varies in layers of different density. This causes sound waves to be reflected and refracted and to

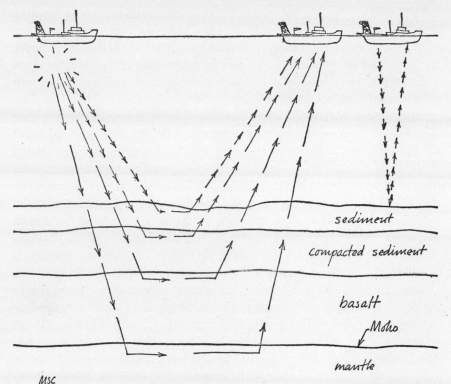

sediment

compacted sediment

basalt

Moho

mantle

MSC

FIG. 6: *Probing with sound: On the left, sound waves from a small under-water explosion are refracted by the different layers of sediment and crust. Right, pulses from an echo sounder give depth to top of sediments.*

arrive back at the surface at different times and places. By studying the arrival times and patterns of these returning sound waves, geologists can determine something of the nature of the crustal layers through which the sound waves have passed. This technique has long been used on land for oil prospecting. It was first used for probing beneath the ocean bottom on research ships from Woods Hole Oceanographic Institution at Woods Hole, Massachusetts, by Dr. Maurice Ewing, now director of Lamont Geological Observatory, in conjunction with Drs. Allyn C. Vine and J. Lamar Worzel of Lamont and Dr. George P. Woollard of the University of Wisconsin.

World War II interrupted this work, but it was taken up again and extensively developed as soon as peace came by Ewing, by Dr. Russell W. Raitt at Scripps, and by a group at Cambridge University in England under Sir Edward C. Bullard. At first, explosives and seismographs were placed on the sea bottom, but this was found to be unnecessary. As now used, the technique requires two boats working as a team. One of them shoots off explosions of known intensity, while the other picks up the sound waves through electronic hydrophones.

Except for a few advanced techniques such as echo sounding and seismic probing, however, the main data-collecting methods of the oceanographer had until recently changed little since the days of the *Challenger*. They were largely refinements of the time-honored method of throwing over a bucket and seeing what it brought up. In a sense, these older systems have been merely extensions of human arms and hands. Men float on the sea surface and reach down, so to speak, to touch and grasp what they can. The sounding lead and line were just a deep-sea version of the arm-and-stick method for measuring the depth of a pond. The dredges, bottom samplers, tow nets, and water-sampling bottles can be thought of as a grandiose system of grabbing what one can put one's hands on in blindly groping about the sea.

Considered in this perspective, the newer instruments and methods are the beginning of a revolution. The swift flight of a sound pulse has replaced the fish-and-feel method of measuring depth. Hauling up of water samples for analysis may soon give way to instruments now under development that can measure such things as pressure, temperature, salinity, and oxygen content directly at any depth and relay the information to the surface by electric cable. In shallow water the limitation of blindly groping from the surface has been overcome by the freedom of SCUBA diving ("SCUBA" for self-contained underwater breathing apparatus such as the Aqualung) and by underwater television. Biologists now can study many of their subjects in the natural environment. Geologists can go see for themselves what the shallow bottom looks like. Even the deep sea is becoming accessible to direct observation. Deep-water cameras have already brought back pictures from depths of 24,600 feet and are capable of operating in the deepest trenches. They are giving tantalizing glimpses of abyssal scenery that soon will be accessible to direct observation as the deep-diving submarines, such as the bathyscaphes, come into wider use. (See Plates 1, 19 & 20.)

The bathyscaphe, which will be described in detail in Chapter Eleven, was invented by Auguste Piccard, one of the famous twins who soared miles above the earth in some of the first stratospheric balloons. It is essentially a pressure-resisting steel chamber with observation ports that is supported by a float filled with gasoline. It is a kind of undersea balloon whose descent and ascent are regulated by siphoning off small amounts of gasoline and dropping ballast. The French Navy has used an adaptation of an early Piccard bathyscaphe for several years for explorations by Georges Houot and Pierre Willm. Meanwhile, and at this writing, the U. S. Naval Electronics Laboratory at San Diego is trying out the latest Piccard model in the Pacific.

Thus the exploration of the sea is at a critical juncture in its evolution as a science. Long-standing research limitations are being overcome at a time when governmental interest in the field is increasing. It seems likely that support for oceanographic research will be increased substantially in the next few years. For one thing, the international ocean research begun during the IGY is being continued. A special international scientific committee, called SCOR (Special Committee on Oceanographic Research), has been appointed to plan and co-ordinate this work. This continuing international activity is in itself bound to invigorate ocean research and help strengthen its support.

Beyond this, the Harrison Brown committee of the National Academy of Sciences in the United States has recommended a greatly increased American oceanographic effort which would involve an expenditure by the United States Government of $651,410,000 over the next ten years. At this writing, the indications are that the Brown report is being considered seriously both by Congress and by various administrative agencies, even though the Academy itself is a nongovernment institution.

The activities of bodies such as SCOR and the Brown committee demonstrate a growing interest in oceanography. The science of the sea appears to be entering a period of growth and activity as ebullient as that which followed the explorations of the *Challenger*. Within a decade much of today's oceanographic knowledge will be outmoded by a flood of new information. Thus the following chapters are as much a prelude to the future as they are a summary of accomplishment.

TWO

Beginnings

Wʜᴇʀᴇ have the oceans come from? How old are their waters? When and how did life arise in the ancient seas? These are fundamental questions of oceanography that have yet to receive definitive answers. They are inseparable from the larger question of the creation of the earth itself.

Up to a few hundred years ago Christian cosmologists thought this perplexing problem of beginnings had been solved once and for all by the biblical account of creation, which many scientists and clergymen alike accepted literally. By studying such things as the ages of post-Adamic generations listed in the Bible, a seventeenth-century Irish clergyman, Archbishop James Ussher, fixed the epoch of creation at just 4,004 years ʙ.ᴄ. His computations were popular around 1650, but subsequent scientific analysis and discovery have freed geology from this kind of dogmatic dating. Yet even today one can't talk about the origin and age of earth and its oceans without taking part of the story on faith. The Nobel Prize-winning chemist Dr. Harold C. Urey of the University of California notes wryly that when it comes to cosmic origins "even scientists have a marked tendency to call for miracles whenever some phase of the subject moves outside their own specialities." Because no one was there to see, this may always be the case. On the other hand, science has learned enough to have something meaningful to say on the subject of creation even though its competing theories are constantly in flux.

To trace the genealogy of the sea, oceanographers have joined with chemists, geologists, and astrophysicists in trying to reconstruct the birth and early history of our planet from processes and phenomena that can be observed today. For one thing, they have found that Archbishop Ussher hit very wide of the mark. The ancient Hindus came closer in compiling their sacred book, the Manusmitri, which received its final form in the second century B.C. The mystical cosmology spelled out there fixes the earth's age at just under two billion years, a figure that is at least of the right order of magnitude. At this writing, scientists put the earth's age at somewhere between five and six billion years, which is close to the age of the sun itself. How do they know? As Dr. Urey points out, there is a bit of miracle-working mixed with the computations, but here is one way to estimate it.

The "Atomic Clock"

From estimates of the extent to which the sun's initial charge of nuclear fuel (hydrogen) has been used up and from comparison with stars in its astronomical neighborhood, the sun is thought to be about six billion years old. This age may be in error by a factor of ten and almost certainly will be revised as more is learned about stellar processes. Nevertheless, as today's best-informed guess, it puts an upper limit on estimates of the earth's age, for it is inconceivable that the planets formed before the sun. A lower age limit can be set simply by reading some accurate "atomic clocks" that have been running throughout geological time. These are the natural radioactive elements, such as uranium, thorium, rubidium, or potassium, that lie fixed in ancient rocks and decay at a known rate into other non-radioactive elements. Let's take uranium for example.

Natural uranium comes in two slightly different varieties. Chemically, these are indistinguishable. But one weighs 238 atomic weight units and the other weighs only 235. For comparison, hydrogen has an atomic weight of 1. Atoms of the same element that have different weights are called "isotopes" of that element. The uranium isotopes are called U-238 and U-235, respectively, and there is 139 times as much of the former in a sample of natural uranium as there is of the latter. Each type of uranium decays radioactively into a particular isotope of lead. This means that a given uranium atom emits radiation and simultaneously initiates a nuclear process that turns it into an atom of lead. However, there is no chemical affinity between uranium and lead. Thus, if several per cent of lead is found in a uranium mineral, it is generally assumed that the lead is the decay product of the uranium. By measuring accurately the ratios between the amounts of the various lead isotopes and the amounts of the uranium isotopes that produce them, it is possible to tell how much uranium was present when any given sample was formed. Then, since uranium turns into lead at a known fixed rate, the sample's age can be estimated. Half of any given amount of U-235, for example, decays into lead-207 in 8.8 hundred million years. This is called the "half life" of U-235 and is a fundamental constant in determining the age of uranium-bearing rocks. Of course this technique will work only if the uranium and the lead it produces have kept together and intact in the sample and if there has been no contamination from other sources of lead. Fortunately the relationships between all of the isotopes involved are understood well enough to guard against errors of this sort.

Before they learned how to read the "atomic clocks," geologists dated rocks by their structures and the fossils they contained. These gave rough results at best. But by studying the order of succession of fossils found in the different layers of stratified rocks and by comparing observations from many parts of the world, geologists worked out a relative time scale for the past 500 million years. They split these years into three main divisions called "eras," which encompassed major phases of biological evolution. They named them the Paleozoic, Mesozoic, and Cenozoic eras in that order, the latter being the present era. The eras, in turn, were subdivided into "periods." The earliest period, which began some 500 million years ago, is called the Cambrian, while the current period, covering the past million years, is called the Quaternary. Some of the periods are further subdivided into "epochs."

But while these methods gave some idea of the relative timetable of geological history, they were no good for fixing absolute ages or for dating rocks older than the Cambrian. Prior to that period, the fossil record is dim. The "atomic clock" has eliminated much of this chronological uncertainty. It is a relatively new tool, having been in use for only a decade or so. Geochemists are still developing their analytical techniques, refining procedures, and improving accuracy. Some of the presently accepted age determinations may be changed as they are checked and rechecked over the years. Nevertheless, the "atomic clock" has already fixed the age spans of the geological periods and eras far more accurately than was ever possible before. And, reaching much farther back in time than the fossils, it has dated the oldest-known crustal minerals—pegmatites from Africa, Australia, and North America—at just under three billion years.

This is the span of the earth's history that can be read in the rocks. It sets a minimum age for the earth. But certainly our planet is older

GEOLOGICAL TIME SCALE

Era	Period	Epoch	Age in millions of years	Principal Events
CENOZOIC	QUATERNARY	Recent	0.01 (10,000 years)	Crustal folding, volcanoes.
	QUATERNARY	Pleistocene	1	Glacial epoch with four ice ages separated by warm periods, fluctuating sea levels. Rise of man.
	TERTIARY	Pliocene	13	Crustal folding, volcanoes.
	TERTIARY	Miocene	30	Sea invades many lowland areas. Plants and animals evolve rapidly, mammals become dominant.
	TERTIARY	Oligocene	40	
	TERTIARY	Eocene	60	
	TERTIARY	Paleocene	70	
MESOZOIC	CRETACEOUS		130	Crustal folding, Small mammals.
	JURASSIC		165	Pacific border folding. Marine reptiles, first birds, dinosaurs.
	TRIASSIC		195	Volcanoes. First mammals.
PALEOZOIC	PERMIAN		230	Crustal folding, continental uplift, volcanoes. Glacial epoch with at least five ice ages separated by warm periods, glaciers in equatorial belt, extremes of cold and aridity. Rapid biological evolution.
	CARBONIFEROUS	Pennsylvanian / Mississippian	290	Warm humid climate; swamp forests and coal formation, ferns and mosses. Amphibians, first insects.
	DEVONIAN		330	Mountains uplifted (some never again submerged). Fishes are dominant.
	SILURIAN		370	Crustal folding, volcanoes. Seas invade widespread low areas. Warm, locally arid climate. Coral reefs widespread, first land life.

Era	Period	Age in millions of years	Principal Events
PALEOZOIC	ORDOVICIAN	425	Seas spread widely over low continents, mountains uplifted. Shelled invertebrates, trilobites, first fishes appear.
	CAMBRIAN (Recent unconfirmed measurements indicate Cambrian may be 200 million years older.)	520	Seas advance and withdraw, at one time covering much of North America. Abundant fossils of marine life. Eocambrian glacial epoch.
PRE-CAMBRIAN		3000	Earliest known rocks and mountains. At least five glacial epochs. Faint traces of seaweeds and invertebrate animals.
UNDECIPHERED		4600	Solidification of mantle. Beginning of geological time.
PRIMORDIAL		6000	Sun and planets, the earth and moon form from cosmic nebula.

than that, for these rocks are not the first that were formed. Older crustal rocks have melted, sunk far out of sight, or been changed so that their "atomic clocks" can no longer be read. Then too, at best, these clocks will date only the solidification of the earth, not its true beginning. This is estimated from astronomical considerations.

For example, radioactive dating of the meteorites that occasionally fall out of the sky indicates they solidified at the same time as the earth's mantle, which has itself been radioactively dated as 4.6 billion years old. The meteorites are assumed to be either fragments of the asteroids, which are small chunks of planet material that whirl about the sun in an orbit between the orbits of Mars and Jupiter, or to be material left over from the formation of the asteroids by the breakup of a planet. In either case, it is further assumed that since the earth and asteroids solidified at the same time, their primordial material was assembled at the same time as well. Allowing time for this material to compact, melt and solidify, present calculations put the epoch of the asteroid's (and presumably the earth's) initial formation at between five and six billion years ago.

Birth of a Planet

What happened at that dim time is any expert's guess. Perhaps it was something like this, to quote a theory popular in the last half century. Because of a collision or near collision with another star, a great fiery mass was expelled from the sun. Flying outward, it eventually settled into a planetary orbit. This "protoearth," as we shall call it, was a seething mass of incredibly hot gas. But as it radiated its heat into the vastness of space it gradually cooled. First it became partly liquid. Then, with further cooling, the outer crust began to form. Meanwhile the materials of the protoplanet were sorting themselves out. The heavier ones moved toward the center, the lighter ones toward the outer parts. Gases, such as water vapor, collected as an atmosphere. This resulted in the layered earth we know today with its dense fluid metallic core, its semi-plastic (but extraordinarily rigid) mantle, and its outer crust.

With the solidification of the outer layers, cooling of the inner parts was slowed tremendously. Even today the core is thought to retain most of its primordial heat. But the young planet was in constant turmoil. The thin crust broke in many places, letting through fiery lavas, while overhead the face of the sun was hidden by a thick curtain of perpetual clouds. Soon after this the oceans began to form. But let's leave the story at that point and return to it later, for this is only one way it might have happened.

Some experts think that a chance encounter between our sun and a star is too unlikely to consider even on the epochal time scale of cosmic events. There have been a number of theories of the planets' origin, some of which have a long ancestry. The cataclysmic one just described was proposed early in this century by the American geologist Thomas C. Chamberlin and the astronomer Forest R. Moulton, and subsequently elaborated by the British physicists Sir James Jeans and Sir Harold Jeffreys. It was popular for fifty years and still crops up in spite of its improbability and certain highly technical objections.

In 1796 the famous French mathematician Pierre Simon de Laplace suggested that the planets evolved from material originally thrown off as a series of rings by a condensing mass that eventually became the sun. Others took this theory more seriously than did its author, who never published it in exact scientific form. It was dominant for almost a century, but it was shown to be theoretically impossible and dropped out of vogue. Prior to Laplace, in 1750, Thomas Wright in England suggested a theory, later elaborated by the famous philosopher Immanuel Kant, that sun and planets developed as centers of condensation in a cloud of cosmic dust and gas. It stirred little interest at the time.

In recent decades there has been a spate of cataclysmic theories in which the sun is either the survivor of a collision between a double star and a third star or is the surviving member of a double star whose companion exploded. The planets, of course, would form from the debris that remained. These theories, along with the related ideas of Moulton and Chamberlin, were effectively demolished by the American astronomer Lyman Spitzer, Jr. He found that the debris from a stellar collision or a wisp of material pulled out of the sun would be blown off into space almost explosively from the pressure of its own or of the sun's radiation. Under these conditions, planets would never have a chance to form. Then too, the cataclysmic theories have never been able to answer objections based on technical consideration of the motions of the sun and planets.

At this writing, an adaptation of the old Kant-Wright theory is in vogue. It was revived in 1944 by Carl von Weizsäcker in Germany and O. J. Schmidt in the Soviet Union. Since then it has been developed and expanded, especially in the United States by Urey, Spitzer, and Gerard P. Kuiper. The theory holds that it is highly likely that sun and planets condensed from the same mass of dust and gas roughly at the same time. So here, briefly, is another story of how the earth was born.

As far as stars themselves are concerned, it is generally accepted that they begin as a loose association of the cosmic dust and gas which exist in great abundance throughout the universe. Local concentrations form in a cloud of this dust and gas, which, through the pulling together of the mutual gravitational attraction between the cloud particles and the action of electromagnetic forces and perhaps even the pressures of cosmic gas and radiations, slowly contract into discrete bodies. As such a "protostar" contracts, it heats up from compression until at some point it is hot enough to kindle the thermonuclear reactions that are the source of stellar heat and light. These are akin to the thermonuclear reactions that power a hydrogen bomb. This contraction to stellar dimensions may take anywhere from a hundred thousand to tens of millions of years. Thus a star is born of a contracting dust cloud, condensing its fires from the cobwebs of the universe. So it was with our sun.

But as the protosun shrank, it left behind some of the primordial cloud as a rotating nebula. This nebula was cold to begin with. And as the developing sun shrank, the nebula radiated much of what little heat it had into space. At this time the sun itself gave only feeble light and heat in return, so that the nebula soon reached the unimaginable cold of 370° below zero Fahrenheit (minus 223° Centigrade) and perhaps even lower. Under the influence of cold and gravity, the nebula became disk-shaped, and soon local concentrations began to form within its turbulent, whirling mass. These were the protoplanets, one of which was to become the earth.

Thus, instead of a fiery mass torn out of a full-blown sun, the proto-earth, according to this theory, was formed from a cloud of dust and gas in the incredible cold of interstellar space at a time when the sun itself was still dark. It had 500 times as much mass as the earth does today. Its diameter was 1,800 times that of the final globe. Much of this mass was subsequently lost to space as gases escaped from the evolving planet.

At first the planetary matter condensed into fine grains which grew rapidly in size. These, in turn, began to spiral in toward the center of the protoplanet to form a nucleus. The materials involved were essentially those that make up the earth today, including a good deal of water, much of which may have been frozen. Thus the planet grew. And as the rain of matter continued, it gradually heated up from the effects of compaction, chemical reactions, and radioactivity, which was 15 times as intense as it is today.

Slowly the protoearth began to melt. Its materials separated into the constituents of core, mantle, and eventually the outer crust. This melt-

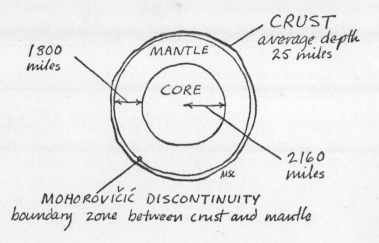

FIG. 8: *The earth's layered structure shown schematically in cross section.*

ing and final freezing of crust and mantle took something like a billion years. Thus geological history began with solidification of the mantle 4.6 billion years ago, and the young earth was ready to receive its oceans.

Origin of the Seas and Their Basins

Until recently it was widely assumed that the great ocean basins have remained much the same throughout geological time. There have been changes at the edges as continental lands rose and sank and waters advanced into or retreated from the low-lying inland areas. And there have been some changes in the deep ocean bottom itself. But, by and large, the great basins that cover two thirds of the globe today were thought to have remained relatively unchanged. The question then was, how were they formed in the first place?

Some have thought the birth of the moon may have played a leading role in shaping such features of the earth's crust. According to this view, first advanced in 1878 by Sir George Darwin, son of the famous naturalist, the moon was torn out of the earth after the crust had begun to form but while the mantle was still fluid to some extent. Here is how it might have happened. In those distant days the sun's gravity was the major tide-producing force on earth. It pulled the viscid outer layers into enormous tidal bulges whose peaks grew progressively higher. They built up steadily until, after a few hundred years, it was more than the young planet could stand. A chunk of the earth broke off to become the moon. Held as a satellite by gravity, the moon gradually moved away from the earth and is still moving away today. The basin of the Pacific Ocean, according to this theory, is the scar left by the cataclysmic separation.

Those who hold this view point out that the mean density of the moon is similar to that of the outer layers of the earth. Also, they note that other ocean basins have a thin covering of granite, while much of the Pacific does not. Perhaps its original granite cover now is swinging through space as part of the moon's substance. The other ocean basins may have been formed at this time too. As the moon matter tore away, the new crust broke, wrinkled, and shifted, especially on the opposite side of the planet. The result was a migration of great crustal blocks to become continents and the opening of basins to receive the ocean waters.

But over the past two decades this theory has been seriously questioned. For example, Sir Harold Jeffreys has shown it is extremely unlikely that the peaks of the solar tides could have risen more than 200 feet. This would be impressive if seen from the ground, but it would not have been enough to throw off the moon. Instead, the nebula theory of earth's origin suggests that the earth and moon formed simultaneously. Two condensation centers may have formed in the cold mass of dust and gas that became the protoplanet. The larger one became the earth and the secondary center formed the moon. Consequently, the moon is not regarded as a satellite of the earth but rather as the lesser partner of a double planet system, analogous in origin to the many double stars found throughout the Galaxy. On the other hand, the moon may have formed from its own part of the primordial cloud and then been captured by the protoearth early in its history.

As for the ocean basins, perhaps these were formed as part of the general and violent solidification and settling processes of the crust that followed solidification of the mantle. Whatever their origin, the early scene was one of appalling desolation. Everywhere there was only hot bleak rock broken by innumerable volcanic fissures. Then as the planet continued cooling, the atmosphere released some of its load of water vapor and it began to rain in an endless torrent. Water that had been held in the primitive atmosphere as vapor condensed and fell. At first the hot rocks sent it back as steam. But gradually the rocks cooled and oceans began to form. The rain continued for decades, even centuries. It eroded the rugged landscape, beginning the long process of carrying the minerals of the land into the seas and helping to make them salty. When at last the sun shone again, the earth had become a water planet, ready for the great adventure of the evolution of terrestrial life.

But it is questionable that the earth received the bulk of its oceans at that time. The protoplanet lost much of its mass before the earth finally took on its present shape. Most of the water it managed to keep was probably trapped chemically or physically in the subsurface rocks. For example, William Rubey of the United States Geological Survey estimates that only 5 to 10 per cent of the present oceans were formed initially, the rest of the waters having escaped from the earth's interior throughout geological time. Indeed, this is part of a dynamic new view that geologists have begun to take of the earth's atmosphere and oceans. In recent years they have begun to wonder if any of the major exterior features were formed once and for all in a single epoch.

Summarizing the present state of knowledge of the earth's crust, Dr. J. Tuzo Wilson of the University of Toronto, until recently president of the International Union of Geodesy and Geophysics, explained that "it seems reasonable to conclude from the many sources of information which modern geophysical science has placed at our disposal that the atmosphere, the oceans and the crust of the earth have all been brought forth from the interior by volcanic and seismic activity during the planet's long history. Thus oceans and continents, with their vast ridges and trenches, valleys and mountains, have gradually been constructed on top of the original surface of the earth. This now forms the base of the crust. It is hidden and only known to us from the echoes of seismic waves it reflects. This view is a new one and not yet widely understood, but it seems forced upon us by our expanding knowledge. Consideration of the rate at which gases, steam and lava are poured forth by volcanoes has led to the idea that the atmosphere, oceans and rocks of the crust have all been produced by volcanicity. Studies of their composition and abundance strengthen this view. A rate not much higher than that at which volcanoes emit lava today would have sufficed to build the entire crust during [geological time]."

But whatever the origin of the oceans, it is certain that the earth has had a good deal of water for a very long time. The oceans are not only a product of earthly evolution but are a contributing factor to geological change. Time after time the restless forces beneath and within the crust have heaved up great mountain ranges. And time after time the erosive forces of wind and water have worn down these ranges, carrying great masses of land material into the seas. Some of this material has dissolved and been distributed throughout the waters to add to their hoard of minerals. Some of it has undergone chemical change or been picked up by organisms and subsequently has settled out in a different form. Some of it settled out directly. This gradual settling formed bottom sediments that, in the slow cycles of geological time, became sedimentary rocks—limestones, sandstones, shales, and the like. These were deposited over large continental areas during extensive invasions of the sea. In their turn they were often uplifted into mountains and again worn down and carried to the sea in a complex cycle. There have been some half dozen such mountain-building epochs since Cambrian times. The sea plays its role in erosion processes too, for its waves are constantly eating away at coast lines and islands. But the grandest part the ocean has ever played in the evolutionary drama has been as the womb for the rise of earthly life.

The Rise of Life

The first faint traces of fossils date back nearly two billion years. But biological evolution had been going on for a long time before that. Here again no one really knows just what took place. It is believed that the primitive oceans contained a variety of chemicals, greatly diluted and spread throughout their vast waters. Interactions between these chemicals and constituents of the primitive atmosphere were going on constantly, stimulated by radiation from the sun and perhaps by electric discharges in the atmosphere.

It is fairly certain that conditions of this kind could produce many of the organic chemicals that today are associated with living cells. For example, several years ago Dr. S. L. Miller of Columbia University, then a graduate student working with Harold Urey at the University of Chicago, ran an electric discharge through an atmosphere of methane, hydrogen, ammonia, and water vapor and produced a variety of organic compounds. These included substances called amino acids, which are the building blocks of proteins. The gases used in this experiment are thought to be among the main constituents of the primitive atmosphere.

For his own part, Urey has examined many kinds of chemical reactions he thinks could reasonably have taken place. He has concluded that if half the carbon now present on the surface of the earth had existed as soluble organic compounds in early times, and if the primitive oceans had only 10 per cent of the present amount of sea water, these oceans would have been approximately a 10 per cent solution of organic compounds. Thus the chemical turmoil of that distant age turned the ocean into a complex mixture and solution of chemicals that were favorable for the rise of a primitive form of life. It was a dilute nutritious soup that, with the advent of life, began to consume its own substance.

If life arose in this way, as is now widely believed, it may have been a long slow process of trial and error, to judge from the pace of evolution today. On the other hand, the British biochemist J. B. S. Haldane thinks that evolution may have been a good deal more rapid in that early epoch. He suggests that there may be a relatively short critical period in the early years of a planet when life has an opportunity to evolve. The fact that it has arisen on the earth then indicates that it must have evolved quickly in the beginning to take advantage of this period. He further points out that evolution proceeds by mutation. For one of today's complex organisms, mutation is usually a relatively minor inheritable change which may or may not affect its evolutionary course. But for primitive life where species were little more than living molecules, mutation could be a sudden drastic change in which molecular species superseded one another quickly and evolution could proceed at a fast pace.

Whether the process was quick or slow, in those formative times many substances must have appeared that came close to being what we would consider alive, only to disappear again in the constant chemical shifting of the primordial "brew." Indeed, if an observer could go back in time and sample the seas at different periods, he would be hard put to say just when life did appear. The line between living and non-living has proved an impossible one for biologists to draw. Does the capacity to eat and grow, to reproduce, to organize the environment define life? Does a system have to have only one of these characteristics or all of them to be called living? Or does the criterion lie elsewhere? Viruses that are inert crystals when isolated and viable entities using the apparatus of living cells to reproduce themselves when they enter a host are an enigmatic case in point.

It is likely that a number of systems we would recognize as living appeared, struggling to keep their integrity in spite of the incessant chemical attack of their environment, competing with each other for the materials they needed to survive. At some unknown time, at least one line of these systems must have gained an advantage, however slight, that set it on the long road of biological evolution. Perhaps it was the first to evolve a means for altering hitherto unusable chemicals so that it enlarged its food supply. Perhaps it was the first to build a protective wall that would admit needed nutrients but keep out destructive compounds. Whatever its evolutionary advantage, it was the ancestor of the first living cell, the basic unit of life, which is one of the most complex chemical systems known.

A. I. Oparin, the Soviet biochemist who has long been a world leader in this field, and others have pointed out that the earliest living organisms could have developed directly from dense globules of carbon compounds. At first these could live and grow by taking necessary chemicals out of the surrounding water. But as one or more of these nutrient substances grew scarce, only those organisms could survive that developed ways of using new materials as a food supply. This process would continue as these materials in turn became scarce. In this way very simple organisms would continually increase in complexity through the exigencies created by dwindling food supplies.

Primitive one-celled plants probably arose early in this evolutionary process. Animals could not have evolved until later, for only plants are able to perform the magical transformation of sunlight into living substance that is the basic sustenance of all earthly life. These simple plants probably got along without oxygen, as some primitive bacteria do today, since the atmosphere and ocean at that time were probably oxygen-poor. But the great adventure had started. Through the gradual processes of evolution, modifications were made as changes in the environment permitted. Oxygen began to increase as the plants released it, and oxygen-breathing organisms arose. As the plant cells proliferated, some of them modified so that they no longer used sunlight to turn inorganic materials into organic substances. They fed directly on the primitive plant cells and perhaps on each other. These were the first animals. From such shadowy beginnings, the rich proliferation of life slowly evolved throughout the periods of geological time.

A Bit of Crystal Gazing

Just as there are no cut-and-dried answers to the question of beginnings, so there is no sure forecast of the future. Nevertheless, the latest theories show an interesting trend. Instead of cataclysms, sometimes bordering on the miraculous, they envision the earth's history as a slow process of evolution guided by principles that are generally considered valid throughout the universe and wrought by forces acting over long periods of time. These principles are still valid, and many of the forces are active today. One can at least project their possible effects into the long-term future. Here is what that projection foretells.

Left to its own devices, the earth's future evolution would probably be undramatic. Over eras measured in billions of years, the heat of radioactivity would slowly diminish in the outer layers of the mantle and crust. And with the cooling of these underlying masses, the volcanism and mountain-building forces that have constantly reshaped the surface would die down. Slowly the processes of erosion would wear away the land no longer being renewed by upthrusting mountains, carrying its substance into the seas. During this period some of the atmospheric gases would escape to space, but these would be renewed by leakage from the earth's interior. Since water vapor, in particular, escapes very slowly, the earth would retain its great oceans. And as the lands eroded, these waters would slowly spread until eventually they might completely cover the planet. The time scale for this course of events would be on the order of at least ten billion years.

But the earth will not be left to its own evolutionary devices. Over the billions of years of the future, the development of the sun will again become the dominating factor in the earth's evolution even as it was at the beginning. The sun is burning up its nuclear fuel at a prodigal rate. As its hydrogen supply is used up, the sun will gradually increase in size and brightness until it becomes what astronomers call a red giant star. Then, with its fuel supply exhausted, it will collapse again to become a white dwarf star, its fires slowly cooling over an indefinitely long time.

There is reason to believe that the sun has already started down this evolutionary road. Its brightness now is some 20 to 25 per cent greater than it was when the young sun first condensed from its protostar. Its diameter also has started very slowly to increase. In another three to four billion years it will have become a red giant perhaps ten times as bright as it now is and emitting perhaps a hundred times as much radiation. But its evolution will have had serious consequences for the earth long before that point is reached.

As the solar brightness grows, the earth will heat up. Sometime around two billion years from now the oceans will begin to boil. Soon their water masses will be transformed into clouds and vapor in the atmosphere. There is no reason to think these will be lost to space. But the surface will be hot and dry. Like Venus, the earth will probably be wrapped in perpetual clouds. After another billion years or so the sun will shrink. If the earth has not been engulfed and vaporized by the expanded sun—a not unlikely event—it then will cool. The air will give up its moisture in a primordial rain and the ocean basins will again be filled. But this time the shrunken sun will be considerably dimmer. The earth will cool until its waters freeze and its lands are covered with perpetual snow.

Is this to be the end of our planet—to drift through space, the frozen companion of a dying sun? It is impossible to foretell. Certainly this is one logical result of evolutionary trends as we know them today. However, Dr. Gerard P. Kuiper of the University of Chicago's Yerkes Observatory, a leading theoretical astronomer, has suggested an alternative. It is possible, he says, that the frozen earth might be rejuvenated. He bases this on mathematical studies of the evolution of the entire universe.

Our stellar universe seems to be expanding. It has been expanding for a long time and will continue to do so for an indefinite time in the future. But Dr. Kuiper has worked out a mathematical theory for this expanding universe and has found that it need not go on expanding forever. There are solutions to the mathematical equations that suggest the universe someday might start contracting. If it did, it would heat up as its contraction proceeded. The earth itself might warm again as part of the general heating, its oceans melt and its continents thaw. But it would be a catacylsmic reawakening, for the universe would be on its way to a nuclear holocaust. Its contraction would progress until its temperatures could support the basic nuclear reactions that would rework its matter anew and start it again on a great creative expansion. "Nothing could be more dramatic," Dr. Kuiper observes, "than the dissolution of the earth and all that is on it in the mad rush of stars and planets during the concluding moments of the present cycle of the universe."

THREE

The Unseen Landscape

Some of the earth's most spectacular scenery lies under the sea. Upthrusting mountain ranges and plunging trenches, awesome canyons and escarpments, all are hidden under hundreds and often many thousands of feet of water. If they could be viewed from the deep-sea floor, they would be found in many cases to excel the scenic grandeur of the continents. Here is a vast unseen landscape that men have scarcely begun to explore. Here, if anywhere, is the last great frontier for geographical exploration. Even the forbidding interior of Antarctica has begun to yield to the map makers under the concerted attack of the International Geophysical Year expeditions and their successors. But the ocean floor remains a challenge to man's ability to chart what he cannot see.

According to Dr. Roger Revelle of Scripps, "Only about two per cent of the deep sea floor has been even moderately accurately surveyed. As far as our understanding of the topography of the sea floor is concerned, we are now about where we were a hundred years ago in surveying the land . . ." It is easy to see why the Brown committee said that men know less about many parts of the ocean bottom than they do about the near face of the moon.

Men have been studying the sea bottom for the better part of a century. The first true deep-sea sounding was made in 1840 when Sir James Clark Ross plumbed a depth of almost 2,000 fathoms with a weighted hemp line. Oceanographers, however, first took the measure of the sea floor during the Challenger expedition. These soundings gave a general idea of the outline and average depths of the major ocean basins, but they scarcely hinted the true complexity of submarine geography. For decades thereafter the ocean floor was thought to be primarily a smooth monotonous plain, its original features buried under sediments accumulated throughout geologic time.

This, after all, was the way the sea bottom appeared to be when all the oceanographer had was hemp or steel sounding lines and a few crude instruments for sampling the uppermost sediments. But with the advent of the echo sounder, oceanographers began to discover the submarine landscape. Much of this landscape remains to be explored, as Revelle's statistic illustrates. On the other hand, enough of the former blank spaces have been filled in on the charts so that one can, figuratively speaking, take at least a generalized tour of the ocean bottom. This general topography of the sea floor, as it is known today, is shown on one of the endpaper maps. Because of the small scale to which the map is drawn, only the major features can be indicated. Nevertheless, they help orient one in this unfamiliar world beneath the sea.

The Threshold

The transition from continent to ocean is rarely sudden. To the casual eye of a landsman, the sea begins at the water's edge. But to the sound beams of the oceanographer, the boundary is less distinct. Almost everywhere the land is bordered by shallow "continental shelves" where land and sea merge into one another. They are the threshold over which one must pass to enter the deep ocean.

Or, to look at them another way, the shelves geologically are part of the continents—the pedestal, so to speak, upon which the land rises above the water like a monument. The United States gave legal recognition to this viewpoint when it took possession of the mineral rights on the continental shelves adjacent to American territory by presidential decree in 1946.

But however one looks at it, the shallow-water transition zone has in many ways been the most important part of the undersea landscape for practical human purposes. This is where the great commercial fisheries are found, such as those of the North Sea and of the Grand Banks off Newfoundland. If trawlers had to fish the abyss miles below their ships rather than the few-hundred-foot depths of the shelves and their banks, they would find it cumbersome and prohibitively expensive ·in gear and operating costs, even if the sparse abyssal fauna were worth hauling in.

The shelves also have long been both a hazard and an aid to navigation. Navigators must constantly be on the lookout for shoals and sand bars. At the same time, by comparing soundings with those on their charts, they can help guide themselves in their coastwise sailing. Thanks to this practical importance to navigators and fishermen, the shelves are the best-surveyed areas under the sea, at least off the coasts of maritime nations.

For the purposes of the 1946 presidential decree, the continental shelf was defined as the shallow-water area out to a depth of 100 fathoms. This is useful as a legal definition, but the shape of the shelf rarely fits the 100-fathom contour line. The shelves end in more or less distinct breaks where the bottom begins to slope more steeply, sometimes precipitously, into the abyss. This break is their natural limit. Thus by international agreement the continental shelf is defined geologically as the "zone around the continents, extending from low water line to the depth at which there is a marked increase in slope to greater depth." If the "marked increase in slope" comes in two breaks instead of one, as it often does, then the sharpest break marks the edge of the shelf, provided this break is no deeper than 300 fathoms.

However, not all of the world's continental shelves have been well enough surveyed to be delineated in this manner. Because of this, and because there would be no serious distortion for the scale with which they are drawn, the shelves are delimited on the endpaper map by the 100-fathom line.

In some places the shelves are wide, as in the North Sea area off Europe or along the Arctic coast of Asia. In other areas they are narrow or virtually nonexistent, as off the eastern tip of Florida. On the whole, to give a few general statistics, they have an average width of about 42 miles, an average depth of 180 to 210 feet, an average slope toward the sea of about 10 feet in a mile ($0°7'$), and an average depth at the outer edge of 432 feet.

These valuable undersea margins are thought to be a gift of the last ice age. At its peak, 18,000 years ago, so much water was locked up in the ice that the general sea level fell anywhere from 250 to 500 feet. This was an ice-age phenomenon that affected all the seacoasts of the world, even those far removed from the glaciers themselves. Waves can quickly erode soft materials. Thus, when extensive new coast areas were exposed by the retreating seas, wave-cut terraces were formed. Then with the rise of the seas as the ice melted, and perhaps aided by the slow sinking that many coastal areas are known to be experiencing, the continental shelves were created by submersion.

The shelves, especially in the glaciated areas, still show the marks of their ice-age origin. In many places glacial rubble has been dredged up, while off northern Europe and North America the topography of the shelf shows the same glacial scouring as the adjacent land. The fjords, in particular, are believed to have been carved by the ice.

Elsewhere the shelves have a varied topography. In some places they are hilly or rolling. Occasionally they are very smooth. There are many basins, banks, sand bars, and remains of drowned river valleys, while the material covering the bottom is a veritable patchwork of muds, sediments, and rocks.

The most common sediment is sand. Some of this, the "terrigenous" sand, is land-derived. Some of it is organic, such as the "calcarcenite" sands made up of coral fragments, the shells of microscopic animals of a type called Foraminifera, and the calcium carbonate remains of other organisms. There are also the so-called "chemical" or "authigenic" sands that are deposited by chemical processes in the sea. Besides the various sands, there are muds, silts, and clays, which are respectively made up of finer and finer materials, all finer than the sands. Last, there are gravels, pebbles, cobbles, and boulders—stones ranked according to increasing size—which cover the shelf in some places.

One of the more curious and occasionally valuable features of the shelves are the salt domes, such as those found off the Gulf coast of the United States. These sometimes are associated with oil and have been used as a cheap source of high-quality salt and sulphur. These domes, which look like rounded hills, are really oval plugs of salt, sometimes over a mile in diameter, that rise up from deep underlying salt beds. They have been pushed upward by subterranean forces until they rise with vertical walls through thousands of feet of sediment. Where they have risen, these mountains of salt are surrounded by uptilted sediment beds. Oil is often found in these beds. Being lighter than the water that is also present in the sediments, it floats up through the tilted sediments until it is blocked by the wall of salt.

By definition, the shelves end where the sea bottom begins to drop more steeply into the abyss. These more inclined areas are called the "continental slopes," and it is here that the deep sea really begins.

Descent to the Abyss

Depending on one's point of view, the continental slopes are either the edge of the ocean basins or the rising flanks of the continents. But, however one looks at them, these are the greatest slopes and escarpments on the earth. There is nothing on land to rival them. Indeed, some of them are steeper and more awesome than the famous southern face of the Himalayas.

Off the west coast of South America, for instance, the east wall of the Peru-Chile Trench combines with the adjacent slopes of the Andes to give an average vertical rise of some 42,000 feet. That is practically twice the rise of the southern Himalayan slope. The greatest height difference known on the earth is found in this same ocean area where, at one point, the crustal surface rises from an undersea depth of 25,000 feet to a mountain height of 23,000 feet. This is a vertical rise of 48,000 feet (just over nine miles) within a horizontal distance of 100 miles.

Even where the shelf is too wide for the slope in which it ends to be considered contiguous to land elevations, steep escarpments are sometimes found. Furthermore, and unlike escarpments on land, the great undersea slopes stretch for thousands of miles, surrounding entire

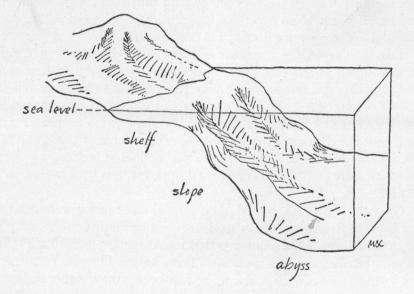

FIG. 9: *The descent to the abyss.*

continents. Of course they are not everywhere as steep as those off western South America. In some places they are much more gradual. In other places they are broken up into intermediate plateaus and basins so that they descend to the deep-sea floor in somewhat stepwise fashion. In a few places they are virtually nonexistent because there is no perceptible change in the slope of the shelf until it reaches the

C*

abyss. Nevertheless, as a general feature, the "continental slopes," as they are called, would afford some of the most impressive scenery on the planet if they could be viewed from the deep ocean bottom.

In general, these slopes have not been as extensively surveyed as the shelves. The 1,000-fathom line seems to be the limit of most detailed coastal exploration, at least as far as published information is concerned. In the United States much of the recent detailed data or undersea topography has been kept secret because of its military value as a navigational guide to submarine commanders. On the other hand, except for the shelves, the continental slopes are the best-known features of the unseen "landscape." Again, to give a few general statistics, the inclination of the slopes ranges from about 1°20′ to 5°40′ (roughly 100 to 500 feet per mile) and more for the steepest areas. The steepest continental slopes are those of the Pacific, which average 5°20′, while the gentlest are those of the Indian Ocean at 2°55′. The Atlantic and Mediterranean slopes fall between at 3°05′ and 3°34′, respectively. Almost everywhere, these slopes end in a gentle apron known as the "continental rise" or, over local areas, as a "deep-sea fan."

Like the shelves, the slopes are often covered with a variety of sediments—about 60 per cent mud, 25 per cent sand, and a scattering of gravel, rocks, and oozes. But, unlike the glacially influenced shelves, the slopes are believed to be the product of large-scale adjustments in the crust. At one time it was thought the slopes were simple piles of sediment and debris built up off the end of the shelves. But the modern view is that they are at least originally the product of faulting, a process in which huge blocks of the crust are dropped vertically or moved horizontally.

Once the slopes are formed, their relative steepness and irregularity are thought to be preserved by landslides and turbidity currents in spite of the continual fall of sediments that would tend to bury their profile as snow blankets a winter landscape. These loose sediments, permeated with water, are easily set to sliding by slight earth movements and even by their own weight on steeper parts of the slope, so that the slopes themselves retain many of their original jagged features.

The so-called "turbidity currents" do a similar job of preservation. If bottom sediments are stirred, as in an earthquake, they fill the water with a cloud of fine suspended material. This silt-laden water is a small fraction of one per cent heavier than the surrounding water. But the slight weight difference is enough to make the turbid water settle. If there is any incline at all to the bottom, it will run off as a "density" or "turbidity" current, which some experts think can become quite powerful. Certainly these currents and landslides seem able to keep the steeper parts of continental slopes relatively clean of sediments and thus to preserve their original form.

A third factor affecting both the slopes and the shelves are the major ocean currents, which often distribute or carry away sediment. An example of this is the action of the Gulf Stream in shaping shelf and slope, as off the southeast coast of the United States. South of Cape Cod, the edge of the shelf curves ever closer to the land until, off the western tip of Florida, it virtually disappears. But beyond the shelf edge there is a plateau, the Blake Plateau, about 2,400 to 3,600 feet deep, which runs more or less smoothly out to sea until it terminates in a steep escarpment with inclinations of 15 degrees and more. This is roughly the area off the southeastern United States between the 1,000-fathom contour line and the 100-fathom line marking the edge of the shelf as shown on the endpaper map. It is one of the geological curiosities of the continental slopes.

Dr. Henry Stetson of Woods Hole Oceanographic Institution and a team under Dr. Maurice Ewing, director of Columbia University's Lamont Geological Observatory, have found that the sea bottom on the Blake Plateau is either rocky or covered by a hard calcareous material with little or no soft sediment. Furthermore, the Lamont geologists have dated rocks from the edge of the plateau and from the adjacent slope as being quite old, dating back to Cretaceous and Miocene times (see table page 56). Northward, rocks this old are deeply buried under more recent sediments, but on the Blake Plateau they lie at the surface. The plateau itself is flat enough to be considered part of the shelf if it did not lie so deep. It looks as if the top of the shelf had been sliced off with a great knife, like the frosted top layer off a cake. The reason for this curious geological feature is thought to be the flow of the Gulf Stream.

This massive current is believed to have started flowing through the Florida Strait early in the Tertiary period. Once started, the current stopped sedimentation in the Blake Plateau area except quite close to the coast. Meanwhile the sea floor slowly sank as part of the general subsidence that is known to have occurred throughout all areas off the North American coast. It once was thought that the Blake Plateau was due to downfaulting of a large crustal block or to the erosive action of the Gulf Stream. Although there may be some erosive action, the plateau and the lack of a significant shelf off southern Florida are now considered to be the result of a slow general sinking of the sea floor, which has continually been swept clean of upbuilding sediments by the Gulf Stream. As will be explained in the next chapter (pages 122, 123), there is also reason to think the plateau is an ancient drowned coral reef. But however it was first formed, the fact that it has not been buried by sediment is a striking illustration of the power of an ocean current to shape major sea-bottom features even when it does nothing more violent than keep an area clean of sediments.

The continental shelves are also the location of a much-debated geologist's puzzle, the great submarine canyons that rival and often excel any the land can boast. It would seem obvious that, built on the scale of the Grand Canyon of the Colorado River, they are simply drowned river valleys. But so far they have defied all attempts at explanation, although there is strong circumstantial evidence to support modern theories of their origin.

Canyons in the Deep

The great submarine canyons cut the continental slopes at a number of places throughout the world. Sometimes they are located off adjacent land valleys, as in the case of the canyon off the mouth of the Hudson River in New York or the canyon off the island of Corsica, where every bay on the west coast has its continuation under the sea. But in many places the submarine canyons bear no obvious relation to the adjacent terrain.

These undersea canyons are generally too small in relation to the scale of the endpaper map to be shown there. However, if you look carefully at the east coast of North America, Long Island can be seen southwest of Cape Cod. Just south of Long Island there is an indentation in the continental shelf so narrow it appears simply as a short solid line. This is the location of the canyon off the Hudson River. Actually the canyon head is some distance from the shore, but this is difficult to show exactly on so small a map.

The canyon walls reach a maximum height of 4,000 feet. Many short tributaries feed into the main valley, which runs to some 180 miles in length. This includes the inner canyon that cuts the continental slope and a shallower trench that Lamont geologists have traced across a huge deep-sea fan that extends into the western basin of the Atlantic. At its outer end the canyon system is 14,000 feet deep.

Although this canyon is unusual in that it is located off a river valley, its dimensions typify the majesty of these undersea formations. One has scarcely a hint of this from a mere listing of dimensions. But to geologists who have dived into these submarine valleys and for the extent to which they have been able to penetrate, it has been like swimming through the upper reaches of the Grand Canyon. How were these magnificent gorges created and what keeps them from filling up with sediments? There is no simple or generally accepted answer, but the forces involved link the canyons with long riverlike channels that have in recent years been discovered on the deep-ocean floor.

The first of these channels, a long winding depression tied into the mouth of the La Jolla submarine canyon, was discovered in 1948 by Dr. Henry W. Menard, Dr. Robert S. Dietz, and E. C. Buffington, who at that time were working from the United States Naval Electronics Laboratory at San Diego. Similar channels were found about the same time in the Atlantic by Bruce C. Heezen of Lamont. Since then a number of them have been found in both oceans, sometimes associated with submarine canyons on the slopes and sometimes by themselves on the abyssal floor. Menard, now with Scripps Institution, has found a puzzling twist to twelve deep-sea channels off the North American west coast which no one has yet explained. All twelve hook to the left. None hooks right or extends straight from the adjacent shelf.

The longest of the deep-sea channels, the Mid-Ocean Channel, was discovered and partially surveyed by expeditions from Lamont in 1949 and 1952. It begins off the tip of Greenland, where it may be a two-prong system with many branching tributaries, and runs for nearly 2,000 miles to end in a deep basin of the west-central North Atlantic, reaching as far south as the latitude of Washington, D.C. It ranges in width from two to four miles and from 150 to 600 feet in depth.

The Bay of Bengal offers a striking example of a sea-floor channel that appears to be an extension of a submarine canyon. Analyses of echo-sounding records made in 1948 across the entrance of this bay by the Swedish research vessel *Albatross* indicate several channels in the bottom. The largest is some four miles wide and 240 feet deep. It is bordered by symmetrical levees six miles broad and rising 90 feet above the level of the surrounding bottom. This channel, which is eight times as wide and five times as deep as the Mississippi River at its southern end, is thought to run northward for some 1,100 miles, where it ties into the huge submarine canyon off the Ganges River.

The echo-sounding records of these channels look very much like the profiles of big land rivers that build natural levees on their banks.

On land, the levees are built when sediment-laden rivers overflow. Running fast at flood stage, the water of such rivers suddenly slows down when it spills over the banks and spreads over the countryside. Much of the heavier sediment it carried when it flowed faster is deposited along the banks, where over the years it builds up into levees. Manmade levees for flood control are often built on top of the natural ones.

Similar "levees" show up on the echo-sounding profiles of most of the deep-sea channels. In fact, this is the way these channels usually are spotted. They are only a few miles wide and a few hundred fathoms deep at most and had been overlooked in the general roughness of the deep-ocean bottom until relatively precise and continuously recording echo sounders became available to oceanographers after World War II. Since then the characteristic levees have become a kind of identification tag.

The phenomenon that gouged these channels, that could flood and build up levees on a plain already covered with several miles of water, is also involved in the origin and maintenance of the submarine canyons. In each case, marine geologists think density currents probably play a major role. In the case of the canyons, these are primarily turbidity currents. In cutting the deep-sea channels currents of water made dense by cooling and by its relatively high salt content are also thought to be a predominant factor.

Forces of Mud and Silt

In 1936 the Harvard geologist Dr. Reginald A. Daly first suggested that turbidity currents could erode the sea bottom. Few other geologists took him seriously until a Dutchman, Dr. Philip Kuenen, showed in 1951 that substantial turbidity currents could be generated in a 100-foot-long tank at Groningen University in Holland under conditions analogous to those of the sea. This lent support to the turbidity-current theory.

Meanwhile, in 1947, during a cruise of the Woods Hole Oceanographic Institution's research ship *Atlantis*, a plain over 200 miles wide was discovered in the deepest part of the western Atlantic, where the first 15-foot layer of the sediment was made up of sand and silt like that of a New England beach. Finding this material in the deep ocean where the bottom usually consists of fine oozes and clays was startling. It seemed totally out of place, with no apparent explanation for being there.

Then in 1949 the *Atlantis* again set out for the plain, this time tracing the Hudson submarine canyon westward from the edge of the continental shelf. Bottom samples showed the canyon was cut through ancient clays millions of years old. Moreover, sand, gravel, and the shells of shallow-water animals that live near shore were found along the canyon floor. All of this suggested one thing—turbidity currents. Perhaps these currents with their suspended silts and sediments could have carried shallow-water materials even to the newly discovered abyssal plain. Then came Kuenen's demonstration that the concept of such currents flowing over the ocean floor was valid. But could these currents, flowing because their turbid fluid is just a little bit heavier than the surrounding water, generate enough force to erode canyons and reach distant parts of the deep sea?

Ewing and Heezen at Lamont thought this was the case. When they looked about for evidence, the transatlantic telegraph cables gave them a clue. If turbidity currents strong enough to cut canyons actually flow down the slopes and over the abyssal floor, they reasoned, those that occurred in the northwestern Atlantic may have broken some of the cables. Looking over the records, they found circumstantial confirmation in the severe earthquake that shook the Grand Banks south of Newfoundland on November 18, 1929. Cables lying within 60 miles of the earthquake epicenter broke instantly. But for 13 hours thereafter cables on the downslope side from the epicenter continued to break one after the other in a regular sequence, starting with the ones farthest upslope and ending with one in the deep-ocean basin 300 miles from the epicenter. It looked as though some kind of massive flow had moved down the slope.

Ewing and Heezen concluded that there had been a turbidity current. From the records of the precise times of the respective cable breaks, they calculated that the speed of the current ranged from about 50 miles an hour on the steep slope to 15 miles an hour in the depths. Here was a current powerful enough to erode canyons on the continental slope and to cut channels along the deep-sea floor. The levees that border many of these latter could easily be accounted for by the same process that took place on land. As the turbidity current overflowed the channel banks it would deposit some of its load and build up the levees.

Subsequent investigation in the western North Atlantic by the Lamont group showed that the area where the deepest cable break had occurred in 1929 was covered with just the thickness of silt to be expected if a turbidity current had flowed there. In 1954 an earthquake in the Mediterranean yielded additional evidence of strong turbidity currents based on cable breaks similar to those of the Grand Banks quake.

Ewing and Heezen also noted that there is a network of submarine canyons in the Caribbean off the mouth of the Magdalena River in Colombia where an underwater cable has broken seventeen times since it was laid in 1930. In the case of at least two of these breaks there were concurrent earth slides near the river mouth which gave rise to turbidity currents. These, in turn, flowed down the canyon and deposited sediments on the floor of the adjacent sea basin where shallow-water sand and shells and the remains of land plants have been found.

All of this added up to impressive circumstantial evidence for the existence of turbidity currents strong enough to have eroded the great submarine canyons of the world. But as often happens in science, there is more than one way of interpreting the evidence. Professor Karl Terzaghi of Harvard University, one of the world's foremost authorities on soil mechanics, has recently taken an interest in the cable-breaking problem. He points out that it is quite possible for loosely packed and water-soaked sediments like those found on the sea bottom to be temporarily liquefied by mechanical shock such as that caused by an earthquake. This shock influence would travel swiftly out from the earthquake epicenter, causing progressive liquefaction of the sediments on which the cables rested. As the bottom suddenly gave out under any particular cable, it would snap from the strain.

Here is an alternative explanation of the cable-breaking evidence. It does not rule out the simultaneous generation of turbidity currents, which would leave telltale signs, such as the distribution of silt. But it does explain how the succession of cable breaks occurred so rapidly, in a way that seems more satisfying to those geologists who were unable to conceive of 50-mile-an-hour turbidity currents developing on the gentle slopes off the Grand Banks and against the substantial friction of the surrounding water.

One of these skeptical geologists is Dr. Francis Shepard of Scripps Institution. He has been unusually well located to study submarine canyons, since Scripps is close to the head of the sizable La Jolla submarine canyon systems. Unable to accept the concept of really powerful density currents, Shepard has suggested that these canyons may be a combined product of river erosion and turbidity flows. Geologists have objected to the theory that the canyons are drowned river valleys because many of the canyons are not associated with land valleys and many of them extend into quite deep water. Sea levels would have to be dropped an unbelievable amount for rivers to have cut these canyons. Shepard points out, however, that if the canyons are many millions of years old, rather than geologically recent formations, river erosion in their initial stages is no longer out of the question.

It is entirely possible that the present continental shelves and slopes stood much higher in the early Tertiary period. At that time they may have been above sea level and rivers could have eroded them deeply. Then, as they sank beneath the sea, the underwater canyons would have been preserved while the corresponding land valleys in many cases would have long since been modified beyond recognition. What preserved the form of the submarine canyons? What kept them relatively free of sediments through millions of years? This, Shepard suggests, has been the action of landslides and turbidity currents.

In support of his theory he points out that almost every coast that is inside a submarine canyon is underlain by thousands of feet of sedimentary rock which contain evidence of having been laid down at much higher levels than those at which they now are found. This indicates that over a long period of time, perhaps twenty million years, substantial sinking has occurred along such coastal areas. He also notes that in the La Jolla submarine canyon there has been no net fill during the more than twenty years that Scripps oceanographers have been watching depth changes in the canyon system. This is in spite of the rapid sand movement in the area which is sufficient to fill the canyon head in a few years. He attributes this to the periodic landslides known to occur in the canyon head and to resulting turbidity currents that carry the sediment out along the length of the canyon and deposit some of it in basins and troughs farther out to sea.

In this way, Shepard says, he thinks turbidity currents help preserve the canyons, but the great undersea gorges could not have been sculptured by turbidity flows alone. Among other things, he notes that Kuenen and others have found relatively coarse sediments deposited by turbidity currents on top of finer deep-water sediments in which worm tracks had been untouched by the passing current. This casts doubt on the power of these turbid flows to erode canyons that have been cut into bedrock.

On the other hand, it still is possible that turbidity currents could have cut some of the shallow deep-sea channels in soft bottom sediments over long periods of time. According to Dr. Robert Dietz, however, many of these channels seem to be primarily the product of flows of cold, saline water, which would also carry some sediment and could build levees. Perhaps, he says, these channels are evidence of one of the most fundamental processes in the ocean, the formation of cold bottom water and its movement equatorward. He notes that many oceanographers now think the cold water that underlies all the major oceans is formed at very selected spots and at irregular intervals in high Arctic and Antarctic latitudes. Perhaps some of the deep-sea channels were formed in areas where the surface water, becoming cold and dense, cascades down to the abyssal floor and pours out along it, bringing Arctic cold to the depths of tropical seas.

Mountains beneath the Sea

Like the submarine canyons, the huge channels on the deep-ocean floor are relatively too small to be shown on the endpaper map. On the other hand, the map does show the known major features of the ocean floor. With towering mountain ranges and deep trenches, it is as varied a "landscape" as anything the continents can boast. And, unlike the continents, it is not subject to erosive forces of wind, rain, and large temperature changes. Once formed, its major geological features tend to persist unless altered by forces within and below the crust itself.

Although the first accurate soundings of the deep oceans were taken by the *Challenger* expedition, a physicist named A. D. Bache had made a fair estimate of the average depth of the Pacific before the *Challenger* sailed. He did it by measuring the time it took waves generated in conjunction with earthquakes off Japan to reach the west coast of the United States. Bache fixed the time of the earthquake with the help of an early-model seismograph and detected the arrival of the waves with tide gauges. Then, using the physical principle that the speed of these waves depended directly on the depth of the water, he estimated the average depth of the Pacific to be about 2,000 fathoms (12,000 feet). The *Challenger* findings confirmed his estimate as a fair average for the world's abyssal depths.

By way of comparison, the average depths as known today for the three largest oceans—the Pacific, Atlantic, and Indian—are, respectively, 2,340 fathoms, 2,150 fathoms, and 2,180 fathoms. If one includes adjacent seas such as the Caribbean or China Seas, these average depths are, respectively, 2,200 fathoms, 1,820 fathoms, and 2,140 fathoms.

But while Bache and the *Challenger* scientists could estimate average water depths, the varied topography of the bottom remained largely unsuspected until the German ships *Meteor* and *Altair* began running lines of echo soundings across the North and South Atlantic about thirty-five years ago. From these soundings, rough charts of major bottom features were drawn up. Even then the submarine topography could not be worked out in more than a generalized way until the continuous-recording echo sounder became available to oceanographers after the war.

The endpaper map gives only a rough idea of the complex relief the sea-bottom explorers have found. In the Pacific, for example, Menard estimates some 90 per cent of the ocean-basin floor is rough and irregular. Much of the remaining 10 per cent smooth area borders continents and islands where sediments eroded from land have covered over the rough bottom. Moreover, the exceptions to this general picture are mountains and deep trenches rather than the smooth monotonous plains that were once thought to be the rule.

The Atlantic, on the other hand, does have some sizable abyssal plains. They lie in the long wide basins that flank the Mid-Atlantic Ridge and may be partly due to sediment deposition by turbidity currents. These basins are largely between 12,000 and 18,000 feet deep, with a few deeper spots. The most striking feature of the Atlantic floor, however, is the Mid-Atlantic Ridge. This great mountain chain extends in an almost unbroken line from Iceland to about 55° South Latitude. It rises on the average some 5,000 feet above the basins at its sides and splits the North and South Atlantic neatly. Menard has pointed out that a line drawn equally distant from the continental slopes that border these oceans falls on top of the ridge throughout most of its length. In places the mountains of the ridge break the surface to form islands such as St. Paul's Rocks, Ascension, and the Azores. But for the most part they are submerged.

Lines of soundings across the ridge show it to be as rugged and as complex as the North American Rockies. There are chains of mountains interspersed with valleys. Terrace-like platforms are ranged along the sides of the ridge. They look very much like basins which were blocked off by natural dams and which turbidity currents then filled with sediments just as silt piles up behind man-made dams. And, reminiscent of the Rocky Mountain Trench—a fault valley in the northern Rockies—a steep-sided valley with a flat bottom several miles wide has been found along the ridge north of the Azores.

Ewing and Heezen have suggested that this trough may run the full length of the ridge and around Africa into the Indian Ocean. There they think it splits into two branches running, respectively, up the Arabian Sea and around Australia into the eastern Pacific. They estimate it is a 40,000-mile-long "crack" in the earth's crust. This will be a major geological discovery if it is confirmed. But until the necessary soundings have been taken, it will remain simply an intriguing speculation.

In any event, the well-established trough in the ridge north of the Azores is thought to be a fault valley created by movements of the crust. It is an active earthquake region, as are many areas along or bordering the ridge. In this connection, Shepard has suggested that the deep-sea channels associated with the ridge in the western North Atlantic may have been created by faulting rather than erosion by density currents. Once opened, they would then form channels along which turbidity currents could flow and deposit sediments.

In addition to the deep basins, the sea floor on either side of the Mid-Atlantic Ridge is broken by a number of transverse ridges and rises extending laterally from the central ridge or out from the bordering continents. To draw the geologists' distinction between "ridges" and "rises," the former are defined as elongated elevations with steep irregular slopes, while the latter have smooth gentle sides.

Bottom features such as ridges, mountains, and canyons play an important role in the general water circulation. By blocking and channeling the movement of deep water, they influence the mechanism and rate by which the oceans are stirred and overturned. As will be explained in Chapter Seven, this overturning has a significant and little-understood effect on world climate. It is also possible that some bottom water becomes trapped in deep basins. During IGY surveys in the Caribbean, samples of deep water from the enclosed basin in that sea indicate the water is a stagnant mass left over from previous ocean circulation patterns under different climatic or geological conditions. It is "fossil" water that, like the rock-bound remains of ancient animals, has been sealed off by the encircling basin and preserved.

To draw another technical line, ocean "basins" are distinguished from "trenches" in that basins are more or less broadly dimensioned depressions in the ocean floor, while trenches are long, narrow depressions with relatively steep sides. An ocean "deep" is the deepest area of a given depression when the depth exceeds 18,000 feet. With very few exceptions, the deep-ocean trenches are found in the Pacific.

Unlike the Atlantic, the Pacific has no single dominant ridge to set the pattern of its "landscape," although it does have major mountain ranges, as a glance at the endpaper map will show. The topography of the Pacific however, is nowhere near as well known as that of the Atlantic. The former embraces a hemisphere, while the latter is relatively circumscribed. It will take many more years of surveying before the whole Pacific floor has been charted in even a generalized way.

It is doubtful, though, that any more striking feature will ever be found than the deep trenches. It is in these that the greatest recorded depths of the ocean have been plumbed. Besides the *Vitiaz* deep of 36,056 feet officially reported from the Marianas Trench during the IGY (a subsequent sounding of 36,173 feet was reported by Moscow Radio), soundings in the other trenches indicate maximum depths in the range of about 35,000 feet. It is hard to imagine a chasm so deep that seven Grand Canyons could be piled up on top of each other in it, and so long that it would stretch from New York to Kansas City. Yet this is the way Roger Revelle and Robert L. Fisher of Scripps have described a typical Pacific trench, the Tonga Trench, which Scripps' oceanographers have studied extensively.

Some of the trenches are V-shaped. Others are slightly flattened at the bottom to form more of a narrow U-shaped cross section. They ring the Pacific from Indonesia to South America and are shown on the endpaper map as narrow elongated areas of solid color. Almost everywhere these trenches are associated with mountain building, active volcanism, and earthquakes. They are one of the most geologically interesting features on the surface of the earth, and we shall hear more of them in the next chapter.

One other feature of the Pacific floor should also be mentioned, although, like the trenches, its geological history will be discussed in the following chapter. This is the peppering of individual, often isolated, undersea mountains that rise from the bottom. Many of them have rounded peaks. These are called "seamounts." Others are flattened on top and are known as "guyots" (pronounced *gee-yo*, with a hard g as in "get").

There are some seamounts and guyots in the Atlantic, but by far the majority of those known have been found in the Pacific. The seamounts seem to be scattered all over that ocean, while the guyots for the most part have been found along three lines. One of these, along the line of the Emperor Seamounts, runs south of Kamchatka. A second is associated with the Mid-Pacific Mountains, and the third stretches between the Marshall and Marianas islands. A group of ten guyots has also been found in the Gulf of Alaska.

Seamounts, built up by repeated undersea volcanic eruptions and lava flows, are easy to account for, but the guyots are more puzzling. Their flat tops, beveled at the edges, appear to have been carved by waves at the surface. But, as will be explained later, they lie now at depths of several thousand feet, intriguing geologists with suggestions of ancient sunken islands. (See Plate 3.)

The Arctic and Indian Ocean basins are even less well known than those of the Pacific. But, such surveys as have been run indicate that they are, in general, equally deep, with depths averaging over 12,000 feet. It should be noted that the landlocked seas—the Black Sea, Caribbean, Gulf of Mexico, and Mediterranean (whose basins are sealed off even though their uppermost waters are not completely enclosed)— also have true oceanic depths, exceeding 12,000 feet over large areas. The Gulf of Mexico and the Black Sea are comparatively flat-bottomed, while the other two seas have a number of ridges and basins.

The Indian Ocean has been singled out as an object of special study by SCOR in its plans to carry on internationally co-operative ocean investigations where the IGY left off. Meanwhile preliminary studies indicate that the floor of the Indian Ocean has its mountain ranges too. In particular, there are indications of a large central ridge with numerous transverse ridges in the Arabian Sea.

The Arctic Ocean floor, as everyone who followed the voyages of the United States submarines *Nautilus* and *Skate* knows, is studded with jagged mountain peaks. Traveling under the ice, navigators of these submarines often had to pick their way through mountains with the aid of sound-ranging devices, just as pilots of small planes visually guide their aircraft through passes in land mountains. The Arctic basin is split by the great Lomonsov Ridge discovered in 1948 by Soviet explorers stationed on drifting islands of ice. Rising some 10,000 feet from the ocean floor, it stretches between Ellesmere Island, the northernmost part of Canada, and the Soviet islands Novosibirskiye Ostrova off northeastern Siberia. A large submarine peninsula, Chukchi, lies off the northwest tip of Alaska.

Soviet and Western geophysicists again manned ice-island stations during the IGY. One of these, Station A, which carried an American team, drifted across a second mid-ocean ridge about 850 miles northwest of Barrow, Alaska, and 550 miles from the North Pole. The ridge in that area rose steeply to within 4,500 feet of the surface in its central

4-5000 meters; 3000 meters; ——— 200 meters.

FIG. 10: *Arctic Ocean bottom topography.*

part from depths of 10,000 to 15,000 feet on either side. It is hard to judge the extent of this ridge from the relatively few soundings taken from Station A. However, Kenneth Hunkins of Lamont, who reported the discovery, said there are indications that the ridge is a major bottom feature running parallel to the Lomonosov Ridge.

The Dustfall

One of the most characteristic features of the deep-sea floor is the sediments. Drifting slowly down from above or spread broadly by currents, sediments accumulate like a slow dustfall. Some of their material has been eroded from the land. Some has drifted down from the life-filled upper waters. There is even a small amount that is meteoritic and has come, so to speak, from the stars.

Many things contribute to the sediments. Rivers carry silts and sands from the land to be spread over parts of the sea bottom as muds. Winds bring more land debris that, gradually settling out of the air, drifts slowly down through the water to combine with traces of volcanic and meteoritic dusts to form the clays that cover many of the deepest basins. A host of plants and animals, many of them microscopic, live in the sunlit surface waters and drop their skeletons when they grow or die. These remains drift down to form various kinds of oozes.

As they slowly accumulate upon the bottom, the sediments, where undisturbed, reflect the climatic and geological conditions under which they were laid down, the deeper sediments corresponding to the earlier periods. Thus the accumulated layers of deep-sea sediments are an ordered record of the ages. The art of reading this record is a subject for the next chapter. Here we are merely describing the abyssal "dustfall" itself.

The most abundant types of sediments are those already mentioned—the oozes, clays, and land-derived muds. The oozes are made up largely of skeletons of microscopic marine plants and animals. They are generally found in shallower parts of the abyss. The most abundant of these tiny animals are the order Foraminifera, of which one genus, *Globigerina*, often dominates the sediments. Foraminiferal and globigerinal oozes are found widely throughout the major oceans. On the other hand, in some equatorial oozes and especially in the Pacific, the siliceous (silica-containing) remains of tiny animals of the order Radiolaria predominate.

A third type of ooze is found extensively around Antarctica and in the Pacific northeast of Japan. Here the siliceous remains of microscopic one-celled plants called diatoms predominate. Individual diatoms are encased in little glass shells made of silica that, in some species, look exactly like tiny glass boxes. It is these that make up the diatomaceous oozes.

The various organisms named here are present in many different parts of the ocean, whether the sediments are classified after them or not. The name of a particular ooze simply indicates that one type of organism is relatively more abundant than others.

Many of the deeper parts of the ocean basins (below about 14,000 feet) are covered with a clay-like sediment. This has been misnamed

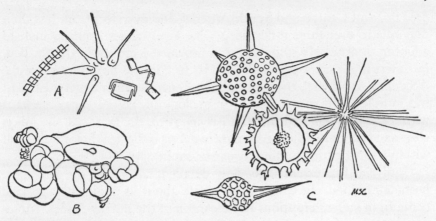

FIG. 11: *Ooze makers: A—Diatoms; B—Foraminifera; C—Radiolarians.*

"red" clay because the first samples found in the South Atlantic happened to be red. But it is more often brown or buff-colored than it is red. As already mentioned, it seems to consist largely of air-borne dust and fine current-borne land debris, a little volcanic dust, and traces of meteorites.

Around the continental margins, the sediments deposited as deep-sea fans are mainly muds with large amounts of silt and interlayered with sand. The occasional appearance of sand and the remains of shallow-water animals in these fans or even on the bottom of the deep basins used to puzzle oceanographers. It now is explained as the deposit of turbidity currents.

The sediments already listed are the principal ones you would find in a standard oceanographic textbook. But so little is known about the ocean bottom that the subject is far from closed. While this chapter was being written, Dr. J. Lamar Worzel, assistant director of Lamont Geological Observatory, reported discovery of a vast layer of clean white ash in the sediments of the tropical eastern Pacific. Discovered and announced during an extended cruise of Lamont's research ship *Vema*, the ash consists of very fine-grained fragments of volcanic glass. It is similar to material that has been classed as volcanic ash in other deep-sea deposits. But unlike these other deposits where the ash is dispersed through normal sediments, Worzel's material is a layer of pure ash of great extent, according to initial reports.

So far the ash layer has been traced at least 750 miles north of the equator and about 825 miles south of it. The area is within a few hundred miles of Central and South America and in waters from less than one mile to over three miles deep. The layer ranges from an inch to a foot in thickness. In some places it lies on the surface of the sea bed, in others it is buried as deeply as 120 feet in the bottom sediments. According to Worzel, the ash probably covers a much larger area than was sampled, and was deposited in geologically recent times, perhaps within the past hundred thousand years. Also, the fact that the ash is clear and free from other sedimentary debris indicates that all of it fell within a short period, within a year or so, he says.

Until the full extent, age, and detailed nature of the ash have been determined, one can only speculate about its origin. It may have come from violent eruptions of volcanoes in the nearby Andes. Moreover, if the deposit can be correlated with those from other areas, it may turn out to be evidence of world-wide volcanism. The ash layer has been traced partly by sensitive echo sounding that picked out the echoes returned by this sub-bottom material. In a paper accompanying Worzel's report in the "Proceedings of the National Academy of Sciences," Ewing, Heezen, and David B. Ericson of Lamont noted that a re-examination of echograms taken by the *Vema* indicates similar sub-bottom echoes had been recorded in the South Atlantic and Indian oceans.

The paper noted that most of the ash fragments, called shards, "are in the form of curved, fluted or crumpled films of glass." It added that "since it is very possible that the shards of the Worzel layer were thrown to a great height in the atmosphere by an explosive eruption or eruptions, and since the shards, because of their peculiar shape, would settle more slowly in both air and water than [more] nearly equidimensional . . . particles, an ocean-wide or even global distribution of the Worzel ash is a real possibility." A rich ash layer has already been found in the Gulf of Mexico at the same depth as the Worzel layer in the Pacific. But, unlike the latter, the Gulf ash is dispersed in normal sediments, as is similar ash long known in the North Atlantic.

According to the Ewing-Heezen-Ericson paper, "Apparently we require [to account for the Worzel ash layer] either a single very large volcanic explosion, or simultaneous explosion of many volcanoes, or conceivably a cometary collision [which would have spread its debris over the planet]." But at this writing, the *Vema* is still at sea. Until detailed study of the data and bottom samples she has gathered can be made in shore laboratories, the nature of the Worzel layer is a matter of speculation.

In any event, this layer is only the latest puzzle of the sediments. The surprising thinness of the sediment accumulation in general has mystified marine geologists for a number of years. For a long time oceanographers thought the entire ocean bottom was covered with sediments that had accumulated throughout geological time. As recently as 1950, Kuenen published an estimate in the English edition of his *Marine Geology* that the average thickness of sediments thus accumulated in the ocean basins would be about three kilometers, or 9,800 feet. But extensive seismic surveys have failed to confirm his calculations. Instead, the average thickness of unconsolidated material on the bottom of the Pacific is about 1,000 feet, while in the Atlantic, where there is less area for river-borne sediment to spread out, it is about 2,000 feet. In many places there is little or no recent sediment cover.

The action of deep currents in redistributing some of the bottom material may partly explain the present sediment pattern. But it doesn't answer the question of why the sediments are so relatively thin if they have been accumulating at presently observed rates throughout geological time. Perhaps the older deeper sediments have become compacted into a hard material that has different sound properties than the unconsolidated muds, clays, and oozes. In that case the thinness of the sediments would only be an illusion of the echo sounder. Or perhaps the oceans are much younger than has generally been believed, so that the "dustfall" has had a relatively short time to accumulate. The history of the sediments is bound up with the geological history of the ocean basins themselves. But that is a subject for the following chapter.

FOUR

Probing the Deep-Sea Floor

Finding out what lies under the ocean floor is an exercise in indirection. The marine geologist is like a space traveler trying to study a planet into whose atmosphere he cannot descend and whose surface is veiled in perpetual cloud. If this planet were the earth, one can imagine how misleading a picture the explorer might get when all he had to go by were samples of ground scraped up from the surface or the profile of the land traced by radar.

With increased use of deep-diving submarines like the bathyscaphe, this blindness will gradually be overcome in studying the sea floor. But, as of today, beyond the 180-foot practical depth limit of SCUBA diving, the marine geologist is essentially as limited in his explorations as our imaginary interplanetary visitor.

Yet by extracting the maximum information from available clues, marine geologists have managed to sketch at least a generalized picture. In seismic studies they listen to the distant echoes of explosions to trace rock layers in the crust and the juncture of crust and mantle. They extend long fingers of steel into the sea bed to measure the heat flowing up from below which hints the great thermal unrest beneath the crust. They measure minute changes in the pull of gravity to find out something about the density of underlying material. And by learning to read a language far more ancient than the oldest human tongue—the signs and symbols buried in the slowly accumulated sediments—they can piece together some of the history of past epochs.

The Record of the Sediments

To penetrate a few dozen feet into the sediment-covered sea bottom is to go back millions of years in time. Wherever the sediments have been undisturbed by bottom upheavals or eroding currents, the story

of past climates and geological events can be read by those who know
the "language." Experts are still learning the subtler points of its gram-
mar and enlarging their vocabulary. But they already can extract a good
deal of meaning from what to a layman looks no more informative than
the colored clays with which children play.

For one thing, the sediments often are neatly layered, indicating
sudden changes of climate or certain geological events in the past.
Sometimes distinct layers of glacial sediments are found. These are
usually characterized by stones dropped by the numerous icebergs that
broke off from the edge of the ice sheets. Also, the sediments are full of
fossils of tiny marine plants and animals that help date the layers and
tell something of past climates as well.

Take the Foraminifera, for example. This order of tiny animals has
been one of the most useful for oceanographic research. They have been
widely abundant for several hundred million years, and over 15,000
living and extinct species have been identified. With few exceptions
they are microscopic. They generally have a calcareous shell, although
in some species the shells are formed of sand grains cemented together.
Some of the shells look like those of tiny snails. Others are elongated
or globular, sometimes formed into little clusters of crystalline bubbles
of calcium carbonate. Most of them have several communicating
chambers and are perforated by many tiny holes through which the
animal protrudes bits of its body as pseudopoda, or "false feet." Hence
the name Foraminifera, the "hole bearers."

The shells of these animals are easy to spot in microscope studies of
sediments. Some species live their lives floating and drifting near the
surface as part of the plankton. Others live on the bottom even
at abyssal depths. Many species also have fairly narrow temperature
ranges, while extinct species often are typical of specific epochs in the
past. Because of this, these curious little animals have been extraordinarily useful in dating sediment layers and in estimating the temperatures of the surface and bottom waters at the time their shells were
laid down.

Before oceanographers could read the sediment record, they had to
devise ways of recovering that record intact. A simple grab or dredge
will suffice to find out what kind of sediment is on the bottom. But to
take advantage of the time-ordered layers, oceanographers need a deep
and undisturbed sample. They get it by cutting out a sediment core with
a kind of hollow pipe dropped into the soft bottom material, like cutting
the core out of an apple.

As with many other "firsts" in oceanography, the first deep-sea cores were taken from the *Challenger*. They were only about a foot long and scarcely penetrated the upper layers. In fact, no really long cores were taken until after World War II. Because of this inability to penetrate deeply, the pre-war interest in coring was relatively slight. The German *Meteor* expedition accounted for a good many of the cores taken in those years. Even with heavy weights attached, coring tubes could penetrate no more than a few feet with only gravity to help them punch into the sediments. At one point Charles Piggot of the National Research Council in the United States tried to improve matters by shooting the tubes into the bottom with a special kind of gun. But the method was cumbersome—being as likely to shoot a hole in the bottom of the ship as in the bottom of the sea—and the cores were only up to 10 feet long. Woods Hole oceanographers were already getting cores of that length with the less hazardous gravity corers, and the coring gun was abandoned.

The problem was finally solved during the war by what looks in retrospect like a simple and obvious invention. The inventor was Dr. Börje Kullenberg, now head of the Oceanographic Institute at Göteborg, Sweden. Kullenberg fitted a long coring tube with a piston. In practice, a tripping weight hangs below the corer as it is lowered through the water. Hitting the bottom first, this weight releases the core barrel, which then falls freely, sliding past the piston as it drops. At the same time, the piston is held stationary from the deck of the ship by stopping the winch handling the corer's cable.

The effect of the heavily weighted coring tube sliding past the stationary piston is the same as if the piston were being slowly withdrawn up the tube and "sucking" in the sediment core as it went. In this way cores of undisturbed sediments over 60 feet long are easily forced into the tube.

Kullenberg demonstrated his invention on the Swedish Deep-Sea Expedition (the *Albatross* expedition) led by Dr. Hans Pettersson in 1947–48, when over 300 long cores were taken in the Atlantic and Pacific. Since then, use of the piston corer has spread widely, although gravity corers, punching out samples by weight alone, still are used in many cases. Thousands of long "piston" cores from the major oceans now have been taken for study and deposition in "core libraries" at oceanographic institutions. For this purpose, corers are often lined with plastic tubes which are removed with the cores and in which the cores

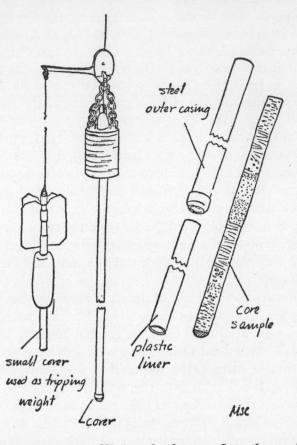

steel
outer casing

plastic
liner

small corer
used as tripping
weight

corer

core
sample

Misc

FIG. 12: *Kullenberg corer. Hitting the bottom first, the small corer releases the main coring tube. In this way (see text), sediment samples up to 70
feet and more in length have been taken. The small corer collects a comparison
sample of the upper few feet of sediments, which are the part of the sample
most likely to be compressed and distorted in the long core.*

can be stored for future study. The Soviets appear to hold the length
record. A scientist named Zenkevich has reported cores up to 111 feet
long being taken from the *Vitiaz*.

Meanwhile, during the past decade, oceanographers have been learning to read the record the long corers are bringing up with new clarity
and precision. In addition to classifying characteristic fossils, they now
have a chemical thermometer for reading ancient temperatures and a
short-term "atomic clock" for dating fairly recent deposits.

1. Lowering deep-sea camera from the *Atlantis*.

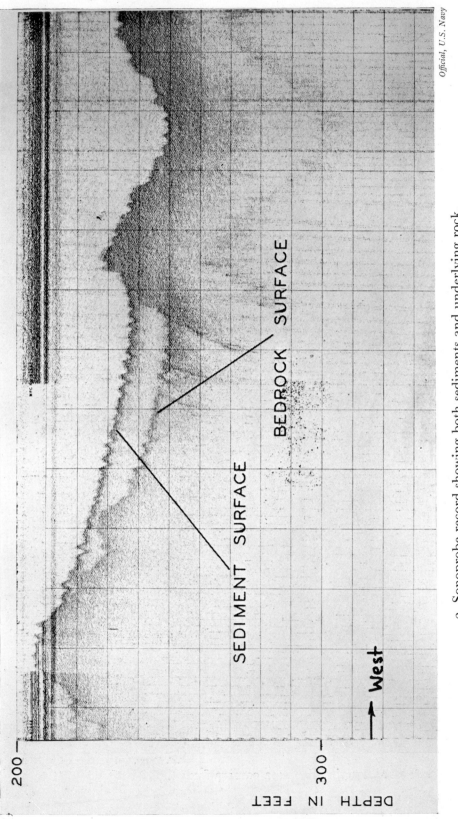

2. Sonoprobe record showing both sediments and underlying rock.

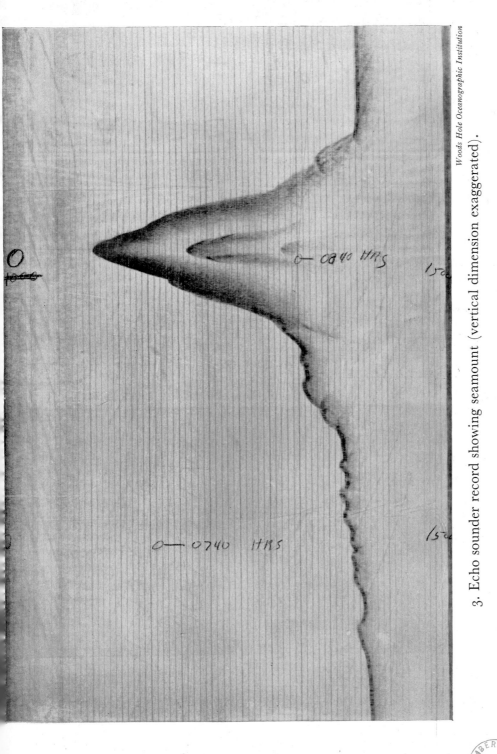

O

O — 0840 HRS

O — 0740 HRS

150

150

Woods Hole Oceanographic Institution

3. Echo sounder record showing seamount (vertical dimension exaggerated).

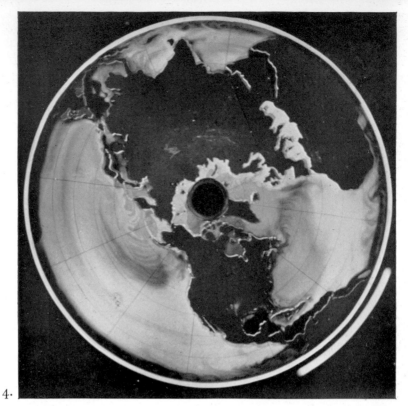

4.

William S. von Arx, Woods Hole Oceanographic Institution

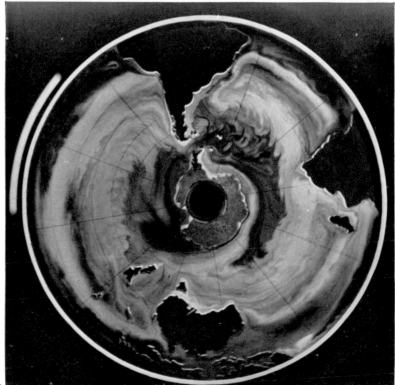

5.

6.

Ocean circulation patterns can be simulated in rotating cylindrical tanks which are cooled at the centre and heated at the rim just as a hemisphere on the real earth is cooled at the pole and warmed at the equator. The two photographs on the left show one such device used at the Woods Hole Oceanographic Institution in which major land masses are represented by movable blocks and currents by a coloured fluid in water. Configurations for the northern and southern hemispheres are shown. Above is another type of simulator used at Woods Hole. This is the kind of device in which Stommel's theory predicting the Gulf Stream Counter Current was first tested.

7. Soviet research ship *Mikhail Lomonosov*.

8. Woods Hole's *Atlantis*.

9. The bathyscaphe, *Trieste*, which has carried men to the deepest part of the sea, diving 35,800 feet into the Marianas Trench on January 23, 1960.

The Oxygen Thermometer

Some of nature's most telling distinctions are the slight differences between almost identical materials. The weight difference of three parts in 238 between two isotopes of uranium, for example, is the difference between an atomic bomb and a harmless piece of metal. So it is with the oxygen in the air we breathe and in the water we drink. This oxygen is made up of three isotopes—oxygen-16, oxygen-17, and oxygen-18— the lightest being by far the most abundant. Chemically these isotopes are indistinguishable. But almost imperceptible differences in their relative abundances have become a key to the past.

When water evaporates, the three isotopes of oxygen in the water molecules go off at different rates, the lightest evaporating slightly faster than the others. This leaves the water a little richer in the heavier isotopes. This suggests, among other things, that there should be a difference between the isotope ratios in the continually renewed fresh water of the land and the ratios in the sea, where evaporation has gone on for a long time. Moreover, the compounds involving carbon and oxygen, called carbonates, which make up the shells and skeletons of many aquatic animals, should reflect the oxygen isotope ratio of the water in which they were formed.

With this in mind in 1947, Dr. Harold Urey was studying oxygen isotope ratios in the shells of marine animals when he made an unexpected discovery. He had hoped to find a way to tell whether ancient carbonate deposits, such as limestones, had been laid down in fresh water or in salt. But as often happens in research, he came up instead with something quite unlooked for and much more valuable to oceanographers. His study showed that the relative concentration of oxygen isotopes in the carbonates depends partly on the temperature of the water in which they were formed. In his own words, "I suddenly found myself with a geological thermometer on my hands."

But at that time it was an extremely difficult thermometer to read. For one thing, a difference of one degree Centigrade in water temperature corresponds to a difference of about two hundredths of one per cent in the ratio of oxygen-18 to oxygen-16 in the carbonates. The best that could be done in 1947 was to detect a difference of one fifth of one per cent in isotope ratios. This corresponded to a temperature range of ten degrees Centigrade on the Urey thermometer. Given the relatively

D

stable temperatures of the ocean, this ten degree range of error could be the difference between glacial and temperate climates.

An important part of the subsequent development of the Urey thermometer has been a continuing increase in the sensitivity of mass spectrometers, the instruments used to measure isotope ratios. By the early 1950's, the sensitivity was good enough to fix ancient ocean temperatures to within a very few degrees. This enabled Dr. Cesare Emiliani of the University of Miami to begin temperature analyses of some of the *Albatross* long cores, which were by then available for study, and some of a library of 1,000 cores that had been collected by Lamont using the Kullenberg equipment.

There now was another source of error to be contended with, however. Urey had originally assumed that oxygen was the same throughout the ocean. But studies at sea showed that oxygen isotope ratios vary from place to place. There is a difference between tropical and Arctic waters and between mid-ocean and inshore waters, where local evaporation and outpouring rivers have a noticeable effect. This introduces a corresponding uncertainty in readings of the oxygen thermometer, which are based on estimates of isotope ratios in ancient seas. It is hard to know how true the thermometer reads when the ratios may reflect fresh-water dilution or unknown but normal differences between parts of the same ocean.

For the moment this uncertainty is reduced somewhat by studying fossils of animals that lived in the open sea away from inshore disturbances, and by careful geographical selection of the cores. A second thermometer, based on isotope ratios in silicas and phosphates, which vary with temperature on a different scale from those in the carbonates, is being developed as an independent check. Meanwhile, Emiliani says he is "reasonably confident" that present measurements are exact enough so that any future corrections will be minor.

Starting with three cores brought up from over 10,000 feet in the equatorial Pacific, Emiliani began to develop the general climatic outline of the Cenozoic era, the great age of mammals. He looked first for the long-term trends. These would most likely show up in the bottom-water temperatures. Being formed in restricted areas at Antarctic or Arctic latitudes, this water would be characteristic of the trends of polar climates rather than those of the more variable temperate and tropical zones.

For this purpose Emiliani studied the fossils of bottom-living Foraminifera. These showed that thirty-two million years ago the

Pacific bottom from which the cores had come had a temperature of about 51° Fahrenheit. Twenty-two million years ago it had dropped to 44°F. By the beginning of the Pleistocene epoch one million years ago, it had fallen close to the present bottom temperatures prevailing in all oceans—just two or three degrees above freezing. For the past half million years it has fluctuated around an average slightly lower than the present average bottom temperature.

Thus, according to Emiliani, thirty-two million years ago polar waters were as warm as those of temperate latitudes today. This correlates well with fossil evidence of evergreen forests on Greenland where thousands of feet of icecap now sit. The drop to near freezing temperatures at the beginning of the Pleistocene indicates a frozen Antarctic, while the temperature fluctuations of the past five hundred thousand or so years reflect climate changes associated with the advances and retreats of the glaciers.

The next step was to pin down the chronology of the ice ages. A certain amount of chronology could be deduced from the structures of the cores themselves. But Emiliani needed a more precise frame of reference than the biological characteristics of fossils alone could provide. This is where the short-term "atomic clock" came into the story.

The method is similar to that used in dating rocks, except that in this case organic remains are involved. It was developed by Dr. Willard F. Libby when he was with the University of Chicago. The timekeeper is carbon-14, a radioactive isotope of carbon that occurs naturally in the atmosphere in known concentrations. As long as plants and animals are alive, their bodies maintain the same relative concentration of carbon-14 as found in their environment. But after they die, the carbon-14 slowly decays away at a fixed known rate. Experts use this rate to date organic remains for intervals up to about thirty-five thousand years in the past.

Incidentally, radioactive dating of rocks is unreliable for intervals shorter than about ten million years. This leaves a considerable gap from the early Pliocene to late Pleistocene in which dating is largely guesswork. However, a dating technique based on radioactive ionium, found naturally in sea water, is coming into use that will partly fill this gap up to about five hundred thousand years in the past. Using the amount of radioionium in the newly deposited sediments at the top of the core as a reference, experts can date the rest of the core by measuring how much the ionium concentration falls off in progressively deeper layers. Presumably the concentration of radioionium at the surface gives the rate at which this isotope is incorporated in the sediments as they accumulate on the sea bed. Then, since radioionium decays at a known rate, its concentration down the core is yet another form of "atomic clock" which can date sediment layers. But at this writing it has not yet been applied to dating the ice ages.

To help Emiliani use the carbon "clock," Hans Suess and Meyer Rubin, at the Radiocarbon Laboratory of the United States Geological Survey, undertook to analyze a number of cores from the Atlantic, the Caribbean, and the Mediterranean. This time Emiliani selected Foraminifera that lived within a few hundred feet of the surface, because the glacial record would show up most clearly in fluctuations of surface temperatures. With the help of Suess and Rubin, he found that the peak of the last ice age came about eighteen thousand years ago.

At that time, when the ice reached as far south as Chicago and Berlin, tropical ocean temperatures dropped significantly. In the Caribbean, for example, the surface temperature at 15° North Latitude was 68° to 72° Fahrenheit compared to a present-day 84°F. In the equatorial mid-Atlantic the temperature was 62°F. compared to a current surface temperature of 78°F. More recently David Ericson of Lamont, using oxygen temperatures found by Emiliani and carbon-14 dates worked out at Lamont by W. C. Broecker and J. L. Kulp, has shown that the Atlantic and Caribbean waters warmed up significantly about eleven thousand years ago to mark the probable end of the last glacial stage.

With the radiocarbon dates for the first thirty-five thousand years well established, Emiliani was then able to work out a tentative chronology for earlier parts of his cores. One way of doing this was to assume that the sediments accumulated throughout the core at the same rate they accumulated during the well-dated period. In itself, this was unreliable, because the rate of accumulation for bottom clays can vary by a factor of ten or more with different geological and climatic conditions. But by comparing his cores with others dated by other techniques, such as careful study of fossils, he cut down the margin of error.

He then checked the record of fluctuating temperatures with the advances of the ice sheets on land. The cores correlated exactly with glacial land evidence for the past hundred thousand years. After that the correspondence was hazier. However, if Emiliani's dating scheme is correct, the present glacial epoch began three hundred thousand years ago. This is two hundred thousand years later than had previously been estimated as the most recent possible date for the start of this epoch. But Emiliani's date is also a guess. Until a more exact dating system is employed, the real date could fall anywhere from three hundred thousand to a million years ago.

Beneath the Sediments

For the most part, the upper few dozen feet of sediment, such as Emiliani has been studying, is the only part of the sea bottom directly accessible to the oceanographer's instruments. All that is known about what lies below that level has been inferred from such things as seismic, gravitational, and heat-flow studies. These are the tools that point the way for exploring by indirection.

As far as you and I are concerned, the slight variations in gravity from place to place on the earth's surface are a geophysical refinement we can forget about. The small fractions of an ounce that are involved are of little consequence for most practical purposes. But they are a useful tool to geologists in studying masses beneath the surface that they cannot reach directly.

One way of doing this is by timing the swing of a pendulum. The time it takes for a pendulum of given length and mass to make one complete swing back and forth—the "period" of the pendulum, as it is called—depends on the local pull of gravity. This pull depends in turn on distance from the earth's center and on the mass of the underlying material. The greater the pull of gravity, the faster the pendulum swings, and vice versa. Thus careful timing of a pendulum gives a clue to the heaviness of the material under the instrument. Salt domes, for example, can be detected in this way because they have a different density than the surrounding sediments have.

The first gravity measurements at sea were made on the steamship *Fram* when it was locked in the arctic ice during Fridtjof Nansen's polar expedition of 1893–96. With the ship trapped, Nansen had a stable platform from which to work. Since it is hard to time a pendulum on a rocking ship, further gravity measurements at sea had to wait until some way was found to get a stable platform on the open ocean.

Vening Meinesz, a Dutch geologist, found such a platform in the submarine. Submerged beyond the play of wind and waves, a submarine is stable enough to work with a pendulum. Meinesz made his first gravity measurements at sea in 1923 and thereafter studied gravity in all the major oceans. But submarines are not readily available to oceanographers. As recently as the start of the IGY, only about five thousand gravity measurements had been made at sea throughout the world, and twelve hundred of them were taken by Meinesz himself before the end of World War II. These measurements had added to geologists' knowledge, but their total was insignificant compared to the vast area of the ocean. Then the invention marine geologists had been waiting for came along.

On November 22, 1957, Worzel of Lamont made the first successful measurements of gravity from a surface ship in the open ocean. He used an instrument designed by Anton Graf of Munich, Germany, which was mounted on a gyro-stabilized platform on board the navy ship U.S.S. *Compass Island*, one of the few ships on which such a platform has been installed. Unlike the pendulum whose bob responds to the slightest roll or pitch of the ship, the Graf instrument detects gravity variations by measuring slight shifts up or down in the end of a horizontal aluminum boom. The small boom is suspended and pivoted near one end by specially designed springs. These both support the boom and allow its other end to move up or down with changes in local gravity. This arrangement is much less susceptible to outside interference than a pendulum, yet is sensitive and accurate. Combined with the gyro-stabilized platform, it mastered the problems of measuring gravity at sea.

Meanwhile, Roger Revelle of Scripps and Arthur Maxwell of the Office of Naval Research in the United States and Sir Edward Bullard at Cambridge University in England have in the last ten years developed an ingenious way of measuring the heat flowing out of the ocean bottom. In particular, Revelle and Maxwell, who was formerly at Scripps, have used this technique widely in the Pacific. The instrument involved is simple. It is essentially a probe about 10 feet long and 1 to 1.6 inches in diameter which measures the temperature difference in the sediments at points near its top and bottom. At the same time, a core is taken. Back in the laboratory, the rate at which the material in the core conducts heat is measured. By using the observed temperature difference, the heat flow in the sediments can then be calculated. Thus an important geophysical effect that can't be measured directly can be determined indirectly by using the physical laws of heat conduction to interpret other characteristics that can be measured.

These various ways of probing the sea bottom have revealed a quite different structure from that underlying the continents. For one thing, the seismic studies confirmed that the earth's crust is relatively thinner under the oceans. Geologists had suspected this ever since gravity studies made during the first geodetic survey of India in 1855 indicated a thinning of the crust seaward from the subcontinent.

Because the different bottom layers are revealed by the different speeds at which sound travels through them, geologists often talk about them in terms of their characteristic speeds of sound. Thus the typical downward sequence of bottom layers as they now are known is as follows: first at the top there is a layer of sediment where the average sound velocity is 7,000 feet per second; then comes a rock layer of 16,000 feet per second; then a second rock layer of 22,000 feet per second. Below this is the mantle, where sound travels at an average speed of 26,000 feet per second. There is a distinct break or boundary between

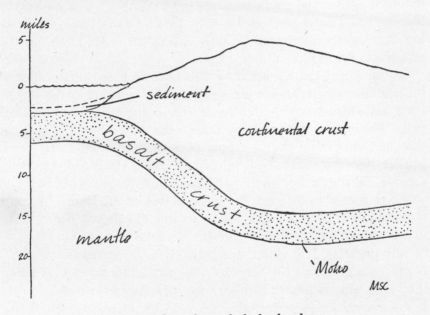

FIG. 13: *Crust beneath the land and sea.*

the non-crystalline material of the mantle and the next higher rocky layer, where the speed of sound is significantly lower. This is the "Mohorovičić discontinuity," or more simply the "Moho," which separates the crust from the mantle. Beneath the continents, the Moho is 20 to 25 miles deep. But under the sea it comes within three to eight miles of the ocean floor.

Finding a thin crust under the oceans has helped geologists explain the deep basins which formerly were something of a puzzle. The relatively high sound velocity in the mantle has been taken to mean the mantle material is denser than that of the crust above. Geologists believe that the light crust literally floats on the heavier mantle. Thus, if the crust under the oceans were as thick as it is under the continents, the ocean bottom should float as high as the land. But with a thin, somewhat heavier crust, the ocean basins would be expected to float lower.

Both gravity and seismic measurements show the thin crust of the oceans is indeed heavier than that under the land. The lower layer may be a volcanic rock called basalt, while the upper layer might be some kind of sedimentary rock, such as limestone, or even a lava. In any event, the studies show that, on the whole, the ocean crust is nicely balanced against the continents, just as a relatively thin and dense block of wood floats lower in the water than a thick lighter one. Finding this "isostatic balance," as it is called, has helped tidy up the geologists' over-all picture of the crust.

On the other hand, the heat-flow data have been a surprise. Much of the heat flowing up through the continents is generated by radioactive materials which have been concentrated in the granitic continental rocks. The thinner igneous rocks of the ocean crust don't have much of this "hot" material. The heat flow there was expected to be much smaller, since it would be due mainly to the slow cooling of the earth's interior. Yet the average heat flow upward through the sea bed has been found in general to be about the same as that of the land. This hints that radioactivity under the oceans is still distributed through the mantle, where its heat causes unrest and convection even in the hard mantle material. This material is believed to be as rigid as steel yet plastic enough to flow like very cold molasses under forces that act on it for long periods of time. Although the meaning of the heat-flow data is still unclear, this interpretation fits with the other indications that the Pacific is bordered by regions where the interior of the earth is unusually restless.

The Pacific's Ring of Fire

The scene of the planet's most intense earthquakes is the zone of trenches that circle the Pacific. As shown on the endpaper map, all run parallel to upthrusting island archipelagoes or nearby continental mountain ranges and are accompanied by lines of explosive volcanoes.

This zone is well characterized by its geological nickname, the "ring of fire."

What causes the great downbows or creases in the crust we call trenches, downbows that seem to be maintained against the prevailing force of gravity? Why do they mark such a volcanically and seismically active zone? This is one of the problems marine geologists have to study by indirection, and they can only guess at answers. Nevertheless, the known facts do provide some clues.

The earthquakes, for example, show a suggestive pattern. Quakes occurring along the trenches are generally of shallow focus with their centers lying close to the surface. But landward of the trenches, the quakes originate at progressively greater depths. There is a line about 200 miles landward where all the quakes are what geologists call "deep focus," meaning they originate more than 200 miles below the surface. The lines of volcanoes that often parallel the trenches seem to lie over zones where earthquakes have an intermediate depth of origin.

FIG. 14: *Trenches of the Pacific (shaded). See endpaper map also.*

D*

Another interesting feature is the fact that the trenches of the western Pacific seem to be naturally divided from the island arcs by a change of rock types. The division is called the "andesite line" because the islands consist of a continental type of rock, andesite, rather than the basalts of the ocean floor. This is not a generally accepted division, however, since elsewhere the boundary between oceanic and continental rocks is much closer to the continents.

Heat-flow and gravity measurements in the trenches are also quite unusual. Measured heat flows have been only about half that of the average for the earth as a whole, in spite of the fact that heat flows through most of the sea bottom at about the same rate as through the continents. The pull of gravity, for its part, is much smaller than would normally be expected.

As explained earlier, the sea floor and the continents are in a kind of equilibrium, floating on the underlying mantle material like rafts of

FIG. 15: *The Pacific's Ring of Fire: The band of earthquakes and volcanoes paralleling the line of the trenches.*

different density floating in water. One effect of this "isostatic equilibrium" is that there is relatively little variation of gravity between continents and ocean areas in general, the lighter material of the continents being balanced by the heavier crust under the sea. But the gravity measurements in the zone of the trenches are significantly lower than they would be if isostatic equilibrium prevailed there. They show what geologists call a "negative anomaly." This implies that the underlying material is much lighter than one would expect considering the great depth of the trenches. It should float higher than it does, but it is being held down against its buoyant tendencies by whatever forces are forming the trenches. In other words, the lighter material of the crust is being downbowed into the mantle and held there against the gravity-induced pressure that would displace it with the heavier material in which the crust would normally float.

To some geologists such as Dr. H. Benioff of the California Institute of Technology, the evidence suggests that the trenches are the surface expression of a fault deep inside the mantle. It looks as though a great split or series of splits have developed that angle down on the landward side of the trenches. Stresses build up along this split—or fault, as it is called—until they are relieved by slippages which cause earthquakes. The trenches themselves result from compression of the crust and downbowing along the fault line.

But this is only one way of looking at the evidence. Dr. Roger Revelle and Robert L. Fisher of Scripps have suggested an alternative. Perhaps the low heat flow through the floor of the trenches is the result of convection currents in the plastic material of the mantle. In that case, relatively cool rock is moving slowly downward under the trenches and tending to drag the crust down with it. In this connection, Revelle notes areas of exceptionally high heat flow, such as the Easter Island Rise off the west coast of South America, where relatively hot rock may be rising to the surface to complete the convective cycle.

All such theories are speculative, for the indirection of the oceanographers is based on fairly sparse data. The deep trenches spread over a vast ocean area are difficult to explore. But, to follow Revelle's speculation a bit further, the trenches may develop somewhat as follows. Formed by forces deep within the mantle, a V-shaped trench "bottoms out" at about 35,000 feet. Crustal material and accumulating sediments may still be dragged down by the trench-forming forces. But the depth remains about 35,000 feet. This may explain why the deepest trenches appear to be sediment-free even though they are natural sediment traps.

The early stage of trench formation is accompanied by violent earthquake and volcanic activity. Then, as the formative forces relax, the
trench begins to fill up, becoming flat-bottomed and U-shaped as sediment accumulates. The sediments pile up so high that, when isostatic
equilibrium is eventually re-established, the top of the sediments is

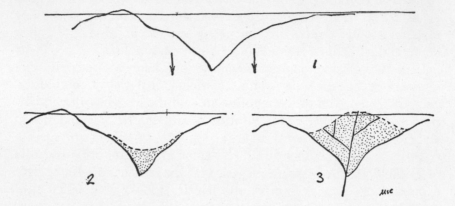

FIG. 16: *Geological history of a trench: According to one theory, the Pacific
trenches result from convection currents in the mantle. 1—relatively cool rock
moves downward under a trench, dragging the crust with it. 2—when formative
forces relax trench begins to fill with sediment. 3—eventually the sediments
rise above sea as islands. With the sediments insulating the heat flow from
below, the deep rocks melt and, flowing upward, transform existing rock and
lower sediments into granitic material, thickening the crust in that area. In this
way, continents may grow at the expense of the ocean basin.*

pushed above the sea as islands. Also, since the accumulating sediments
would tend to insulate the heat flow from below, the temperature of the
deep rocks might rise to the melting point. The molten magma flowing
upward would then transform the existing rock and lower sediments
into granitic material, thereby thickening the crust in that area. Such
a series of events, repeated many times in the past, may be the way in
which the continents have grown at the expense of the ocean basins.

Inside its "ring of fire" the Pacific ocean basin seems today to be an
area of almost complete seismic calm. Indeed, for many years geologists
thought the basin had been stable throughout geologic time. But recent
investigations show that this seemingly stable area has also been the
scene of crustal sinkings and uplifts, of volcanism and faulting. Take
for example the great fracture zones Menard has found stretching seaward from the western coast of North and Central America.

For a long time the charts showed nothing much of geological interest in this corner of the Pacific. But by studying old soundings and the results of several Scripps expeditions, Menard found, between 1950 and

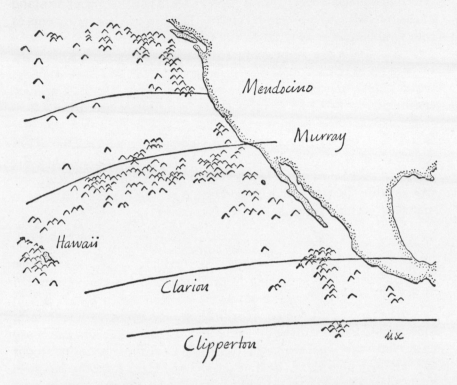

FIG. 17: *Fracture zones in the northeast Pacific.* (*After Menard*)

1953, what he described as "four great bands of unusually irregular topography." These bands were full of narrow ridges, fault scarps, and narrow fault valleys. There were numerous seamounts and some volcanic islands along the bands as well. They looked exactly like huge fractures in the crust and accordingly were named "fracture zones."

The zones are about 60 miles wide and run from 1,600 to 3,300 miles out into the ocean, more or less along great circles, the arc of a great circle being the shortest distance that can be drawn between two points on the earth's surface. The northernmost zone, the Mendocino Zone, may be connected with the famous San Andreas Fault in California. Menard thinks the four fracture zones plus the San Andreas Fault and perhaps also the Hawaiian Island fault line were all formed as one huge fracture system, like an eggshell that has been crushed slightly on one side but has not been completely broken.

No one knows what caused such a fracture, although Menard has suggested two possible mechanisms. The fracture zones seem to be as old as the late Mesozoic or early Tertiary. Perhaps at that time, sixty to eighty million years ago, the North and South Poles migrated from a position in India to their present locations, putting a strain on the crust. Or, alternatively, Menard suggests that great convection currents in the plastic mantle may have caused the crust to break up like thick river ice cracking under the stress of movements in the water beneath it.

Then there is the question of the general stability of the Pacific bottom. Has it stayed more or less as it is throughout geologic time or has it sunk substantially? And related to this is the question of when the Pacific acquired the bulk of its waters. These questions are difficult, but studies of the flat-topped guyots and of the growth of coral islands have suggested possible answers.

Sunken Islands

Marine geologists have long been familiar with seamounts which seem to be simply volcanic mounds that never reached the surface to become islands. But during World War II a young geologist from Princeton University made an intriguing discovery. He was Dr. Harry Hess, who was serving as a naval reserve officer at the time. As navigator and later commander of the transport U.S.S. *Cape Johnson*, he made many voyages in the western and central Pacific. During these voyages and in spite of the press of shipboard duties, Hess kept his interest in the ocean floor alive by studying the ship's echo-sounder records. One day he found a unique profile of a seamount. Instead of the usually rounded dome, its top had been shaved flat as if by a giant carpenter's plane.

None of the charts showed any seamounts like this. It was too big and flat to be a volcanic crater. It looked exactly like a low island whose surface had been eroded by waves. Yet it lay several hundred fathoms deep. Could this be an ancient sunken island that had once lain at the surface when the bottom stood higher or the water level lower, the first of its kind known to geological science?

Hess later found nineteen more of these flat-topped seamounts himself and unearthed a good many more in the records of the navy's Hydrographic Office. He concluded that they were indeed ancient drowned islands, which he named "guyots" after the nineteenth-century French geographer Arnold Guyot.

The next question was: When had these ancient islands been at the surface? Hess thought they were very old, dating back to the Precambrian era, over five hundred million years ago. In his view, they had been submerged by the slow rise in sea level as sediments acumulated since that time, displacing the water and bending down the crust with their weight. But according to the present consensus, the epoch of submergence was much more recent.

One of the most thorough studies of a line of guyots was made by a joint Scripps-Naval Electronics Laboratory expedition to the Mid-Pacific Mountains in 1950. The resulting monograph by Dr. Edwin L. Hamilton of N.E.L. shows that the guyots associated with this undersea range were once a chain of basalt islands that sank quite rapidly in the Cretaceous period, 60 to 125 million years ago.

Although the Mid-Pacific Mountains had been known as a line of seamounts before 1950, the Scripps-Navy expedition was the first to delineate this structurally as a great undersea ridge upon which seamounts and guyots rise as peaks. The geological history of these guyots thus is intimately connected with that of the ridge itself.

Hamilton has worked out the following hypothetical history for these mountains. At an undetermined time in the past, basalt rocks and associated material, like those of the Hawaiian Islands, were extruded from cracks in the sea bed. These formed the ridges and volcanoes of the Mid-Pacific Mountains. Eventually some of the high peaks emerged to become islands.

As the mountains grew, their weight compacted underlying sediments and bowed down the crust until isostatic equilibrium had been established. Actually, the crust under the Pacific is strong and elastic, so that the weight of structures like these growing mountains is borne partly by the crust and partly by the buoyant iscstatic pressures. By the time the peaks had emerged to become islands, much of this downward adjustment had taken place, so the peaks remained above the surface for some time. That is when the waves planed off their tops and when reef corals began to grow.

Then something upset the balance, and the mountains began to sink. They sank so quickly, they reached the 50- to 85-fathom depth limit of the corals faster than the reefs could grow upward. Perhaps the weight of the mountains became too great and the whole range broke through the crust and foundered. Perhaps they sank as part of a more general subsidence of the sea floor. Whatever the cause, to quote Hamilton, "they remain today as the oldest uneroded mountains known on earth. They are fossil landforms preserved in the depths of the sea where they are disturbed only by light currents and the slow rain of . . . material from the waters above."

It is a moot question among marine geologists how much the submergence of the guyots has been due to a sinking of the crust, as suggested by Hamilton and some others, and how much it has been due to a rise in sea level by the addition of new water from deep inside the earth, as some geologists believe is happening. Either mechanism or a combination of them would give the same submergence effect. But before considering this further, let's take a look at the problem of coral reefs and atolls, for these are linked with the guyots in geological history.

Living Reefs

A coral reef is a triumph of life. Exposed to the incessant attack of waves and surf, the corals build firmest where the seas run heaviest. The eroding forces of wind-driven water, which no cliff of dead rock can withstand, have met their match in a relative of the soft-bodied sea anemones and some one-celled plants of the algae group.

Coral polyps, as individual coral animals are called, are little more than flexible bottles with a crown of food-catching tentacles. They be-

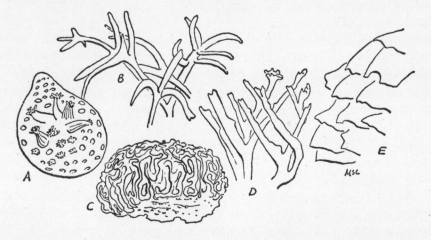

FIG. 18: *Coral colonies:* A—*showing individual polyps;* B—*staghorn;* C—*brain coral;* D—*elkhorn;* E—*shingle.*

long to the great phylum of the Coelenterata, named from the Greek words for "hollow-boweled," and are almost literally "all stomach." Like their close relatives, the sea anemones, they live their lives quietly attached to a solid substratum, eating bits of animal food brought to them by the water. Such unenterprising animals would have been of little account geologically if they had not evolved an ability to secrete a lime skeleton that gives strength and permanence to their otherwise ephemeral bodies.

Coral reefs are essentially accumulations of these calcium carbonate skeletons. But these could not by themselves form a strong enough aggregate to withstand the pounding of waves and surf. That is where the algae, members of the Corallinaceae family, come in. They are hardy organisms that thrive even in the zone of breakers on the seaward edge of the reef. They secrete a hard pink coating of lime that covers and cements the dead coral skeletons into a firm but porous limestone. Sometimes the algal deposit accounts for half and more of the reef material. In the Indian and Pacific oceans the algae also form a low hummocky ridge at the very edge of the reef on the seaward side which acts as a breakwater to protect the flat top of the reef behind. On reefs where this protection is lacking, as in the West Indies, storm waves cause considerable damage.

Some corals live in temperate waters and at considerable depths. But the range of the reef builders is more restricted. They live in harmony with a one-cell algal plant called zooxanthella, which is embedded within them. Biologists call such an arrangement "beneficial symbiosis," a relationship in which two dissimilar organisms live together to their mutual benefit and often could not survive independently. In the case of the corals, the algae get food and carbon dioxide from the animals' metabolism, while the polyps are cleaned of waste products and may also get oxygen and perhaps some carbohydrates in return. The exact nature of the relationship between these organisms is hazy. But as far as active reef building is concerned, the range of the polyps seems to be limited at least partly by the needs of the plants.

The zooxanthellae are photosynthetic; that is, they can live and grow only in waters where the sunlight can reach them. This puts a shallow depth limit on the reef corals and a premium on clear water that transmits a maximum of light. Although some live reef corals have been found as deep as 580 feet, they generally seem limited to less than 300 feet, with an optimum depth, from the viewpoint of the algae, of 12 to 15 feet. Zooxanthellae also grow best in warm waters of normal

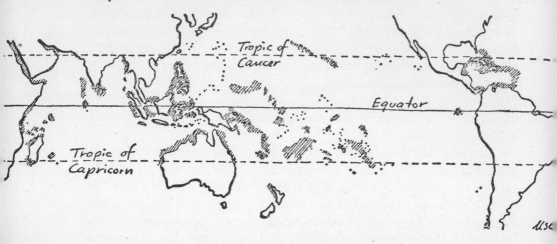

FIG. 19: *Range of the reef corals (shaded).*

salinity. This means a water temperature range from about 68° Fahrenheit to the low 90's, and a salinity range of about 27 to 40 parts per thousand, whereas the ocean average is about 35 parts per thousand. Thus depth or turbid waters that cut down light transmission, suffocating sediments, extremes of temperature, and fresh-water dilution are all enemies of the reef-building coral polyp and its symbiotic algae. They restrict their range to relatively clear shallow waters of the tropics.

The corals reproduce both by the budding of one individual from another and by release of free-floating larvae into the sea. When a larva comes to rest on a suitable substratum, it secretes its skeleton and begins to bud off new polyps. These are all distinct individuals. Yet groups of them remain physically tied together by a common digestive tract in colonies of marvelous complexity. Sometimes colonies grow as large as eight to ten feet in diameter, containing thousands of individuals. Some look like the branching antlers of stags or elks (the staghorn and elkhorn corals). Others form rounded masses whose grooved surfaces look like brain tissue (the brain corals), and so forth. Much of the beauty of the reefs is due to the curious structures of the coral colonies.

Reef corals will grow on any solid substratum where the water conditions are favorable. This results in a variety of reef forms. However, there are three dominant reef types—fringing, barrier, and atoll. Fringing reefs grow out directly from the coasts of many islands with scarcely a break. In some places one can wade out several miles on these shallow platforms. There is little active coral growth on top of such reefs, which

often are covered with an algal crust. But corals live in holes and channels within the porous reef platform and grow profusely at its steep
outer edge, where driving seas bring a continual supply of oxygen and
planktonic food.

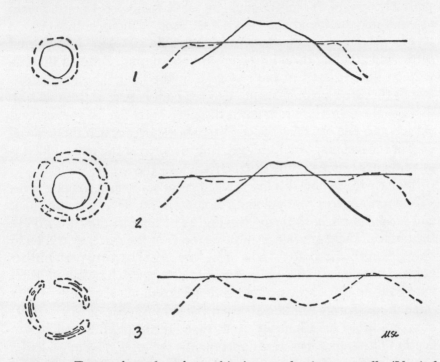

FIG. 20: *Types of coral reef:* 1—*fringing;* 2—*barrier;* 3—*atoll.* (*Vertical
views left, cross-sectional views right*)

Barrier reefs are what their name implies. They are separated from
the coast line and its fringing reefs by lagoon channels up to 180 feet
deep, although these are occasionally cut across by outshoots of a fringing reef. They stand literally as a barrier between land and the open
sea. The most famous of these, perhaps, is the Great Barrier Reef of
Australia extending for 1,200 miles along the northeastern coast. It is
really a series of many individual reefs that are separated by as much
as 150 miles from land at the southern end.

Atolls, such as Bikini and Eniwetok, are essentially coral reefs that
enclose a shallow lagoon. The word "atoll" comes from the language
of the Maldive Islands, where each governmental district consists of a
reef enclosing a lagoon and is called "atolu." Some atolls are ring-

shaped, but more are irregular. They are the most common type of reef in mid-ocean and are found by the hundreds in tropical Pacific and Indian Ocean waters.

Crowding together in shallow surface waters, corals and algae grow profusely upward toward the sunlight, while wanderers from the main colonies may be found 200 to 300 feet deep. Wherever this upward growth reaches the surface, waves continually attack it, breaking off pieces and grinding them into fine white coral sand. Some of this collects on quieter parts of the reef and on the land. The low narrow islands that grow up on parts of atolls are built largely of this material. Some of the debris also rolls down the steep outer face of the reef and collects as a pile or "talus" of coral sediments over which the growing edge of the reef may build seaward. But the vigor of the reef builders is more than a match for the destructiveness of the sea.

It is easy to see how this living mechanism constructs fringing reefs. Wherever there is a gently sloping shore in favorable waters, the corals and algae can establish themselves and grow upward until they break the surface. Then, growing against the forces of the sea, they will build outward until the bottom falls away too deeply to support further growth. But how could these organisms that need shallow sunlit water have built up barrier reefs from the depths offshore where the bottom often drops sharply into the abyss on the seaward side of the reef? Or how could they have built up atolls that rise steeply from mid-ocean depths? These questions were uppermost in the mind of young Charles Darwin in 1835 as he prepared to sail into the Pacific from the western coast of South America during the voyage of H.M.S. *Beagle* (1831–36).

This is the famous expedition on which Darwin served as geologist and naturalist and which, in his own words, "determined my whole career." It is the cruise during which he began collecting the evidence for, and began formulating the central points of, his theory of evolution. But he was also concerned about the problem of the coral reefs.

The subject engrossed him during the last year of the voyage. Indeed, his theory on coral-reef origins was worked out deductively before the *Beagle* left South America and before he ever saw any of the great Indo-Pacific reefs. He afterward noted in his autobiography that it was the only hypothesis he ever formulated that he did not have to change later. The theory was presented briefly before the (British) Geological Society in 1837 and in detail in his first major scientific publication, "The Structure and Distribution of Coral Reefs" (1842). Like the theory of evolution, but on a far less public scale, it was destined to spawn a scientific debate that has remained lively to the present day.

The Coral-Reef Controversy

Darwin's coral-reef theory is simple. If the limestone reefs now extend below the depth range of living coral, then the lower parts of the reefs must at one time have stood higher in the water. For two years he had been studying the evidences for slow intermittent uplifting of some land areas with concomitant erosion and deposition of sediments in low basins which gradually sank under the accumulating weight. He found many effects of these earth movements along South American shores. ". . . it was easy," he explained in his autobiography, "to replace in imagination the continued deposition of sediment by the upward growth of coral. To do this was to form my theory of the formation of barrier-reefs and atolls." Thus, he reasoned, if something caused the sea bottom to sink slowly, and the coral reefs with it, the sun-seeking reef organisms would build the reefs upward in pace with the rate of sinking. Provided the sinking was not too rapid, as Darwin believed, this seemed a simple and adequate explanation of many of the great barrier reefs and atolls.

For example, a volcanic island might rise above the sea. At first erosion and sedimentation would keep the surrounding waters turbid and clear of coral. But eventually the polyps would establish themselves as a fringing reef. Then, as the island gradually sank owing to subsidence of the sea bed, the reef would build upward. The growth would be most active along the seaward edge because quiet waters, sedimentation, and variable temperatures would inhibit it in the shallow waters near shore. The growing outer edge would in time become a barrier reef with a lagoon between it and the sinking island. Finally the island might disappear altogether, leaving the encircling reef as a coral atoll.

This theory explained at one crack both the formation of barrier reefs and atolls and the hitherto puzzling fact that the limestone bases of some reefs were known to rise from below the depth limit of living coral. In spite of this latter fact, geologists before Darwin were inclined to explain reefs as coral growth on top of existing rock platforms. The ring-shaped atolls were said to be built on the rims of submerged volcanic craters.

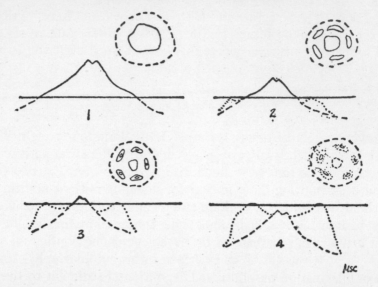

FIG. 21: *Darwin's theory of reef formation: An island rises above the sea* (1). *Eventually corals establish a fringing reef* (2). *Then, as the island slowly sinks the corals build upward. They build most vigorously along the seaward edge, forming a barrier reef* (3). *At last disappearing beneath the sea, the island leaves the encircling reef as an atoll* (4). *(Both vertical and cross-sectional views shown)*

In presenting his subsidence theory, Darwin pointed out that corals could indeed become established on pre-existing shallow platforms and that this might account for some of the barrier-reef and atoll formations. But he discounted this explanation for the larger groups of Indo-Pacific atolls. "The idea of a lagoon island, 30 miles in diameter being based on a submarine crater of equal dimensions, has always appeared to me a monstrous hypothesis," he explained in a letter sent home in 1836.

Darwin's ideas found quick support from the American geologist Professor James Dwight Dana of Yale. He marshaled corroborating geological evidence, pointing out, among other things, that the lower reaches of river valleys on many barrier-reef-encircled islands now lie under the sea. This suggested the islands had sunk relative to sea level since the valleys were first eroded. With Dana's support, Darwin's theory was generally accepted for almost a quarter of a century. Then opposition developed.

For one thing, geologists didn't understand how the sea bed could subside. Today this would probably be explained as isostatic adjustment. As the weight of an upthrusting island and its accumulating coral overloaded the crust, the island would sink lower in the plastic mantle. It would act like a buoyant object which, when thrown into a tar pit, slowly sinks until it reaches its proper level for floating. Or perhaps a more general adjustment involving large areas of sea bed would be invoked. But in Darwin's day the theories of isostasy were not yet worked out. Alexander Agassiz, who spent many years studying coral reefs, once remarked that he had found scarcely a reef to illustrate Darwin's theory.

Then too, Sir John Murray, who had studied bottom sediments during the *Challenger* expedition, gave considerable authority to a view exactly opposite to that of Darwin. He revived the argument that the reefs grew up from pre-existing platforms, perhaps craters of extinct volcanoes. If these were not close enough to the surface to begin with, they would be built up by sediments until the reef builders could establish themselves, Murray said.

Toward the end of the nineteenth century the German geologist Albrecht Penck suggested still another possibility. The reefs, he explained, might be the result of upgrowth during the rise of sea level after the last ice age. Meanwhile it had been discovered that the lagoons inside even large atolls have shallow floors all the way across, rather than a deep moat just inside the reef with a rising bottom toward the center where the island had sunk, as one might expect from Darwin's theory. Supporters of the theory pointed out that the moats were probably filled by sediments and coral growth. But added to Penck's suggestion, the absence of the moats was a rallying point for skeptics, among whom Professor Reginald Daly of Harvard University eventually became the chief symbol and proponent.

Daly elaborated Penck's idea into a full-blown theory of reef formation based on what he called "glacial control." As the glacial ice sheets built up, sea level dropped, the oceans cooled, and erosion from the newly exposed beaches made offshore waters turbid. These effects, said Daly, would kill existing coral reefs. Then, during the periods of low glacial sea levels, and without the protection of living reefs, small islands would be cut away to form banks, while broad sediment platforms would be built up around the larger islands. As the ice melted and the seas again rose, corals would re-establish themselves in the warming waters. New reefs would grow upward on the glacially created banks and platforms in pace with the rising waters, while the lower

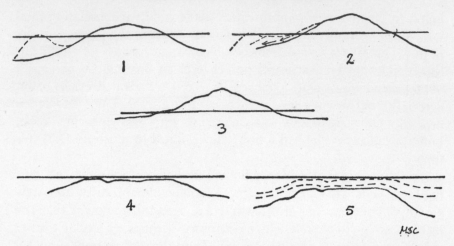

MSC

FIG. 22: *Daly's theory of reef formation: As glaciers grow and sea level drops, reefs surrounding islands (1) are killed off by exposure, cooling of the water, and by sediments eroded from newly exposed beaches (2). During low water, broad sediment platforms form around larger islands (3), while smaller islands are cut away to form banks (4). When waters rise, new reefs grow upward on the glacially created banks and platforms (5).*

parts of river valleys cut during low water would be submerged. This implied, among other things, that all living reefs are no older than the last ice age; that is, not much more than ten thousand years old.

Here was a theory to rival that of Darwin, and for many years it held the field. It was strengthened by studies in the West Indies, where living reefs were found to be merely thin encrustations over older wave-eroded terraces. In no case did they appear to be great piles of coral skeletons extending to thousands of feet in depth and accumulated over long ages of slow subsidence.

But Daly's case had a weak point, for he insisted that glacial control could account for reefs everywhere, that subsidence had played no significant part in any living reef formation. The attacks on the Darwinian theory from this viewpoint were particularly strong in the thirty years prior to World War II. But during that same period the question was put into new perspective by an American geologist, William Morris Davis.

Davis showed that the glacial sea-level shifts had indeed had major effects on reefs along the continental margins such as those of the West Indies. Their effects, however, had been relatively slight on reefs in the deep Indo-Pacific basins. In other words, the reefs Darwin had studied and those of the West Indies which were being used to refute his theory were quite different cases. Each had to be studied and discussed in terms of its peculiar circumstances. No one theory could claim to explain all cases or exclude other theories.

One of the reasons there has been so much speculation and so little agreement on the history of coral reefs is that this is another of the problems marine geologists have to tackle by indirection. The reefs build too slowly for their growth to be watched. Geologists can only infer what happens by studying reefs in various stages of development and trying to put together a general picture. Even this kind of study has been hampered by the difficulty of finding out what lies under the surface of the reefs. It was relatively easy to discover that West Indian reefs were only thin crusts over old rock platforms. But until recently the great Indo-Pacific reefs remained an enigma. "I wish," Darwin once wrote Agassiz, "that some doubly rich millionaire would take it into his hands to have borings made in some of the Pacific and Indian atolls, and bring back cores for slicing from a depth of 500 or 600 feet."

Darwin's "millionaire" turned out to be the Royal Society, which in 1897 commissioned drillings that penetrated 1,100 feet into Funafuti Atoll in the Ellice Islands. The drillers found nothing but coral. Darwinites considered this a victory for their side. But skeptics replied that the boring had actually been made through the mound of coral fragments that litter the seaward slopes of reefs and over which the living coral sometimes extends, rather than through the main reef structure itself. The same ambiguity held true for subsequent drillings made by several countries up to World War II. Then came a series of really deep drillings to prepare for the United States nuclear tests in the Pacific.

The first of these was made in Bikini Atoll in 1947. The drill reached a maximum of 2,500 feet and still failed to get to the bottom of the coral. Again the Daly school insisted this was only coral talus and not the reef itself. But their insistence was broken by the second series of American drillings, this time in Eniwetok. Under the direction of Harry Ladd of the U. S. Geological Survey, a major effort was made to drill through to the underlying bedrock. Holes were bored on both sides of the atoll. The borings finally hit lava at depths of 4,630 and 4,222 feet, respectively, drilling through coral all the way. Careful analysis of the drill cores proved conclusively that they had gone through the reef proper. They showed an orderly sequence of coral skeletons from the

Eocene to the present, an uninterrupted structure that started growing sixty million years ago. Throughout that time Eniwetok has been subsiding at a rate of two millimeters a century. Darwin had at last been vindicated, at least as far as major Indo-Pacific atolls are concerned.

But while the importance of subsidence has been confirmed, this doesn't mean that all details of Darwin's theory have been accepted even for the atolls. Shepard thinks that at least some present-day reefs, instead of growing around sinking volcanic islands, may have first become established on wave-beveled platforms and partly eroded volcanoes many millions of years ago, perhaps during the Cretaceous period. Since then, these platforms have gradually sunk, with the reef builders constantly extending the reefs upward in pace with the sinking. Where coral growth was slight or inactive, or where the sinking was too rapid for upbuilding to keep pace, these platforms have become guyots.

Also, Shepard explains, the reefs would probably have been affected by glacial changes in sea level. Atolls, for instance, may show this in the narrowness of the encircling reef. Temporary emergence during low water would have exposed the reefs to erosion by waves and to the dissolving action of rain water. With the rise again of the seas, renewed growth at the rim of the eroded reef could have produced present-day atoll formations. In this case, the shallow lagoons would be underlain by old reef material rather than by the sunken and sediment-covered tops of submerged volcanic islands.

The continental shelves of the West Indies and the southeastern coast of the United States are another interesting example of how different reef-forming processes have all played a part in the geological history of an area. The present coral formations in that area are postglacial in origin. But Dr. Norman D. Newell, professor of geology at Columbia University and curator of historical geology and fossil invertebrates at the American Museum, points out that the area may also be underlain by vast fossil coral reefs similar to those of the Indo-Pacific.

Biologically, the West Indian area is isolated from other regions. But at one time it was inhabited by the same organisms that thrived in Indo-Pacific and Mediterranean waters, which interconnected at that time. Then during the Miocene epoch (thirteen to thirty million years ago), interchange of shallow-water life was restricted to the east by the rise of a land barrier at the far end of the Mediterranean and perhaps also by the deepening of the central Atlantic basin. When the Central

American isthmus later arose in the Pliocene epoch, the Caribbean was cut off from the Pacific as well and became a landlocked sea.

Ever since the Caribbean first began to be isolated and as climatic and geological changes took their toll, the Atlantic reef corals have been on the decline. But Newell says there once was widespread reef building that reached a climax in late Oligocene and early Miocene times. Recent deep borings and seismic and gravity studies show that the sea floor adjacent to Florida and the Bahamas is underlain by over two and a half miles of limestone rocks similar to those laid down by the reef deposits of the Pacific. Also, the edge of the Blake Plateau farther north looks very much like the Great Barrier Reef of Australia. Its steep seaward face slopes as much as sixty degrees for thousands of feet as it drops toward the abyss. In places it is vertical, just as in many coral reefs today. Here is another possible explanation for the origin of the Blake Plateau.

Perhaps, Dr. Newell suggests, reefs were first established along an arc of volcanic islands like the Lesser Antilles. For a long time they grew steadily upward in the Darwinian manner as the sea bed slowly subsided. In time a great barrier reef was built up along the line of the present Blake Plateau. Then, as the waters cooled and became turbid from erosion of newly uplifted lands during Tertiary mountain building, coral growth began to decline.

It died out first in the north. The barrier reef was killed in the Miocene epoch. But growth continued in the Bahamian and Florida areas until the Pleistocene ice ages. Thus the sea bed of the West Indies and off the southeastern United States, according to Dr. Newell, may hide ancient reef formations as magnificent in their day as any the Pacific now boasts. Also, this area, whose minor present-day coral growths have often been cited to disprove Darwin's ideas, once underwent the same history of coral upgrowth on a subsiding sea bottom that Darwin had so aptly proposed to explain the great reefs of the Pacific.

Although the complete story of the coral reefs has still to be unraveled, today the old elements of the controversy have been resolved. The theories of Darwin, Daly, Murray, and others have been incorporated to some degree in the present explanation of reef formations. But Darwin's early understanding of the role of subsidence—his grasp of this important geological phenomenon and the imaginative use of it in his coral-reef theory—was the flash of genuis that has illuminated this difficult geological puzzle for over a hundred years.

Filling the Deep-Ocean Basins

The evidence for the sinking of coral reefs correlates with that of the guyots, the sunken islands, to indicate widespread subsidence of the Pacific Ocean floor. It begs the question: What caused this subsidence and how much of it may be only an illusion owing to a slow rise of sea level?

The origin of the ocean waters is a hazy subject. As explained in Chapter Two, they may have fallen as primordial rains or, in the modern view, have been released from the earth's interior. In either case, many geologists have believed that the oceans received essentially all of their water in Precambrian times. Some still hold to this view. Philip Kuenen, for example, concluded in his book *Marine Geology,* published about a decade ago, that the release of new water from the earth's interior, the only possible source within geological time, has been insignificant since that distant era. Others, such as William Rubey, think the water has been produced continuously throughout geological time. Roger Revelle has extended the latter theory to account for at least part of the submergence of coral reefs and guyots.

In his view, a sizable proportion of the ocean water may have been added in comparatively recent times. The increase began at the end of the Cretaceous period when, according to Revelle, great volcanic outbreaks on the sea floor brought forth large quantities of water and carbon dioxide. This may also explain why the layer of unconsolidated sediments as measured by seismic methods is so much thinner than expected. Earlier deep-sea sediments may have been buried or consolidated by extensive lava flows and other volcanic extrusions.

This probably was also the time when the foraminiferal oozes and other calcareous sediments began to accumulate in quantity. The rate at which they consumed carbon dioxide to deposit the amount of calcium carbonate that has since been laid down must have been far greater than atmospheric sources could supply. This, in turn, suggests a large amount of undersea volcanism.

As new water from the interior accumulated, the sea floor would sink under its weight and under the growing weight of the sediments. Thus, Revelle suggests, the submergence of guyots since the Cretaceous may be due mostly to a rise in sea level and only partly to a sinking of the ocean floor.

On the other hand, Rubey's own calculations of the rate at which new water has been brought forth indicate that only 3 or 4 per cent of the present ocean waters have been added since the Middle Cretaceous. This would have raised sea level by only a few hundred feet, while the guyots now lie at depths of 5,000 to 6,000 feet. Because of this, Hamilton and some others think extensive subsidence is the most likely explanation for their submergence. Perhaps this sinking was regional, occurring in areas overloaded by the growth of mountains and coral reefs, as may have happened in the case of the Mid-Pacific Mountains, or perhaps it was a general subsidence of the sea bed. At this stage no one really knows. The question of rising waters and subsiding sea beds—of when and how the waters have appeared and of the processes at work in the mantle beneath the ocean floor—is one of the fundamental unsolved problems in marine geology. Much of the sea-floor research planned in years ahead will be carried forward with this in mind.

FIVE

Patterns of the Waters

Sᴛɪʀʀᴇᴅ by the winds and by the tide-raising forces of sun and moon, the face of the sea is like a kaleidoscope. It presents an ever changing panorama, sometimes regular, sometimes chaotic, whose patterns often have a meaning. The booming of breakers on a western Pacific shore hints of storms that have raged thousands of miles away, perhaps in another hemisphere. Choppy waters in a channel may tell of tidal currents flowing against opposing winds or swell. The varying heights of incoming waves along a stretch of shore may reflect the character of the offshore bottom, rising higher where there are ridges and breaking with lower crests where they have passed over a submarine canyon. Even the ubiquitous tides bear the stamp of local topography.

Oceanographers have learned to read many of these patterns. They can observe the tides at any given point and, as data accumulate over the years, predict them with fair accuracy. By observing the local characteristics of offshore waters and how they behave under a variety of conditions, seaside meteorologists can include future wave conditions in their local forecasts. This latter technique was developed extensively during World War II, when it was one of the major factors in picking the exact date for the Allied D-day invasion of Europe. In fact, the invasion was postponed a day because of unfavorable wave forecasts. Thereafter, because wave conditions were so important a factor in landing men and equipment on the beaches, the wave forecasters set the pace of these landings. Today wave forecasts are invaluable in building and protecting the offshore oil drillers' platforms and "Texas" radar towers as well as many shore installations.

But a growing ability to read the patterns of waves and tides does not imply precise scientific understanding. Oceanographers know in general what is involved. But neither tides nor waves have yet been encompassed in the kind of comprehensive mathematical theory a scientist has in mind when he speaks of "understanding."

Theory versus Reality

Actually, a mathematical theory of waves was worked out and published in 1845 by Sir George Airy. However, the waves he described are more likely to be found in a textbook than on the surface of the sea. Their crests are straight and long and run parallel to each other, while every wave is identical to the others. Only swell moving over water undisturbed by wind comes close to resembling these ideal waves. Wind-blown waves are distorted from this shape, and a storm-tossed sea is at present beyond all mathematical description.

Oceanographers distinguish between the terms "sea" and "swell." When the wind is blowing up a confused variety of waves of many shapes and sizes, it is called a "sea." When the waves have run beyond the wind and have turned into a low regular undulation of the water surface, their pattern is called a "swell." It is this that most nearly approximates the long, regular, "cylindrical" waves which the theorists are able to handle mathematically.

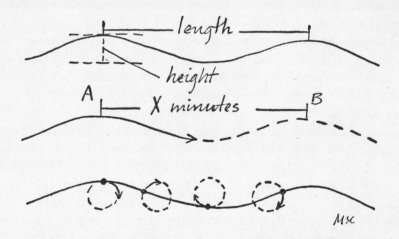

FIG. 23: *Wave elements: Wave length is the horizontal distance from crest to crest. Height is the vertical distance from crest to trough. Period is the time it takes a crest to move a distance of one wave length, i.e., to move from A to B. In a simple wave, individual water particles (represented by dots) travel through small circles as the wave form passes.*

Waves are described in terms of their height, wave length, and period. "Height" is the vertical distance between the high point of a wave crest and the low point of the adjacent trough. "Wave length" is the distance from one crest to the next, and "period" is the time it takes two adjacent crests to pass a fixed point, such as the end of a pier. The mathematics of wave theories are usually concerned with relationships between these and related characteristics. Even though they deal with the ideal rather than the real, such theoretical relationships have helped oceanographers understand the action of ocean waves.

One thing theory tells us is that, except where they slosh up on the shore or when their tops are blown off by the wind, waves are not moving masses of water. It is the shape that moves along, while the water stays more or less where it is. As the wave shape passes, individual water particles move up and down with it, describing a circle or an ellipse. Because of friction there is actually a little forward movement of the particles, like a car wheel spinning on ice and inching slowly ahead. But in deep water the net movement is slight.

These circular motions die out quickly with increasing depth. Heavy storm waves are felt more deeply than others. One-pound rocks have been moved into lobster pots 180 feet deep by storms at the mouth of the English Channel, while off western Ireland rocks weighing several hundred pounds each reportedly have been moved at depths of 100 feet. But, in general, the waves do not stir the oceans deeply. This is why submarines have smooth sailing when cruising underwater.

Sometimes the sea surface appears to be a confusion of waves even when the winds are light. In this case, the confusion has an underlying order. Different wave systems traveling in different directions can interact with one another to create complex patterns. Wherever the crest of one wave more or less coincides with that of another, they add together to build up an extra-high crest. Similarly, wave troughs and crests can cancel one another out. This is called wave "interference." When a number of wave systems interfere with each other, their troughs and crests come together in an endless variety of superpositions. This interference is augmented when the wind is up, constantly generating new systems of waves and adding its patterns to the confusion of the surface. Oceanographers have progressed in their mathematical studies of ocean waves by learning to describe some of the complicated patterns in terms of simple wave systems. These latter can be added together mathematically to represent the observed pattern, while the

E

task of finding the laws that govern these simple waves is relatively easy. But with patterns literally as complex as the waves of the sea, one can understand why the specialists have not yet reached their goal of a comprehensive theory.

The Pattern of the Breakers

Once a wave system has outrun the wind, it can travel for long distances without appreciable loss of energy. If it encounters new winds, the shape and heading of the waves will be altered, while a strong enough opposing wind can quickly destroy them. Under favorable conditions, however, the waves continue more or less in the direction of the original wind indefinitely. Moreover, the longer-period waves travel faster. Leaving many of the small and irregular short-period ones behind, they settle down into the rhythmic undulations of a swell.

Thus the fairly long period breakers characteristic of many windward shores may bring tidings of storms that raged thousands of miles away. Those that break on the California coast in summer, rolling in from the south with periods of eight to eighteen seconds, often originate in the winter storms of the South Pacific east of New Zealand. Across the North American continent, along the eastern shore, short choppy waves from much closer storms are the rule. In the Atlantic, with prevailing westerly winds in its stormier latitudes, the long rolling swells from mid-ocean storms break on the western shores of Europe and Africa.

When a wave leaves relatively deep water and begins "to feel the bottom," it undergoes substantial changes. Velocity and wave length decrease, while height grows. Only the period remains the same. The wave would appear to be dragging over the shoaling bottom until, stubbing its toe, so to speak, it falls over itself as a breaker. This appearance is deceptive, for a wave on water does not behave like a solid body. This is a point at which theory helps one understand what actually happens.

Waves can be thought of as carrying a certain amount of energy, originally derived from the wind and traveling with the wave system. When waves enter shallow water, the energy once carried through a fairly deep column of water is now being concentrated in water growing steadily shallower. Every pound of water has more and more energy stored in it as the wave form passes. Some of this energy makes the water of the crests hump up higher. Some of it increases the speed of the individual water particles (as opposed to the velocity of the wave form itself, which slows down). When the velocity of the water particles at the crest of a wave exceeds that of the wave itself, the wave breaks. In deep water this usually happens when the wave height gets to be about one seventh of the wave length. In shallow water it's the depth that counts. Breakage usually occurs when the ratio of wave height to depth is about 3 to 4. In other words, a 3-foot-high wave would break in about 4 feet of water, although the actual depth of breakage depends on such local factors as the character of the bottom.

With theory as a rough guide, it is easy to see why stubbing one's toe is a poor analogy for a breaking wave. The clumsy human would fall soonest where the bottom is roughest. It is exactly the opposite with waves. Waves travel farther over rough than over smooth bottoms before breaking. The rougher the bottom, the more the wave energy is dissipated by friction. This tends to decrease the amount of energy being concentrated in the water and in turn to cut down the wave height and the speed of water particles at the crest. The wave then breaks at the shallower depth appropriate for its diminished height.

Theory also shows how the pattern of waves can reflect major bottom features. Imagine a wave system coming into a straight shore line over a bottom cut by submarine canyons which are flanked by ridges. As the water grows shoaler, the waves grow higher and move more slowly over the ridges than over the valleys, where the water remains relatively deep. This gives a curving outline to the advancing wave front. At the same time, the breakers over the ridges will be built up as they approach shore, while those over the valley will be diminished. In this way, the pattern of the incoming breakers reflects the topography of the bottom. This makes the head of a submarine canyon an ideal place for launching small boats through the breakers. A difference of ten times in breaker height is not unusual with such offshore topography. This effect was particularly noticeable in the destructive tidal waves that hit Hawaii in 1946. The waves were substantially reduced where they came in over undersea valleys, while those traveling over three ridges on the north side of Kauai Island attained the greatest heights reported.

Broadly speaking, there are two types of breakers, with individual waves showing a variety of mixtures of the two. The "plunging breaker" is by far the more dramatic. It usually occurs on coasts where the bottom rises rather steeply toward the shore. As the wave feels the bottom, its advancing face becomes steeper. Suddenly, at the moment part of this face becomes vertical, the top of the crest shoots forward as a jet. Down it falls in a graceful arc, with the rest of the crest tumbling after. And as it falls it traps a pocket of air. Then crest and air pocket plunge together into the water with a "boom" and a sudden turbulent dissipation of energy.

Where the upward slope to the beach is more gradual, the less spectacular "spilling breaker" is often seen. In this case, the incoming wave tends to keep a more symmetrical rounded crest that gradually grows up in a point until the top part begins to foam and spills down the advancing face of the wave. As the water shoals, the spilling increases and the wave crest slowly disintegrates into an advancing mass of foaming water.

These spilling breakers are the waves the surfboarders ride. Balancing their boards on the advancing wave face, they are perpetually sliding downhill. Ideally, the wave should be just on the point of breaking. Then the velocity of the water particles on the crest where the board is riding will be close to that of the wave itself. The combination of the movement of the water particles and of the board as it slides downhill through the water keeps the surfboarder moving along with the wave.

From the rider's point of view, this is a stable situation. If his board moves ahead too fast, it slows down and the wave catches up. If it starts to fall behind the wave, it moves backward toward the crest, where it is accelerated forward again. The wave face down which the board is constantly sliding is steepest at the crest, while the maximum forward speed of the water particles is also found there. Thus there is a position on the wave face to which the board will automatically return if displaced backward or forward.

This much is convenient for the rider. His skill is tested, however, by the tendency of the board to "broach to." Since the factors favoring velocity are greatest at the crest, the back end of the board tends to go faster than the front. The board keeps "trying" to swing around parallel to the wave front, and the trick of surf riding is to keep it headed toward the beach.

When an incoming wave breaks, that is not necessarily the end of it. If it hasn't yet hit the beach, the remaining wave energy may re-form into one or several new waves. These, in turn, may break and again re-form until the waves run up onto the shore. Even this may not be the end. Especially on a steep rocky shore, the back-slosh of the water as it returns seaward may still have enough energy to generate yet another wave, a "reflected wave," which can be seen heading back out to sea.

The incoming waves also bring an influx of water. This is due to the slight forward movement of the water particles as the wave form passes. At sea this doesn't amount to much. But at the shore the water piles up against the land and, having no other place to go, it runs along parallel to the shore line. This is the origin of the "longshore currents" and "rip currents" that so often take swimmers by surprise.

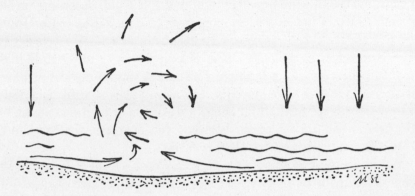

FIG. 24: *Longshore and rip currents: Water brought shoreward by waves tends to run off along the shore until it heads seaward in regions where incoming waves are weaker, sometimes creating a fast-moving current known as a rip. (View vertically downward)*

Usually the longshore currents flow more or less in the same direction as the waves, often scouring out a relatively deep trough parallel to and just outside the beach. If the waves come in from the right, the current generally runs along toward the left, and vice versa, although currents running in the opposite direction may occasionally be encountered. At some point these currents have to return their water to the sea. In the normal pattern of circulation, water flows toward and along the shore in regions of relatively high waves, with a general return flow seaward in regions where the waves are lower. Occasionally there is a second means of escape in narrow, relatively fast currents superimposed on the general pattern. These are the rip currents or, as they are often inappropriately called, the "rip tides."

Longshore currents, which develop speeds of a mile per hour or more, can be quite a challenge to the average swimmer. The rip currents, funneling the water into a narrow, turbulent flow and heading out to sea, are potentially even more dangerous. They develop speeds two or three times those of the longshore currents. Moreover, they are intermittent. Sometimes they set strongly seaward. Sometimes they die out. They can take a bather unawares, especially if he or she has wandered into a rip-current channel during one of the lull periods.

Many of the drownings attributed to the so-called "undertow" are probably due to rip currents. There is little evidence for the existence of undertow currents that physically pull a swimmer down, although near shore the rip currents do extend to the bottom, becoming surface currents farther out to sea. Swimmers becoming exhausted or frightened in a rip or caught unexpectedly by one of its sudden reversals may find themselves in difficulty. This is probably why life guards make many of their rescues in the rips. The easiest way to extricate yourself if caught in one of these currents is to swim across it until slack water and perhaps a shoaler bottom are found outside of the rip channel. On the other hand, for skilled surfboarders and boatmen, the rips can afford a free ride out through the breakers.

Similar currents develop on coral reefs. Water from waves and swell that occasionally top a reef runs off to sea through eroded channels. To reach these channels, it may flow for some distance along the landward side of the reef. Any one channel carries water collected from a wide area of reef and can develop a substantial current. Like a rip, this current is intermittent and can catch a wader off guard.

The longshore and rip currents are also important transporters of sediment. They help distribute and redistribute the sands of beaches and erode channels for themselves in the process. The rip channels in particular can become quite deep with steep sides, an additional hazard bathers should be wary of when jumping up and down in the surf on what is otherwise a shallow bottom.

The incoming waves and breakers that provide most of the sediment these currents carry can also cause considerable erosion. They cut back beaches or, conversely, pile up sand to build them. Of the two types of breakers, the plunging variety causes more direct erosion of the sea bed where they break. But the spilling type stirs the bottom over a wider area and may, in the long run, have a greater total effect. During high waves especially, water made muddy by erosion and carried to sea by wave-generated currents has sometimes gotten into the offshore circulation and been traced for hundreds of miles from the coast. This dynamic interplay of waves and currents, transporting sediments and tearing down or building up the beaches, is forever reshaping the shore.

Shifting Sands

A beach is never finished. It is always in the process of becoming. Built of water-borne materials, it is constantly being worked over by the waves. Much of the sand supply for the beaches comes from rivers. These bring eroded material to the sea, where waves and currents move it along the coast, depositing it in favored locations. Other sands, such as coral and shell sands, come from the sea itself, sometimes in prodigious quantities. Bulldozers have been quarrying sand on many shell beaches for years; yet the beaches remain pretty much the same. Foraminifera and other shallow-water animals living near shore produce a continuous supply of new shells which the waves bring to the beaches in abundance. On the other hand, if the bulldozers stopped operating, the beaches would go on building up until they reached what geologists call an "equilibrium profile," in which the normal pattern of waves would neither add nor take away any significant amount of material. Then the surplus shells would be moved along the coast to be deposited on another shore.

The waves are constantly working to establish such profiles of equilibrium. In each instance, these depend on the type of material deposited. You can see this if you look at the seaward slope, the "foreshore," of different beaches. Coarse sands pack together loosely. When you walk on this kind of beach your feet sink in. The loose material lets slosh from incoming waves drain through, depositing suspended material with relatively little backwash. The slope of such a beach will build up until it reaches a steepness where what backwash there is allows no more material to accumulate. Fine sand, on the other hand, packs together. Water does not sink in as readily. This enhances the backwash from waves, which more easily carries off the sand in suspension. This is why beaches of fine sand have a gentler slope than those built of coarser materials. Also, the former pack into a harder surface, so that cars can be driven on fine sand beaches but would become mired on coarse sands.

Wave patterns change and the beach profiles change with them. One good day's storm surf can completely alter the build-up of several weeks or even months. Some beaches undergo a regular seasonal cycle. During summer months the fair-weather waves bring in sand, building thick wide beaches. A beach is usually defined as extending landward to the farthest point that waves carry sand. The inner part of the beach, where

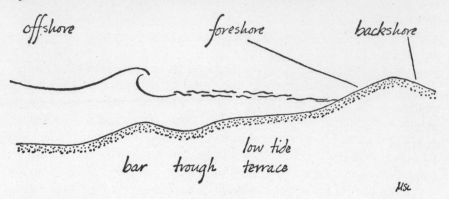

offshore　　*foreshore*　　*backshore*

bar　*trough*　*low tide terrace*

MSt

FIG. 25: *Principal elements of a beach profile. The bar and trough are formed by wave action.*

it is horizontal or even slopes toward the land, is called the "berm" or "backshore." During the summer this berm area may be built out several hundred feet as waves pile up sand on the foreshore.

When winter comes, heavy storm waves batter the foreshore, stirring the sand into suspension and cutting back the berm. The suspended sand is carried off by longshore currents until these find a rip which, in turn, carries the sand seaward. Sometimes the sand is deposited offshore, to be brought back again next season. Sometimes it is shifted to a nearby beach, where it remains until a change in wave pattern brings it back again. Other times it may simply be carried off, to be replaced by fresh supplies of sand moving in from another area. Occasionally a beach will go on building up over several seasons. The berm may widen so much that its inner part becomes dunes and for a while joins the land. But the waves are apt to reclaim their own at any time.

Thus beaches go through cycles of growth, denudation, and replenishment. There are short-period cycles associated with a single storm. Longer cycles, like those just described, are correlated with the seasonal patterns of waves and weather. Still others may be associated with long-term weather trends measured in years.

Because a beach is never static, it is wise to know exactly what you are getting in buying beach property. That beautiful sandy shore you saw last summer may disappear after a couple of winter storms. It is well to observe it at all seasons or, better still, to find out what has happened to it for a number of years past.

There is even greater need for caution in building breakwaters or jetties near sand beaches. These may improve anchorage facilities, but they can also destroy the beaches. The normal sand supply may pile up behind the jetty while the beach below becomes eroded and denuded. At Redondo Beach, California, for example, this effect was augmented when a jetty was built at a point where the edge of a sub-marine canyon caused waves to converge, enhancing their erosive attack. Before the jetty was built, sand coming in from the north had counteracted this effect. When the sand supply was cut off, the waves kept eating away at the beaches and then at the land itself, destroying valuable property.

On the other hand, by taking beach dynamics into consideration, one can have the protection of jetties and keep the beaches too. A number of harbors have been made this way along the straight Florida beaches where nature has provided no convenient anchorages. The jetties have indeed cut off the supply of quartz sand normally brought in from rivers emptying to the north. But an abundance of shell sands from off-shore waters has maintained the beaches south of the jetties.

When storms and high winds drive waves against the shore, the water that shapes the beaches attacks the land itself. It chips away at rock cliffs and man-made structures with tenacity. Here is another and more violent factor that sculpts the shore. (See Plate 10.)

The Force of Waves and Spray

With driving winds behind them, ocean waves become careen-ing giants. At sea they can grow to heights of 75 feet and more. Waves over 100 feet high have been reported. But R. C. H. Russell, the British wave authority, in a comprehensive review of the subject, gives 75 feet as the highest reliable estimate. At the same time, he points out that the most damaging waves are "freak waves found in freak storms," and it is impossible to give figures for their dimensions.

Just imagine a solid wall of water rearing as high or higher than a medium-sized house! The greatest danger to ships from such a wave lies in its breaking or having its top blown off by the wind so that a mass of water crashes onto the deck. Damage to shore structures, on the other hand, is inflicted in a variety of ways. The wind-driven water sometimes picks up sand and pebbles which it uses as an abrasive to grind away at cliffs and walls. It undermines marine foundations. It tosses huge boulders like cannon balls and develops momentary pres-

E*

sures that even the stoutest man-made structures cannot always withstand.

Russell cites several illustrations of the force of such waves. For example, he tells how a massive breakwater at Wick, Scotland, was twice destroyed, even though, from his description, it must have been an impressive structure. It was a mass of concrete rubble tied with steel to a foundation of huge stones cemented together. It measured 26 feet by 45 feet by 21 feet thick and weighed 1,350 tons. Yet in 1872 it was shifted bodily by wave action in a gale. The breakwater was rebuilt, this time weighing 2,600 tons. In 1877 it was swept away again. Russell does not say what happened after that. Or take the case of Tillamook Lighthouse on the United States east coast. In one storm a 135-pound rock was thrown above the light and came down vertically through the roof. Yet the roof stood 91 feet above low water!

If waves can toss such rocks about, one can imagine what enormous forces must be involved. Russell calculates that it would have taken at least a pressure of 2,440 pounds per square foot to move the Wick breakwater. He further estimates that the storm waves over 40 feet high which have been observed at Wick could develop pressures of more than 4,000 pounds per square foot, quite enough to account for the damage.

The simplest kind of wave attack occurs when a more or less vertical wall is sited in deep water. In that case, incoming waves don't break against it. Instead they are reflected and interact with each other to set up a pattern called "clapotis." This is an example of the wave interference mentioned earlier in which the crests and troughs of different waves act to reinforce one another or to cancel each other out. In clapotis, the crests and troughs of reflected waves and of the incoming waves always meet in the same place, so that a stable or "standing wave" pattern is set up. Individual waves still move in, are reflected, and move back out again. But to the observer there is no horizontal movement of the crests and troughs produced by the interference. In other words, the apparent wave pattern doesn't move toward or away from the wall. It just stands where it is. In shallower water, where the bottom begins to affect the waves yet is still not shallow enough to make them break, this standing wave or clapotis pattern is modified. As in the case of the true standing wave, incoming and reflected wave crests meet in the same places, except now one can see them moving and passing through each other.

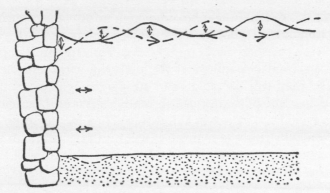

FIG. 26: *Clapotis: Individual waves move in, are reflected, and move out again. But their crests and troughs coincide so that the over-all wave pattern stands where it is, crests and troughs always appearing in the same place. Water particles in the standing crests and troughs simply move up and down (vertical two-headed arrows). A quarter wave length away particles move horizontally back and forth, often eroding the bottom in front of the wall.*

Since the waves are not breaking and hurling water against the wall, the total pressure exerted by clapotis is not especially great. The water simply moves up and down the wall, and the pressure at any point is about the same as would be exerted by still water of similar depth. On the other hand, if water gets into cracks or open joints, this constantly fluctuating pressure can pry facing stones loose. Also, the water movements set up near the bottom by the clapotis can erode and eventually undermine the structure unless special precautions are taken. Unlike traveling waves, where water particles go through a more or less circular orbit as the wave form passes, the water in the standing crests and troughs simply moves up and down. At the bottom this motion dies away, causing little or no erosion. But just a quarter wave length away from the crests and troughs, the water particles move horizontally back and forth. This motion goes right to the bottom and can cause substantial erosion. Thus just a quarter wave length away from the wall the bottom may become badly eroded.

Clapotis is a fairly simple phenomenon. It is easy to study both theoretically and with models in laboratory tanks. Marine engineers can cope with its problems relatively well, as in the case of structures along Mediterranean shores. Here, where the tide range is rarely more than a foot, structures can usually be placed in water deep enough so that waves won't break against them even at low tide. Then the engineers' chief concern is to build them heavy enough not to be overturned and to ensure that erosion won't undercut the foundations.

But where structures have to take the force of breaking waves, clapotis is a secondary problem. If the walls can withstand the attack of breakers, they will be more than strong enough to stand up to clapotis. Where the tidal range is substantial, structures cannot always be sited to avoid breaking waves at low tide. Then too, there are reasons for siting some structures so that waves will break against them anyway, as in the case of many seawalls. Here the problem is to withstand the hammering of moving masses of water, and that hammering can be intense indeed.

When a storm wave breaks, a jet of water usually shoots out from the crest at about twice the speed of the wave itself. The full force of a breaking wave hitting a wall is generally equivalent to that of any other water jet traveling at comparable speed. It is a solid mass of water slamming into the wall, exerting pressures for a second or two which are capable of moving breakwaters and causing considerable damage. Much of the damage to marine structures comes from forces of this type. Moreover, if a wave breaks in a certain way, shock pressures may develop for a few hundredths of a second. These have been estimated at over 14,000 pounds per square foot.

The highest shock pressures are generated when the breaking wave traps a pocket of air and compresses it against the wall. If the pocket is relatively thick, it will merely cushion the impact. If its thickness is much less than half its height, it will begin to exert shock pressures.

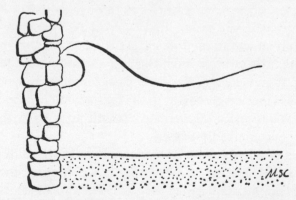

FIG. 27: *When a breaking wave traps an air pocket, compressing it against a wall or cliff face, tremendous shock pressures are often generated, causing the air literally to explode and throwing up powerful plumes of spray.*

These will be greatest where the pocket is thinnest. It is not known how much damage these shock pressures themselves cause, but the compressed air literally explodes, throwing the water up in high-speed plumes of spray that leave little doubt of their power.

Pressure developed by such spray has been estimated at 16,800 pounds per square foot. The pressure estimates given here have been taken from Russell. They were made by a combination of observation and theoretical calculations. The theory, in turn, was based on experiments made in laboratory tanks. Thus the estimates only hint at the actual power of the spray under natural conditions. Russell again cites a case that illustrates this power more graphically than numbers.

In 1864, another English wave researcher, Thomas Stevenson, described groups of huge stone blocks on the Skerry islets in the Shetlands lying well above sea level and looking as though they had been dislodged by storms. A typical group of the blocks ranged from 9½ tons down, with one 19½-tonner standing a little to one side. The blocks had been moved dozens of feet above the low-water mark and several hundred feet beyond it. There were gashes and scores in the rocks below to mark the routes by which the blocks had been dragged or pushed up from lower down on the shore where they had been broken off by breakers. Yet the tide range here is only six feet, indicating that the blocks had been moved by the force of spray. In one instance, a 5½-ton block was found 72 feet above the sea and 20 feet from a hole in the rock into which it fit exactly. It had been quarried out of solid rock by flying spray.

It is little wonder that wind-driven waves have been a powerful factor in carving the shore lines. They can attack and remove even solid rock cliffs, often creating curious shapes such as rock pinnacles standing a little way from shore or joined to it by a natural bridge. Similarly, waves can hollow out caves in the rock. Then, having eroded a cave, they may pound upward until they break through the roof. One sometimes sees spray shooting up out of apparently solid ground behind the main shore line.

On the other hand, some of the most destructive ocean waves have nothing to do with the wind. These are the misnamed "tidal waves" generated by seismic disturbances or by submarine landslides. Geologists call them "tsunamis," from the Japanese term for "large waves in harbors." They are appropriately named. Rising from the sea without warning, they engulf even the shores of sheltered coves.

"Tidal Waves"

On April 1, 1946, a tsunami struck the Hawaiian Islands, the first of any consequence since 1877. The waves had been generated by a disturbance along the Aleutian Trench over 2,000 miles away to the north. From there they had raced as a low swell at an average speed of 450 miles an hour until, feeling the rise of the sea bottom, they reared up to flood over the land. Dr. Francis Shepard was vacationing at Kawela Bay on northern Oahu at that time. The following excerpt from his eyewitness account given in his recent book, *The Earth beneath the Sea,* is a colorful description of what it is like to be caught off guard by one of these huge waves:

. . . we were sleeping peacefully when we were awakened by a loud hissing sound, which sounded for all the world as if dozens of locomotives were blowing off steam directly outside our house. Puzzled, we jumped up and rushed to the front window. Where there had been a beach previously, we saw nothing but boiling water, which was sweeping over the ten-foot top of the beach ridge and coming directly at the house. I rushed and grabbed my camera, forgetting such incidentals as clothes, glasses, watch, and pocketbook. As I opened the door I noticed with some regret that the water was not advancing any farther but, instead, was retreating rapidly down the slope.

By that time I was conscious of the fact that we might be experiencing a tsunami. My suspicions became confirmed as the water moved swiftly seaward, and the sea level dropped a score of feet, leaving the coral reefs in front of the house exposed to view. Fish were flapping and jumping up and down where they had been stranded by the retreating waves. Quickly taking a couple of photographs, in my confusion I accidentally made a double exposure of the bare reef. Trying to show my erudition, I said to my wife, "There will be another wave, but it won't be as exciting as the one that awakened us. Too bad I couldn't get a photograph of the first one."

Was I mistaken? In a few minutes as I stood at the edge of the beach ridge in front of the house, I could see the water beginning to rise and swell up around the outer edges of the exposed reef; it built higher and higher and then came racing forward with amazing velocity. "Now," I said, "here is a good chance for a picture." I took one, but my hand was rather unsteady that time. As the water continued to advance I shot another one, fortunately a little better . . . As it piled up in front of me, I began to wonder whether this wave was really going to be smaller than the preceding one. I called to my wife to run to the back of the house for protection, but she had already started, and I followed her just in time. As I looked back I saw the water surging over the spot where I had been standing a moment before. Suddenly we heard the terrible smashing of glass at the front of the house. The refrigerator passed us on the left side moving upright out into the cane field. On the right came a wall of water sweeping toward us down the road that was our escape route from the area. We were also startled to see that there was nothing but kindling wood left of what had been the nearby house to the east. Finally, the water stopped coming on and we were left on a small island, protected by the undamaged portion of the house, which, thanks to its good construction and to the protecting ironwood trees, still withstood the blows. The water had rushed on into the cane field and spent its fury.

My confidence about the waves getting smaller was rapidly vanishing. Having noted that there was a fair interval before the second invasion (actually fifteen minutes as we found out later), we started running along the emerging beach ridge in the only direction in which we could get to the slightly elevated main road. As we ran, we found some very wet and frightened Hawaiian women standing wringing their hands and wondering what to do. With difficulty we persuaded them to come with us along the ridge to a place where there was a break in the cane field. As we hurried through this break, another huge wave came rolling in over the reef and broke with shuddering force against the small escarpment at the top of the beach. Then, rising as a monstrous wall of water, it swept on after us, flattening the cane field with a terrifying sound. We reached the comparative safety of the elevated road just ahead of the wave.

There, in a motley array of costumes, various other refugees were gathered. One couple had been cooking their breakfast when all of a sudden the first wave came in, lifted their house right off its foundation, and carried it several hundred feet into the cane field where it set it down so gently that their breakfast just kept right on cooking. Needless to say, they did not stay to enjoy the meal. Another couple had escaped with difficulty from their collapsing house.

We walked along the road until we could see nearby Kawela Bay, and from there we watched several more waves roar onto the shore. They came with a steep front like the tidal bore that I had seen move up the Bay of Fundy at Moncton, New Brunswick, and up the channels on the tide flat at Mont-Saint-Michel in Normandy. We could see various ruined houses, some of them completely demolished. One house had been thrown into a pond right on top of another . . . Another was still floating out in the bay.

Finally, after about six waves had moved in, each one apparently getting progressively weaker, I decided I had better go back and see what I could rescue from what was left of the house where we had been living. After all, we were in scanty attire and required clothes. I had just reached the door when I became conscious that a very powerful mass of water was bearing down on the place. This time there simply was no island in back of the house during the height of the wave. I rushed to a nearby tree and climbed it as fast as possible and then hung on for dear life as I swayed back and forth under the impact of the wave. Like the others, this wave soon subsided, and the series of waves that followed were all minor in comparison.

After the excitement was over, we found half of the house still standing and began picking up our belongings. I chased all over the cane fields trying to find books and notes that had been strewn there by the angry waves. We did, finally, discover our glasses undamaged [the sand, being coral, did not produce scratches], buried deep in the sand and debris covering the floor. My waterproof wristwatch was found under the house by the owner a week later.

"Well," I thought, "you're a pretty poor oceanographer not to know that tsunamis increase in size with each new wave." As soon as possible I began to look over the literature, and I felt a little better when I could not find any information to the effect that successive waves increase in size, and yet what could be a more important point to remember? You can be sure that since then those of us who have investigated these waves in the Hawaiian Islands have stressed this danger . . .

Most of the tsunamis, like the one described by Shepard, have occurred in the Pacific, originating with seismic disturbances along the ring of trenches that circle that ocean. Usually they are associated with exceptionally severe earthquakes that shake seismographs throughout the world and give warning that one of these unusual waves may be on its way. Perhaps the disturbance causes a section of the sea floor to drop. Then as water rushes in from all sides, it humps up on the surface, causing waves to move out in all directions. Similarly, if the sea bottom is suddenly lifted, the water at the surface humps up, sending out waves. Submarine landslides may also cause some of the tsunamis.

These waves are unusually long, with lengths on the order of 100 miles between successive crests and with periods of about 15 minutes. They travel swiftly, averaging some 450 miles an hour, and cover many thousands of miles without appreciable loss of energy. In the 1946 tsunami at Hawaii, a second and even larger series of waves came in from the west 18 hours after the primary waves had arrived from the north. Shepard thinks the late arrivals had been doubly reflected, first by a submarine cliff off Japan and then from an escarpment in Oceania, to come in on what had been the sheltered side of the main island of Hawaii.

The arrival of a tsunami, especially along a steep coast, looks like an erratic and rapid rise of the tide, hence the name "tidal wave." But these waves have no more to do with the true tides than do the floods caused by high storm winds which are also called by that name. Responding to the rhythmic pulse of astronomical forces, the tides do indeed affect the oceans daily as a system of waves. However, they are quite different from the undulations of a tsunami or the wind-driven mass of a hurricane flood. Their basic characteristics are set by the sun and moon and by the shape of the ocean basins. They are a constant disturbance that writes its patterns on the waters on a truly global scale.

The Pulse of the Earth

Compared to the pull of the earth's gravity, the tide-producing forces are minuscule. They amount to only about one ten millionth of that pull at the earth's surface. Yet they leave scarcely a particle of the surface unaffected. You and I take no notice of the small fraction of an ounce increase and decrease they regularly make in our weight. But the land feels their influence and responds with crustal tides that can be detected with sensitive instruments. The atmosphere feels it, too, for meteorologists have found tides even in the heights of the stratosphere. And in the ocean the waters are affected even at abyssal depths. These pervasive forces elicit a response from land, air, and sea that geophysicists have aptly called the "pulse of the earth."

This response is greatest in the oceans, and it is the tides of the sea with which we are concerned here. These tides are rarely the same from one place to the next. Even neighboring coastal towns will often have markedly different tides in their respective harbors. No coast line is unaffected by their universal pulse. At some points this pulse may be so weak that it is masked by effects of wind and weather. Yet in other places it raises and lowers the water level as much as 60 to 70 feet. While there is no mystery as to what causes them, the interplay of factors that produce the tides characteristic of any one location is complex. Not even tidal experts can follow these factors in all their detail. Only a brief review of the major influences can be given here.

It seems paradoxical that the tide-raising forces, one of the most potent influences affecting the sea, should be the result of an almost insignificant astronomical imbalance. The earth and moon pull on each other gravitationally. At the same time they revolve about a common center. Without this revolving motion they would crash together disastrously. But the outward centrifugal force of their motion just balances the inward gravitational attraction, and earth and moon go revolving on together in their orbit about the sun. However, while the earth-moon system as a whole is in balance, individual bits of matter on the earth's surface are not. On the hemisphere directly under the moon, the lunar attraction is slightly greater than the opposing centrifugal forces, while on the opposite side of the earth these latter forces have the edge. The result of this small imbalance is the lunar tide-producing forces.

These forces generally have both a vertical and a horizontal component. Compared to the earth's gravity, the vertical forces are negligible. As far as the tides are concerned, it is the horizontal forces that count. Facing the moon, they pull material toward the point directly under the lunar zenith. On the opposite hemisphere they pull toward the antipodal point, where the moon is at its nadir. If the earth were entirely covered by water of uniform depth, it would tend to gather in two humps, one under the moon and one on the opposite side of the earth.

As this hypothetical water-covered earth spins, it brings the various parts of its surface progressively under the tidal bulges. If there were absolutely no friction between the earth's surface and the water, these bulges would stay under the moon. If, on the other hand, there were a very large amount of friction, the bulges would tend to move with the earth. The actual situation lies somewhere between these extremes. There is enough friction for the earth to drag the bulges along a little bit. The bulges reach an equilibrium point between the forces tending to make them hump under the moon and the frictional forces tending to drag them along with the earth's rotation. This is one reason that a given spot on the surface generally passes under and beyond the moon before it has its high tide.

The tide-producing influence of the more distant sun arises in exactly the same way and is about half as strong as that of the moon. Thus at full and new moon, when sun, moon, and earth are more or less in line, the lunar and solar tidal forces add together. Then the seas literally spring up to reach the highest high- and lowest low-water levels in the appropriately named "spring tides." When sun, moon, and earth form a right angle during the first and third quarters of the moon, the solar and lunar tidal forces oppose each other, producing the "neap tides." In these, the range between high and low water is at its smallest.

Changes in the distances and relative positions of earth and moon and sun alter the tide-raising forces. The moon's orbit about the earth

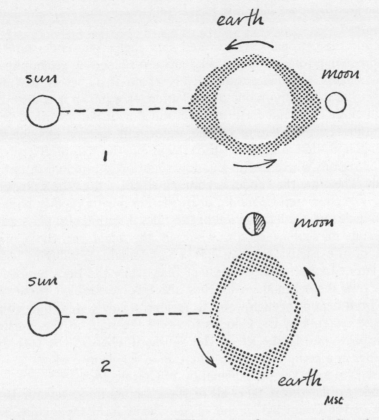

FIG. 28: *Spring and neap tides: When sun and moon are in line they pull together to produce the highest tides, the spring tides (1). But when they are at right angles to each other their tidal forces are opposed, producing the low neap tides (2).*

and that of the earth about the sun are ellipses. This makes the distances between earth and moon and between earth and sun different at different points along the respective orbits. Also, the orientation of these orbits changes slowly, so that the apparent path of sun and moon through the sky changes over the centuries. The position of the moon above or below the earth's equator produces variations in the relative heights of the two daily high tides, in some cases, virtually eliminating one of them. Tidal experts can calculate all these astronomical effects from the laws of celestial mechanics. They can determine what the tide-producing forces were at any time in the remote past or forecast them accurately for an indefinitely long future. Yet they can predict the actual tides only in certain carefully studied cases, for the tide-producing forces are only one factor influencing the ebb and flow of the water.

While the fictional water-covered earth helps one understand the tide-producing forces, the real tides are also shaped by geography and the dynamics of moving water. Every ocean basin, every bay, cove, or inlet has its natural mode of oscillation. If water in it is disturbed, it will slosh back and forth and up and down like disturbed water in a tub. This oscillation of the water will have a characteristic time period determined by the shape of the basin. There will also be regions where the up-and-down motion is minimal or entirely absent. These are the "nodes" about which the rest of the water oscillates. The characteristic modes of oscillation greatly modify both the ocean-wide and the local action of the tides. Friction also plays a role, especially in shallow basins, while in the open sea the Coriolis force of the earth's rotation has a considerable modifying effect. The later effect arises from the fact that, while the tides tend to advance over the ocean as waves, they also involve sizable currents running from regions of high water to regions of low water. The turning of these currents by the Coriolis force, to the right in the Northern Hemisphere and to the left in the Southern, changes the pattern of the tides in a complex manner wherever a sizable area of water is involved. [See page 155 for explanation of Coriolis force.]

Modern tidal theory takes all of these factors into account. If the shape of the ocean basins and of significant local topography were known in enough detail, it might be possible to use high-speed computers to predict the tides for any given locality on the basis of theory alone. This is an impossible task at present. On the other hand, tidal experts can work the problem the other way around. If they have enough records of past tides at any given spot, they can use tide theory to analyze the data to find the significant governing factors. Then with the aid of special tide-predicting machines, they can predict the local tides for many years ahead with a high degree of accuracy.

The interplay of the various tidal influences helps one understand some of the remarkable features of the tides. In most places the lunar influence predominates. Every day the moon rises about fifty minutes later and every day the tides are fifty minutes later too. But at some places, such as Tahiti, this correlation disappears. At Tahiti you can almost tell time by the stage of the tides. High water regularly occurs around noon and midnight, with low water coming more or less six hours in between. The lunar cycle has disappeared and that of the sun predominates. This is probably because Tahiti is in a nodal region for oscillations set up by the moon. The waters here are free to respond to the tempo of the sun.

While sun and moon impress a basic rhythm on the tides, it is the characteristics of the tidal basins that govern their local amplitude and times of arrival. If the period of natural oscillation of a basin is very much smaller than that of the astronomical forces, then the tides tend to follow the waxing and waning of these forces. The water in such a basin, when allowed to oscillate freely, sloshes about relatively quickly, and the oscillation of the tidal forces is able to force the water mass to conform to its own tempo. But when the natural period is considerably longer than that of the tidal forces, the water responds too slowly to follow their oscillations. Then the tides tend to be small and reversed. Low water appears when the tidal forces are greatest, while the water rises highest when these forces have waned.

These are extreme cases, and the actual circumstances may fall almost anywhere in between. Thus the local tides may follow the 24-hour-50-minute daily cycle of the moon, with successive tides being about 12 hours and 25 minutes apart. But the rise of the tides may come several hours after the moon has passed through the local zenith.

The time lag between the arrival of the moon overhead and the actual onset of the next flood tide is called the local "tidal establishment." It is one of the characteristic tidal features that varies widely from place to place. At some places, as in the Gulf of Mexico, there is only one slow rise and fall of the water every 24 hours and 50 minutes.

The natural rhythm of the tidal basins also helps explain why the heights of the tides cannot be predicted from astronomical calculations alone. Again, when the natural period of oscillation is short compared to the cycle of the tidal forces, the rise and fall of the waters correlates well with what one would expect from the play of these forces. When that natural period is relatively long, it is hard to set the waters in motion and rise of the tides tends to be small. But when the natural period of the water coincides with that of the tidal forces, the two types of oscillation reinforce each other. That is when the waters mount to spectacular heights in resonance or "sympathetic" tides. On the southern side of the Bay of Fundy, New Brunswick, which is famous for having the greatest tides in the world, the tidal range is almost 70 feet. Here decreasing width and shoaling side margins accentuate the remarkable resonance tides in this elongated basin.

One of the most striking local effects occurs when the tide enters certain river estuaries. The narrowing of the channel and shoaling of the bottom sometimes change the shape of the incoming flood tide so much that the water surges upstream with a steep front. These "bores," as they are called, can be massive. One of the most famous is that of the Tsientang River in China, where the advancing face of the water reaches heights of 25 feet during spring tides. Another famous bore, called the Pororoca, rushes regularly some 200 miles up the Amazon, often making the river temporarily impassable. It is like a waterfall up to 16 feet high moving upriver at a speed of 12 knots and with a roar that can be heard for miles.

Because the ocean waters are not homogenous, the patterns of their waves and tides are not confined to their upper surface. Wherever there is a sharp vertical change of temperature or salinity marking a boundary between different water masses, there is a "surface" for the play of waves or tides. Thought of in this way, even the top surface of the ocean is an interface between two fluids of different density, air and water. The internal waves of the sea are much harder to observe than those of the surface, however. It takes a rapid series of vertical temperature or salinity measurements to detect them. They can occur even when the surface itself is calm. Some of the internal waves have been related to weather disturbances. Others that have been studied seem to be correlated with tides. For the most part, however, oceanographers know little more about these waves than the fact that they exist and appear to occur even at great depths. Among other things, they may account for the puzzling ripple marks that have been photographed on some parts of the deep-sea bottom, marks that resemble those left by waves on a sandy shore.

Another type of wave little understood beyond the fact that it occurs is the so-called "long wave." These waves have periods shorter than the tides, the longest periodic oscillations in the sea, but much longer than those of ordinary waves or swell. Tsunamis are a kind of long wave. The ones considered here, however, are somewhat different in nature. They have periods ranging from a few minutes to several hours. Sometimes they are associated with seismic activity, sometimes with weather conditions. Many times their origin is not known at all. Like the tides, they are often related locally to the natural oscillations of a basin. Some harbors, for example, have back-and-forth water movements which correspond with their natural period of oscillation and are strong enough to snap mooring cables.

Long waves are believed to travel great distances without much loss of height. If a storm or pressure disturbance happens to coincide with a train of long waves, traveling at the same speed over an expanse of shallow water, the waves may build up into surges as devastating as those of a true tsunami when they finally hit land. The giant storm waves that flooded the British East Anglian coast in 1953 were probably of this type. The peaks of such meteorological surges can last up to three hours and resemble the tides themselves. Fortunately, although the long waves are not understood, meteorologists have been able to set up a fairly effective forecasting and warning system in the shallow North Sea area. The need for this system there, and its effectiveness, is comparable to that of the tsunami warning system of the North Pacific.

During the International Geophysical Year some thirty stations on coasts and islands of the Atlantic and Pacific oceans and a few stations in the Indian Ocean took continuous records of arrival of long waves. They were aided by a special wave recorder that is sensitive to waves of periods from about five to sixty minutes but doesn't respond to the fluctuations of ordinary waves or the rhythm of the tides. These data may eventually increase scientific understanding of the long waves. But as of this writing the state of knowledge is not much better than it was at the beginning of the IGY.

This is typical of the present situation in the science of waves and tides. With the capacity of electronic computers steadily increasing, with more comprehensive and accurate data being collected, and with improvements in mathematical techniques, oceanographers appear to be getting in a position to master these difficult phenomena. Meanwhile they have to live with the uncomfortable fact that some of the most commonplace features of the ocean—features with which practical seafarers long ago learned to cope—have an inherent complexity that so far has put them beyond scientific comprehension.

SIX

The Restless Waters

Seven tenths of our planet's surface is never at rest. Quite apart from the phenomena of tides and waves, the interlocking water masses of the oceans are forever on the move. Sometimes they are in a hurry, as when the Gulf Stream pours past Miami like a millrace. Sometimes they barely creep along, as in the case of the cold bottom currents that may take decades, even centuries, to complete their journey. But somehow, over no one knows how long a time, any given droplet of sea water will find its way to almost every part of the sea's domain.

This constant movement of the waters, this restless stirring which we classify as great current systems, is one of the most characteristic features of the sea. It mixes the oceans so thoroughly that, in spite of the local salinity variations that continually develop, the general composition of their dissolved salts is everywhere the same. It helps even out the unequal distribution of the sun's heating and regulates the weather. It creates vertical upwelling currents that bring nutrient minerals from the depths. These fertilize rich plant growths in many areas, which in turn are the mainstay of the world's great fisheries.

Because the ocean circulation is so basic, it is one of the first things oceanographers must understand to build a comprehensive science of the seas. Yet they have scarcely begun to unravel its puzzle. Relevant observations with an acceptable degree of accuracy have been made only within the past thirty-five years. Even then most of them have been so scattered that it has been difficult to draw comprehensive pictures of the currents. The many fine current charts that have been made are really only averages based on data often taken years apart. They don't begin to show what happens day by day, or even month by month, in the oceans. Think what a fix the weatherman would be in if he had only charts of monthly average winds to guide his forecasting!

Fortunately the meteorologist can draw up maps several times a day which show in some detail just how the atmosphere is behaving. Oceanographers need something equivalent to these "synoptic charts" of the weatherman if they are ever to understand the oceans. Since the ocean is more stable than the atmosphere, however, data for a large area taken over several weeks or months serve the purpose. But until recently this kind of survey was little more than an oceanographer's dream. Ship time is expensive and the ocean is immense. The German ship *Meteor* made a comprehensive survey of the South Atlantic some thirty-five years ago that long remained a lonely example to the rest of the oceanographic world.

The International Geophysical Year changed all that. Twenty-five of the thirty-seven nations that shared the oceanographic phase of IGY put eighty research ships to sea in a co-ordinated effort that has given oceanographers hope of getting the synoptic charts they need. Some of them teamed up to make a comprehensive hydrographic survey of the entire Atlantic. Others cruised the Indian Ocean and made broad sweeps over the half hemisphere of water we call the Pacific. The knowledge they gained is certain to revolutionize this part of ocean science. Indeed, some startling discoveries have already been made, such as that of a current system in the Pacific as sizable as the Gulf Stream, though at this writing the bulk of the data looms as a mountain of analytical work for years to come.

Moreover, the success of the IGY has set a precedent for international co-operation that is expected to carry over into the years ahead. Oceanographers expect to continue their massive surveys and to gather enough data over the years finally to gain the basic knowledge of currents they so badly need. The over-all pattern of these currents as known today is outlined on one of the endpaper maps. It is an interwoven flow that embraces the world in its web.

Pattern of the Currents

If there were no other factor influencing the oceans, solar heating near the equator and cooling toward the poles, plus the ever present force of gravity, would be enough to start the waters circulating. However, the unequal heating sets the atmosphere to moving as well. The wind systems this creates interact so strongly with the oceans that the winds are the major driving force of the surface currents. This vast heat-driven mechanism of wind and water is guided by two all-pervading forces—gravity and the earth's rotational spinning. They grip every tiny parcel of air or water individually, yet they control the courses of the wind and current masses.

The action of gravity is simply the familiar tendency of heavier water to sink and lighter water to rise. You see it every time you boil water in a saucepan and set up convection currents. The action of the earth's rotation is more subtle. If a missile were fired from either pole to hit a point on the equator, it would have to be aimed some distance ahead of the target in the direction of the earth's spin. Otherwise it would miss the mark, because while the missile was in flight the equatorial target would have rotated out of its path. To an observer on the ground it would have looked as if the missile had curved in its path, as though some invisible force had continuously made it shift course. Scientists call this fictitious force the "Coriolis force." It influences every object moving freely over the earth's surface. Of course it really isn't a force at all. It is simply the effect of the planet's turning beneath the objects while they move along. In the Northern Hemisphere it seems to turn them toward the right relative to the surface, and in the Southern Hemisphere toward the left. It is the second guiding influence of winds and currents. Its effect on the currents is to make them flow somewhat to the right of the wind in the Northern Hemisphere and to the left in the Southern Hemisphere. Actually the water starts to move in the direction of the wind but is immediately turned toward one side by the Coriolis force, the degree of turning depending on several factors, including frictional resistance in the water.

The combined result of winds and these guiding forces is an interconnected system of clockwise- and counterclockwise-flowing currents. Oceanographers call these swirling systems "gyrals." You find them in all of the major oceans, current merging into current, weaving their arabesques between equatorial and polar seas.

In near-equatorial latitudes, the driving force of these oceanic rivers is the Trade Winds. Blowing with a force often between 30 and 40 miles an hour, these are the steadiest winds on earth. They blow northwestward and southwestward, respectively, in the Northern and Southern Hemispheres right around the planet, forcing the waters into the strong westward-flowing North and South Equatorial Currents. These are the currents that old-time navigators used to ride. More recently the South Equatorial Current in the Pacific carried Thor Heyerdahl and his raft *Kon-Tiki* on their epic adventure.

In the Atlantic, these currents are diverted by the land mass of the Americas and blocked by the slender Isthmus of Panama. Driven against this western barrier, the waters pile up so that the sea surface slopes upward to the west about three inches in 1,000 miles.

As long as the winds are blowing, the waters flow right on up this oceanic "hill." But between the northern and southern Trade Wind belts there is an area of calm, or at the most light and variable winds, called the Doldrums. Here, with no wind to support it, water runs eastward down the sea slope to form the Equatorial Counter Current. This is most strongly developed in the eastern Pacific but is found in the Atlantic too, flowing eastward just north of the equator. These ocean and atmospheric systems in low latitudes tend to center around the "heat equator" rather than the geographic equator. This "heat equator" is to the heat distribution of the earth what the geographic equator is to the earth's geography and is located somewhat north of the latter as determined by the maximum intensity of the sun's heating.

As the equatorial currents flow westward, the shape of the land barrier shunts them to the north and south. Outside the West Indies, the North Equatorial Current splits. Part of it is forced northwestward to become the Bahamas Current. But the Trade Winds still blow strongly from the northeast, holding the rest of the current on a more westerly course through the Antilles into the Caribbean Sea.

Meanwhile, to the south, part of the South Equatorial Current is turned down the South American coast and becomes the Brazil Current. But only about half of the water can flow this way, for the bulge of Brazil splits the current neatly. Part of it is deflected northward along the coast into the Northern Hemisphere, where it joins the north equatorial waters flowing into the Caribbean.

By now the mass of water has reached titanic proportions. It races through Antillean narrows like a swift river. Urged on by the incessant Trades and funneled by the converging passage between Cuba and the Yucatan Peninsula, it rushes headlong against the land barrier until it piles up into a head of more than seven inches. This is the "pumping system" that drives the Gulf Stream. Forced on by this head of pressure and blocked by the mass of water trapped in the Gulf of Mexico, the bulk of the flow turns sharply north and on into the Atlantic between Miami and Cuba. Here it becomes one of the greatest rivers in the sea, reaching velocities of more than four knots and carrying a water load fifty times that of all the major land rivers combined.

By the time these waters turn north to form the Gulf Stream system, they have been on their way from the eastern Atlantic for several weeks or even months. They have been warmed by the tropical sun all the way and now are carrying this heat energy northward, a striking example of how the ocean currents help balance the heat budget of the planet.

Continuing northward, the Gulf Stream picks up the water that has been diverted into the Bahamas Current, giving it a total transport of some 2,300 million tons of water per minute across the width and depth of the stream. Then it begins to veer right above Cape Hatteras, moving out from the coast and turning until it flows more or less east just off the Grand Banks.

By this time the warm blue mass of the Gulf Stream has run into the icy green waters of the Labrador Current coming from the north to cool the coast line above Hatteras. As these different water systems meet at sea, creating fog banks and mingling their masses, the Gulf Stream slows down, is cooled and slightly diluted by the cold northern water, which is less saline because of melting ice and the influx of northern rivers. It spreads out over the northeastern Atlantic into various current filaments that continue eastward, northward, and southeastward as a diffuse flow called the North Atlantic Drift and driven partly by the prevailing westerly winds. This is the water that warms the coast of Norway and western Europe, too, as part of it drifts southward to become the Canaries Current, thence to feed into the North Equatorial Current once more.

This circuit of the waters completes the North Atlantic gyral. There is a similar gyral in the South Atlantic formed by the South Equatorial and weakly developed Brazil Currents with a return flow off the coast of Africa in the ill-defined Benguela Current. The circuit is completed on the southern end by another of the earth's spectacular current systems.

Between latitudes 40° and 60° South, the winds blow steadily and strongly from the west with no land to block or modify them. Driving the waters before them, they set up an ever flowing current round the Antarctic Continent—the West Wind Drift. The Brazil Current feeds into this circumpolar system.

Like the Atlantic, the Pacific and Indian oceans have two major gyrals, although in the latter they are rather vaguely developed. There is no opportunity for anything comparable to the Gulf Stream in the

Indian Ocean. Instead, the shape of the land forces the North Equatorial Current down the east coast of Africa to join with the similarly diverted South Equatorial Current to form the strong Agulhas Current that flows as far as the Cape of Good Hope. But the northern part of this ocean is dominated by the monsoons, whose regular southwest-northeast seasonal shifting of the winds imposes its own current regime on the waters.

In the Pacific, there is an immense equatorial stretch with no land to divert the westward-flowing currents. Here the South Equatorial Current just spreads diffusely over the whole southwestern part of the ocean. This great gyral is completed to the south by the West Wind Drift of the "Roaring Forties," as old sailing masters called these windy regions, and on the east by the Humboldt Current flowing up the western coast of South America.

North of the equator, the Philippines split the North Equatorial Current after its long journey across the ocean. Part of the current turns south and back to join the eastward-running countercurrent. Part is forced northward where, off Japan, it becomes the Kuroshio, a somewhat weaker counterpart of the Gulf Stream. Again as in the Atlantic, this current turns eastward toward America as the Japan Current, while an icy flow from the north, the Oyashio, cuts in behind it. The gyral is completed by the flow southward down the western American coast of the California Current, which joins the North Equatorial Current off Lower California.

The circulating current systems influence the waters in the broad areas they encircle as well as those immediately connected with their flow. Nowhere is this more clearly seen than in the North Atlantic.

Desert in the Sea

In the middle of the North Atlantic gyral is a calm sunny region of legend and lazily drifting weed—the Sargasso Sea. Columbus ran into it on his first transatlantic crossing. He encountered the weed just west of the Azores, and it increased in abundance until his men began to fear they were in coastal waters and would certainly run aground. But the bottom was almost three miles below and they came through easily. Since then, and in spite of their safe passage, the legend of the menace of the Sargassum weed has grown and persisted through the years. One wonders how many sailors have carefully avoided the area because of this legend. As recently as 1952, Alain Bombard, who sailed alone on a raft across the Atlantic, reportedly planned his trip to avoid the Sargasso because he believed it to be "a major navigational hazard, a terrible trap, where plant filaments and seaweed grip vessels in an unbreakable net."

Actually, such sailors had little to fear. There is plenty of weed, but it floats in relatively small patches with open water in between. The region is really more remarkable for what it is than for what the legends claim it to be. This huge, slowly rotating eddy is one of the great deserts of the sea.

The area covered by the weeds is large and somewhat variable. In late summer it is roughly an oval measuring 1,000 miles by 2,000 miles, with its long axis lying more or less east-west. But the Sargasso water system covers an even larger area. Dr. Columbus Iselin of Woods Hole pointed out two decades ago that it includes pretty much the whole of

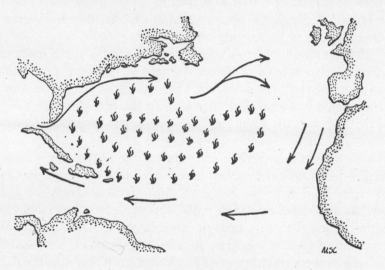

FIG. 29: *The Sargasso Sea.*

the inner portion of the gyral, with the major currents as its boundaries. These impart a slow clockwise rotation to the entire water mass.

More recently Dr. John H. Ryther, also of Woods Hole, described the Sargasso Sea as a shallow lens of warm water floating on the distinctly colder waters of the main ocean. It is sharply separated from these colder waters by a zone of rapidly changing temperature.

As far as is known, this is unique among the great gyrals in the oceans. And the life that is found there is unique as well.

No one knows where the Sargassum weed comes from. It got its name from Portuguese sailors who thought that its air-bladder floats looked like small grapes they called *salgazo*. At one time weeds were thought to come from coastal areas, perhaps in the West Indies, where storms had torn them loose from their beds. Dr. Albert E. Parr, now director of the American Museum of Natural History in New York, made a thorough study of the weeds in the early 1930's. He found that 90 per cent of them consisted of two species that are naturally floating and are never found attached to rocks. Also, he estimated the standing weed crop at several million tons, far too much to be maintained by castaways from coastal beds even if these did exist. The weeds themselves seem well suited to their environment. They grow and reproduce by budding. They are vigorously healthy, often showing new leaves and young shoots. So the mystery remains. Whatever the origin of the weed, the present consensus is that it arrived in the Sargasso Sea a very long time ago and through the slow process of evolutionary adaptation has become a native of these open waters.

With little upwelling or mixing to renew its fertility, the lazily rotating Sargasso is a biological desert. Its rate of plankton production is only about one third the average for the world's oceans. Since the tiny drifting plants and animals that make up the plankton are the basic food that supports the larger marine animals, the Sargasso rates low on the over-all biological productivity scale as well.

But even deserts have their life forms. These often show curiously specialized adaptations that help them overcome the rigors of the environment. So it is in the Sargasso. Almost every clump of drifting weeds has its cargo of small fish, crabs, shrimps, octopi, and many other creatures. Each of these is marvelously adapted to living on and about the weed that gives it sanctuary in a hostile region. If they lost their grip, some of these creatures would sink uncontrollably into the depths, where they would perish.

In some cases the animals have taken on the appearance of the weed itself, so that it takes a sharp eye to spot them. There are weedlike fishes and weedlike crabs. There are sea slugs with folds of skin that enable them to blend perfectly with their surroundings. Various species of worms build houses of lime in which they float with the weeds, taking food from the passing water. There is even one air-breathing inhabitant—*Halobates*, the water strider. This adventurous character runs over the sea surface on six long hairy legs, using the Sargassum as a resting place.

But, in spite of the lively community of the seaweeds, the Sargasso Sea is a sparsely populated wilderness, a strange oceanic desert created by the pattern of wind and currents.

These current patterns give an average picture pieced together from widely scattered data. As an average, it illustrates the general movements of the surface waters and their role in transporting heat around the world. But it hints nothing of the true complexity that oceanographers now are beginning to discover. The familiar Gulf Stream is a case in point.

The Gulf Stream: A Study in Complexity

"There is a river in the ocean. In the severest droughts it never fails, and in the mightiest floods it never overflows—It is the Gulf Stream." That is the way Matthew F. Maury described this mighty ocean current in 1855, and for decades thereafter oceanographers shared this view. Just one hundred years later Frederick C. Fuglister of Woods Hole took a radically different approach. "It is evident," he wrote, "that as more detailed observations of ocean currents are obtained many heretofore unknown structural characteristics will come to light, and the simple concept of a major ocean current 'flowing like a river through the sea' may become a thing of the past."

Here was the first big break with the traditional way of looking at the surface movements of the ocean. Like the concept of the "average man," the picture of an "average current" broke down when it came to individual daily cases.

Scientists had known for a long time that the Gulf Stream was more than a flow of water through a fixed channel. They knew that it meandered and frequently shifted position, that it threw off sizable eddies and mingled confusedly with Labrador waters to the north. After all, the curving coast line of the South Atlantic United States was sculptured by the stream's swirling inshore eddies. Nevertheless, the general concept was of a steadily flowing, well-defined current—literally a "river in the ocean"—that slowly veered northeastward.

This picture of the Gulf Stream system was based on data often taken years apart. It showed how the waters moved on the average over long periods of time. The question was, how much of the natural variability of the current was left in the picture? No one knew and few suspected how different the day-by-day situation really was.

Fuglister became interested in the problem during World War II while preparing charts of water conditions in the northeastern Atlantic. That was when he first began to realize how little is really known about the surface currents.

Unlike many parts of the oceans, the area off Labrador and Greenland had been pretty well covered with continuous observations by the International Ice Patrol. The patrol charted water coming in and out of the Arctic and also the position of the Gulf Stream as it flowed past the Grand Banks and Newfoundland and headed eastward. It hadn't ventured much south of that, since it was interested primarily in iceberg prediction. But the patrol's observations did give some clues to the structure of the Gulf Stream in their area.

It was nothing like a continuous band of warm water. Instead, their data showed a branching system with cool northern water between fingers of Gulf Stream water. Also, there seemed to be some kind of reverse movement within the system, with cool water moving in a direction opposite to the warm as a somewhat weaker flow. From these data Fuglister figured that perhaps the Gulf Stream is not a stream at all but a system of moving water with branches all along its way, or a series of related forward movements interspersed with countercurrents flowing the other way to a lesser degree.

These countermovements had been noticed before. But, since no one had traced them accurately over the ocean, they usually were drawn on the charts as side eddies of the main current. As often happens in tracing air or water movements where data are poor and there is a preconceived notion of what the picture should look like, the chart men simply assumed that the traces of countercurrents were parts of eddies and drew them accordingly. It fitted in with what they thought they knew.

Fuglister was not satisfied with this. To be sure, there actually were plenty of eddies, but these didn't explain all the observations. After the war he set out to find the facts in so far as he could. Working with L. V. Worthington and others at Woods Hole, he began tracing the main Gulf Stream system to see how big it is and where it goes. Here is what he discovered.

The hints of a branching system in the Ice Patrol data were confirmed throughout every part of the Gulf Stream studies. Fuglister calls this a "shingle effect" in which a finger of water moves along strongly for a way and then begins to peter out. Parallel to this and a little distance away (with variations), another current finger seems to develop and in its turn peters out. Still farther along and again parallel, a third current finger develops, and so on for all the courses the ship followed. In be-

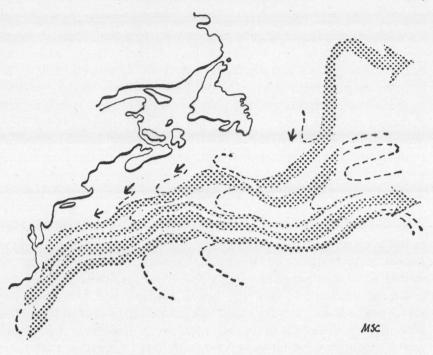

FIG. 30: *Branching fingers of the Gulf Stream (after Fuglister).*

tween these forward movements are the reverse cool currents, also in a shingle effect.

As Fuglister studied this complex system he saw how misleading the average currents shown on the charts can be. This, incidentally, was something that practical sailors had already discovered for themselves. A shipmaster could follow the indications of the chart with fidelity, only to find himself in a countercurrent when he should have been riding the main stream. Current charts fell into relative disuse because of this. Only recently have they begun to make a comeback as more precise navigation aids have been adopted and knowledge of current behavior has grown.

Although he has worked mainly with the Gulf Stream, Fuglister has looked at data from other current systems too. He thinks that all the major currents are more complicated than had been suspected. In particular, the Kurishio off Japan seems to show the same shingle structure as the Gulf Stream. This is why he thinks oceanographers are only at the beginning of a real understanding of the great current systems.

Right now, he explains, all oceanographers can do is to get information on what is happening today. A hundred years hence they may learn something. It will literally take decades to accumulate the information they need. If ocean studies of this kind had been made a century ago, so that today's measurements could be compared with what happened before, oceanographers would know better what they are dealing with—how currents act and change over time and how long any particular mode persists. As it is, they can only make guesses. The waters off Peru give a striking illustration of the need for and potential value of understanding and predicting the vagaries of the currents.

El Niño

As South America stretches its tip toward Antarctica, it catches part of the West Wind Drift, forcing it northward in a broad languid flow known as the Peru, or the Humboldt, Current. This moves on up the west coast of the continent until, a few degrees south of the equator, it swings westward to join the South Equatorial Current. On its shoreward side are the flows and eddies which co-operate with the prevailing coastal winds in a process known as upwelling. A predominantly southerly wind blows surface water away from the coast. This is replaced by water moving up (upwelling) from moderate depths, bringing with it phosphates and other fertilizing minerals that nourish one of the richest populations of marine life in the world.

Life in the Peru Current is incredibly fertile. It supports millions of sea birds whose guano deposits give Peru an endless supply of high-grade fertilizer. In 1956, for example, 330,000 tons of guano were harvested. This means that the guano birds themselves caught over four million tons of a small sardine-like fish, the anchoveta. At the same time, fishermen caught 120,000 tons of the fish directly, plus a substantial haul of larger species that feed on the anchoveta. The abundance of anchoveta is truly phenomenal—and this is just one species. Imagine how luxuriant the plant and animal plankton, the base of the food pyramid in the sea, must be to support such a population!

But every so often disaster strikes. The life-giving flow of the Peru Current slackens or moves out to sea. Close to shore upwelling ceases, surface temperatures of the inshore water rise to abnormal heights, and often a current of warm, less saline water moves in from the north. El Niño has arrived.

The normal fish population dies or moves out to be replaced by tropical forms. Fishermen set their nets deeper to catch the accustomed species if they can. Ar   ano birds, deprived of their food, panic. Many of them aband   lglings and strike out blindly to the north or south. Other   circles, only to die of starvation on the beaches. The   v be reduced from a norm of around thirty millio   to eight million. All along the coast, rotting b   the air. Sometimes there are so many that t   iey release—the same gas released by rotten   on ships, a phenomenon known (from the   ) as the "Callao painter."

Originally El N   the southward invasion of warm water. B   complicated than that. It is a complex o   graphic conditions that has several chara   iich may be more intense in one year t   features may even be normal aspects of   first half of the year, aspects which in El Niño y   ctive proportions.

Conspicuous El Niño out   is have been reported for 1891, 1925, 1941, and 1957–58. Dr. Warren Wooster of Scripps Institution of Oceanography investigated the last of these and came up with a tentative theory of what may cause them.

In El Niño years, he says, there is a general weakening of the atmospheric circulation. This in turn is reflected in a weakening of the southerly prevailing winds that produce upwelling along the Peruvian coast. As the upwelling dies down, no longer bringing cool waters from the depths, the surface waters are heated by the sun. Meanwhile the northern boundary of the Peru Current moves farther south than usual and tropical waters from the north can move down the coast.

These conditions are sometimes accompanied by an invasion of "Red Tide," a bloom of tiny organisms that poison the waters and kill multitudes of fish. Other times the normal fish population may simply move out or go deeper down to stay with the water environment to which it is accustomed, while tropical species come in as their accustomed environment moves south. In either case, the sea birds lose their food supply.

Wooster points out that this theory is really more of an outline of what needs to be studied than it is a scientific explanation of El Niño. As so often happens in oceanography, it highlights an area where scientists could learn much of practical as well as theoretical value if only they had decades of past observations to compare with what they find today.

El Niño is usually associated with Peru. But it is a phenomenon that affects every similar upwelling coast in the world. These include coastal regions of California, southwest Africa, western Australia, and Vietnam. All of these have sizable or potentially sizable fisheries. If these fisheries are to be developed and managed intelligently, El Niño needs to be understood thoroughly. One region where scientists may be able to accumulate the needed data within a reasonable time is the coast of Vietnam, or perhaps of western Australia, where the shifting monsoons make El Niño an annual occurrence.

The shifting structure of current flows, such as El Niño or the shingle effect in the Gulf Stream, is challenge enough by itself. But oceanographers can't be content with their knowledge of the general pattern of the surface currents either. This large-scale picture still has surprises to confound the scientists and make them wary. The most recent of these made headlines around the world during the IGY.

A Second "Gulf Stream"

In 1952 the late Townsend Cromwell of Scripps Institution of Oceanography was fishing in equatorial waters near longitude 150° West when he noticed his gear drifting off in an unexpected direction. At that time Cromwell was working for the U. S. Fish and Wildlife Service, experimenting with Japanese long-line fishing techniques. Several miles of supporting cable had been let out with smaller fishing lines attached. Since he was in the drift of the South Equatorial Current, Cromwell expected his line to move off toward the west. Instead it headed rapidly eastward. This was the first evidence of a vast and unsuspected subsurface countercurrent.

Cromwell himself was subsequently killed in an air crash, but the current which was named in his honor became a prime target for IGY investigation. John A. Knauss of Scripps headed an expedition that traced the Cromwell Current halfway across the Pacific. They found it to be as big and powerful as the Gulf Stream.

Here are the statistics on this mighty current as known at the time of writing. It has been traced for 3,500 miles until it disappeared at the Galápagos Islands. Where it begins and how far westward it extends still are not known. The current itself is about 250 miles wide and flows along at about 3.5 miles an hour. It is found several hundred feet under the South Equatorial Current, which flows westward some 2 miles an hour more slowly than this eastward-moving current. Knauss and his

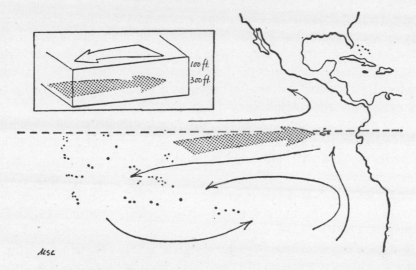

FIG. 31: *The Cromwell Current: A massive eastward flow found beneath the westward-flowing South Equatorial Current in the Pacific.*

co-workers usually found the top part of the current at about 100 feet, with its core at 300 feet. Its total thickness was about 700 feet. Here is a swift-flowing deep-sea "river" that appears to transport about as much water as the Gulf Stream where it emerges from the Florida Strait. The expedition also found a weak third current flowing westward again at still greater depths.

For oceanographers, the Cromwell Current has been both a surprise and an embarrassment. "Just think," Scripps' director, Roger Revelle, observed, ". . . a river in the ocean of this size, and its very existence was not known a few years ago!" One reason its existence was unsuspected is that the water budget of the Pacific equatorial currents balanced out nicely as far as was known. Inflow matched outflow. But now there is an embarrassingly large flow eastward that somehow has to be accounted for.

The newly discovered Cromwell Current carrying 30 million tons of water eastward every second was upsetting enough. But IGY investigations have found just as big an imbalance in the familiar Equatorial Counter Current. Over many areas of the ocean, the surface waters, warmed by air and sun, are separated from the main ocean body by a thin boundary layer where the temperature changes very rapidly with depth. This boundary is called the "thermocline" and is one of the important characteristics of the ocean. Where it exists, it tends to seal off vertical water movements. Tiny plants and animals of the plankton usually will not cross it. The Pacific Equatorial Counter Current had been thought to flow between the surface and this boundary layer, carrying eastward about 20 million tons of water a second. When the IGY team probed this current, it found an even larger flow—30 million tons a second—below the thermocline.

Added to the Cromwell Current, this much stronger countercurrent really unbalanced the old calculations. Here is a total of 80 million tons of water flowing eastward every second—equal to several thousand Mississippi Rivers. Where does it all go west again? Or, if not westward, where does it go? This just doesn't fit any of the present theories, although one expert remarked that they are being "tortured" to try to explain it. The IGY has dropped a major puzzle in oceanographers' laps.

But even though the experts have much to learn about the surface currents, these currents are still one of the most widely known features in the sea. They are often obvious and impressive to sailors who must navigate them, and they usually are part of children's elementary geography lessons. Yet beneath their wandering waters is a complex and considerably less-well-known circulation throughout the depths of all oceans. It operates on a scale more vast than the surface systems. It is one of the principal mechanisms by which the oceans help maintain the earth's heat balance and regulate the climate. Geophysicists will never understand the over-all workings of weather and climate until they have a true picture of these deep-water movements.

The Power of Salt and Heat

The winds that move the surface currents stir the oceans deeply. Their influence can be traced thousands of feet down. But there are other forces stirring the depths as well, forces that arise from the imbalance of water masses when some are heavier than others. This is the process of convection. Light water rises; denser water sinks. Here is a mechanism of great power—power enough to move the tremendous bulk of the oceans. It is a nice question for the theorists where wind power stops and density forces take over. Much of the circulation is a mixture of both.

Sea-water density depends on temperature and salinity. The warmer the water, the lighter it is. The more dissolved salts it contains, the denser it will be. And vice versa. It is one of the wonders of geophysics that relatively small differences in these quantities can generate the forces that move oceans.

Open-ocean surface temperatures range from about 31° or so Fahrenheit in high Arctic and Antarctic regions to around 86° in the tropics. And the difference between summer and winter temperatures at any one place is much less than the difference between these geographical extremes. In the depths, temperatures vary with water masses but generally drop off with depth so that all the deep oceans have bottom layers of about 34° or 35° Fahrenheit. Salinity likewise varies somewhat with the locale. It is higher where evaporation and sluggish or blocked circulation increase the salt concentration of surface waters. It is lower where rivers, heavy rainfall, and melting ice dilute these waters. In the Mediterranean Sea it reaches 39 parts per thousand and as much as 40 in the Red Sea, while in the Baltic it drops to 30 or less. The average salinity for all the oceans is 34 to 35, and 90 per cent of the world's sea water falls within a few per cent of that average, a tribute to the ceaseless mixing of the oceans.

The cold water that underlies all the oceans is one of the most striking features of the deep sea and one of the indicators of its far-ranging currents. Everywhere this bottom water is only a few degrees above freezing. Even in the tropics the warm upper water, which reaches down some 1,500 feet, does not moderate this icy cold. This ubiquitous bottom water must come from somewhere. Its frigid temperatures show it must be formed in cold regions. Studies of dissolved oxygen content, a rough measure of its age, indicate it sinks from the surface in the far North Atlantic and around Antarctica. From these sources it spreads somehow, and at an unknown speed, over the ocean floor.

Above these deepest waters are other water masses, identified by their characteristic temperatures, salinities, and other chemical name tags. To specialists, such characteristics are as distinctive and familiar as the names on neighborhood mailboxes. These water masses are inherently stable. Spread over large areas, they show little vertical mixing, like layers in a cake. But there are also regions with substantial up-and-down movements. These are the places where the action of the density forces that drive much of the deep circulation is most apparent.

The waters around Antarctica are such a region. Here in the cold of the Antarctic winter and around the edge of the polar continental shelf, the water masses that creep under much of the ocean are born. This water is the densest known in the sea. Not only is it cooled to polar temperatures, but it is given an extra burden of salt as ice forms at the surface, throwing out the dissolved salts as it freezes. This dense water sinks to the sea floor and slowly creeps away.

Meanwhile, at the surface and a bit farther out to sea, another water mass is being formed. Here heavy rains and snowfall plus summer melting of the ice dilute the water. Even though it is cold, its salinity is reduced until it is relatively light for that region and it drifts off to the north on the surface.

The combined outflow of this Antarctic Surface Water and sinking Bottom Water brings one of the fundamental processes of the ocean into play. The outgoing water at the surface has to be replaced from somewhere. Thus a deep mass of water that has come down from the north rides up over the sinking bottom water and rises to the surface. As it rises, it brings with it fertilizing minerals that have accumulated in the depths. The result is a prodigious outburst of life that, among other things, sustains the large and famous population of Antarctic whales. Here is a mechanism that produces upwelling in the open ocean. Wherever there is a divergence of water at the surface, other water must upwell from below to take its place. And conversely, wherever there is a piling up, a convergence, of surface water, a compensating sinking must take place. In the Antarctic, there is such a convergence between latitudes 50° and 55° South where the outflowing surface water meets warmer and still lighter water from lower latitudes.

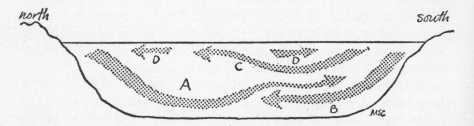

FIG. 32: *The layered flows of the Atlantic (schematic): A—Arctic water; B—Antarctic water; C—Antarctic Intermediate Water; D—Surface flows toward Arctic and Antarctic convergences respectively.*

The Antarctic Surface Water dips down in this region and continues northward as Antarctic Intermediate Water.

The interplay of such water masses is best known in the Atlantic. In the Arctic, cold water, made relatively fresh and light by river outflows, is formed and drifts southward on the surface until it meets the warmer, saltier, and still lighter waters of the North Atlantic Drift brought north

by the Gulf Stream. Here is another mid-ocean convergence. Obedient
to the laws that govern the currents and maintain the water balance of
the seas, the Arctic water sinks and proceeds southward at great depths.
Eventually it returns to the surface as upwelling in the distant Antarctic, completing a vertical circulation that is one of the principal mechanisms by which the Atlantic overturns even its deepest waters.

In the Southern Hemisphere, this North Atlantic Deep Water, as it
is called, joins with other water in the southward-moving mass that
rides over the northward-creeping Antarctic Bottom Water. This latter
itself crosses the equator, merging eventually with the deep water of
the North Atlantic. The Antarctic Intermediate Water also moves over
the equator and, at depths of 1,000 fathoms or less, sends tongues of
relatively cool low-saline water under the salty warm Atlantic Central
Water of the Sargasso Sea. The over-all result of this complex interchange is a flow out of the North Atlantic across the equator of six
million tons of water every second and an equal and opposite compensating flow coming out of the Southern Hemisphere. Some of this
exchange is carried by swift narrow currents such as those that help
originate the Gulf Stream. The rest is carried by the broad slow drifting
of the layered water masses.

There is one other distinctive water mass in the North Atlantic. It
comes from the Mediterranean in a vigorous exchange of water that
makes the Strait of Gibraltar one of the world's famous "millraces."

The Mediterranean is one of the saltiest seas on earth. Evaporation
that removes an average of 70,000 tons of water a second raises the
surface salinity until, in the eastern waters, it may run as high as 39
parts per thousand—five points above the oceanic average. With winter
cooling, this salt-heavy water sinks down at such a rate that rivers and
rainfall can't replace it. Surface water flows in from the North Atlantic
in a shallow current that brings nearly two million tons of new water
into the Mediterranean every second. Beneath this, a compensating current of heavy saline water pours out over the sill at the Strait and
spreads at an intermediate depth over the southeastern North Atlantic.
Each of these currents carries as much water as eight Mississippis. During the last war submarine commanders sometimes tried to ride these
currents to sneak in and out of the Mediterranean without giving themselves away by using their motors.

The deep waters of the other oceans are considerably less well known
than those of the Atlantic. They too have their layered water masses.

But until the International Geophysical Year, these had never been extensively probed. And at this writing the IGY data has yet to be analyzed in comprehensive detail. Even the relative familiarity of the Atlantic waters is deceptive. To describe their broad distribution and give some estimate of their rate of flow between hemispheres is to outline just about all that is really known of them. How they circulate and interact is a major oceanographic puzzle that will take decades to unravel, even with the help of wide-ranging international surveys.

For the most part, scientists know the layered water masses from temperature and water samples taken at different times and places by surface ships. From these usually sparse measurements, they build schemes of how deep waters circulate, based on uncertain theory and individual intuition that none of them takes very seriously. Henry Stommel of Woods Hole, one of the leading theoretical oceanographers, once put it this way: "There are a number of forces acting on the ocean and resulting in currents (winds, density differences, tides). Now which of these actually does produce any one current and how does it do it? That is the unsolved problem." Dissatisfied with previous theories, Stommel decided to try turning the situation around. A few years ago he developed a theory of deep circulations which could itself be tested by direct observations in the ocean. Herein lies the story of one of the major oceanographic discoveries of the IGY.

"Wrong Way" Current

The theory of ocean circulation is an abstruse subject. To understand it takes an expert's knowledge and a fluency in high-powered mathematics. Even the specialists didn't get down to its details before World War II. Since then, however, the theories have begun to sprout and Henry Stommel has been a recognized leader in the field. Without going into the complexities of his mathematics, it will suffice to say that Stommel built his theory around the assumption that density differences, caused by differences in temperature and salinity, and not the winds are the main cause of circulation in the depths. These differences, together with the curvature of the earth's surface and the force of the earth's rotation, in his view, determine the deep-water movements.

This was a bold departure from all previous theories. These had assumed as a matter of course that it was the major wind systems that made the deep waters circulate. Density differences could modify that circulation but could set up no sizable currents of their own. To make matters worse, in 1955 Stommel announced that his theory called for a strong southward-moving current under the Gulf Stream. This is one of the most powerful of the wind-driven currents. It had long been supposed that the influence of the wind was felt all the way to the bottom. Stommel's theory seemed to fly in the face of common sense. But within twenty-four months dramatic confirmation had come from the ocean itself.

Prior to this, Dr. Alan Faller had tested Stommel's ideas in the laboratory, using some ingenious rotating ocean models originally designed by Dr. William Von Arx. These are essentially large tubs, or segments of tubs, that are rotated to simulate the earth's spinning and are heated and cooled in appropriate places to simulate the heat balance of the planet. In one elaborate model, wooden blocks cut in the shape of the major continents can be placed on the tub bottom. In smaller versions the land barriers are simulated by simple straight walls. Currents can be traced in these models by using colored liquids. (See Plates 4, 5, & 6.)

As far as could be told with these laboratory oceans, the development of currents seemed to bear out Stommel's ideas. But that wasn't good enough. He was trying to second-guess nature, and the only way he could find out whether or not he was guessing right was to trace what actually went on in the oceans themselves. Fortunately the means for doing this were already being developed at the National Institute of Oceanography in Great Britain.

Like many another ocean observer, NIO's Dr. John B. Swallow had long been dissatisfied because there was no good way of measuring large-scale deep currents directly. Instruments then used for the purpose gave dubious results at best and had to be operated from the end of a cable tied to a ship. Oceanographers needed something akin to the wind-tracking balloons of the weathermen. Dr. Swallow set out to develop such an instrument. It was ready in time to test Stommel's theory on a joint American-British cruise made in preparation for the IGY during March and early April of 1957.

This undersea "weather balloon" is simply a neutrally buoyant float that sends out an identifying sound "ping". It is an aluminum tube affair about 10 feet long that carries weights, batteries, and a sound generator. By adding just the right number of small weights, the buoy can be made to float at any desired depth. In other words, it can be made neutrally buoyant without a tendency either to sink or rise. There

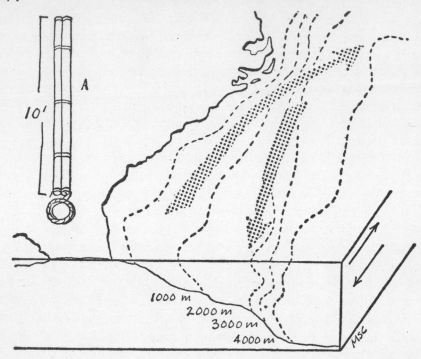

FIG. 33: *The Gulf Stream Counter Current. Inset A shows Swallow's "pinger." Ring hanging from tubes containing electrical equipment produces the sound "pings."*

it drifts freely along with the current, sending out "pings" by which a listener on the surface can track it.

Swallow dropped his "pinger" deep into the waters of the Gulf Stream off the Blake Plateau and followed it on the surface in Britain's research ship *Discovery II*. At the same time, L. V. Worthington in Woods Hole's *Atlantis* accurately traced the position of the Gulf Stream in that area. In all, seven buoys were released at various times. They all moved south at depths between 6,600 and 9,800 feet. Stommel's countercurrent had been established beyond doubt.

On the other hand, this one confirmation doesn't prove the whole of Stommel's theory, even though it does upset old ideas about the deep currents under the Gulf Stream. Many more observations in all oceans are needed. Stommel himself has spelled out several points that can be tested. In the old theories of deep circulation, the bottom water in all the oceans sinks in the far North Atlantic and around the Antarctic

FIG. 34: *According to Stommel's theory, cold water sinks in the Arctic and Antarctic and flows along the ocean floor in relatively narrow currents from which it spreads slowly as indicated by the small arrows (after Stommel).*

Continent. From these source areas it diffuses slowly southward along the bottom of the Atlantic and westward and northward over the Indian and Pacific ocean floors. In the new theory, these broad diffuse flows become strong currents along the western boundaries of the major oceans. The Gulf Stream countercurrent is one of these. Others flow up from the Antarctic along the east side of Africa and around Australia-New Zealand, heading northward toward Japan. Bottom water spreads slowly northwest and southwest from these currents over the rest of the ocean floor. Future surveys, perhaps even analysis of those made during the IGY, will tell whether or not these bottom currents exist.

There is more to Stommel's achievement than just a successful prediction. It is probably the first time that a radical theory of circulation has been worked out in laboratory and study and then tested in the oceans. This pattern of theory followed by experiment has characterized most other sciences. But oceanographers have had too big a subject to do much more than try to grasp its major aspects. They have been primarily explorers because they have had no choice. There is still no way to bring the ocean into a laboratory to experiment with it, except for crude models. But then, astronomers have had much the same problem in studying the stars. They have overcome it in part by simulating stars with mathematical operations on fast electronic computers. To do this, one needs a comprehensive theory which gives results that can be checked against the stars themselves. When this has been done long enough so that the theory checks out well in practice, it can be used to study stellar activities that can't be checked directly with the telescope. Oceanography needs this kind of mathematical theory. Although there is still a long way to go to achieve it, Henry Stommel's work has been a notable first step in that direction.

SEVEN

The Great Heat Engine

EVERY time you start a car, light a fire, or turn on a furnace you are joining in the biggest weather "experiment" ever made. You are adding your bit to the tons of carbon dioxide sent constantly into the air as coal, oil, wood, and natural gas are being burned at unprecedented rates. Collecting in the atmosphere, warming the earth, and influencing massive currents deep within the sea, this gas could in time substantially change the earth's climate. How fast is this unwitting experiment proceeding? What are likely to be its results? These and related questions frame one of the biggest puzzles facing oceanographers today—what is the mechanism of climatic change and what role do the oceans play in it?

At first sight there may seem to be little connection between man's carbon dioxide, the air, and sluggish currents at the bottom of the sea. Yet looked at from the viewpoint of weather and climate, these three factors are intimately related in a complex and as yet unknown manner. Ocean and atmosphere together constitute a heat engine which is "fired" at the tropics and cooled at the polar regions. The power source for this engine is the warming energy of the sun.

Incoming solar energy is divided in several ways. Part of it is "deducted" before it ever enters the earth's heat economy. It is reflected directly back to space by clouds, snow surfaces, ice, and other reflecting materials. This reflection is called the earth's albedo. Recent calculations by the United States Weather Bureau fix the albedo at 35 per cent of the incoming sunshine. The rest of the earth's energy income is used to grow plants, to heat air, land, and sea, and to power the great heat engine.

In spite of this constant energy income from the sun, the earth would be a far colder place than it is if it were not for the heat-absorbing gases in the atmosphere—water vapor, ozone, and carbon dioxide. These invisible gases act like the glass in a gardener's greenhouse. They let solar energy pass right on through to the surface, while they tend to block much of the longer-wave infra-red radiation by which the earth dissipates its own heat into space. The result is a small but significant warming influence all over the planet. This incidentally, is the part of the climate mechanism that man has unintentionally begun to manipulate in the carbon dioxide "experiment."

Most of the heat involved in the ocean-atmosphere system is used to maintain the earth's heat balance. The excess warmth of the tropics is carried north and south and distributed by winds, storms, and ocean currents. Some of it is carried directly as heat. Much of it travels as energy locked up in water vapor which is released when the vapor condenses to form clouds, rain, and snow. Thus every storm, however destructive it may be from man's viewpoint, is an integral part of the heat-distributing system that keeps the planet livable.

While the energy needed to drive this distribution system is small compared with the total coming from the sun, by human standards it is awesome. At any given time the winds and ocean currents have a total energy of movement greater than the electrical energy that could be produced by running all the power plants in the United States constantly for a century. The winds have 98 per cent of this energy. Moreover, the energy is dissipated so quickly through friction with the earth's surface that it has to be replenished every fortnight or less to keep the wind and current systems running.

Much of the lower atmosphere's activity—which means most of the world's weather—seems to be run by sources of heating and cooling over land and water. The land heats and cools rapidly. The ocean, with greater heat capacity, can store more of the solar energy for longer periods of time and spread it widely through its currents. In this heat-engine mechanism the atmosphere can be thought of as the working fluid of the weather. The ocean then becomes a kind of thermodynamic "flywheel," an energy-storage system of vast capacity that keeps the atmosphere working more or less smoothly.

The Thermodynamic Flywheel

The climatic influence of the oceans is familiar to all who live near the sea. Here seasonal extremes are less severe. Winters are milder and summers cooler. The warming influence of the Gulf Stream, which moderates the climate of western Europe, is famous. This direct tempering of regional climates, however, is of secondary importance. The major climatic role of the sea is its function as the thermodynamic flywheel. Actually the icecaps are part of this flywheel mechanism too, for they can absorb and release heat by melting and freezing. But the oceans have by far the larger capacity. If all of the solar energy reaching the earth for two and a half years were marshaled for the purpose, it would just be enough to melt the Antarctic icecap. Yet this same energy would add only about two degrees Fahrenheit to the ocean's average temperature. This great capacity means that a prodigious excess of heat can be stored in ocean waters for long periods of time without appreciably affecting the temperatures of the lower atmosphere. Conversely, the oceans can give up a large amount of heat to the air with hardly any change of average water temperature.

On the other hand, the ocean flywheel can't function efficiently unless there is effective overturning of its deep waters. If the ocean doesn't regularly bring deeper water to the surface and vice versa, its ability to exchange heat with the atmosphere is severely hampered. From the oceanographer's viewpoint, the puzzle of how the ocean flywheel operates breaks down into two broad questions: What are the mechanism and rate of overturning of the ocean waters? What is the "time constant" of the thermal flywheel? In other words, is the overturning of the oceans and their interchange of energy with the atmosphere characterized in terms of decades, centuries, or millennia? Is the overturning a more or less continuous process or, as one expert put it, "intermittent like the flushing of water in a bowl"?

At present, oceanographers can only guess at the answer. They should know a good deal more about it when all the pertinent International Geophysical Year analyses have been completed. Even then it may take decades more of research to find a satisfactory answer. Right now the best guesses at the "time constant" range from a few hundred to thousands of years. Radiocarbon dating of deep-water samples taken off Antarctica during the IGY indicates that the bottom water in that area may be more than two thousand years old. This in turn implies that the circulation period of water layers in the southern oceans may have to be measured in tens of thousands of years. On the other hand, estimates of the age of North Atlantic bottom water have been as short as 300 years. As long as sea water is in contact with the air, it maintains a certain concentration of carbon-14 by absorption. When it sinks, the water can't replenish its carbon-14 and the isotope slowly dies out, as in the case of dead plants and animals. By measuring how much carbon-14 a deep-water sample contains, experts can tell how long it has been out of contact with the atmosphere.

While these age measurements help trace the circulation of deep water, they don't tell the whole story. They indicate this circulation is very sluggish, although there are as yet no good over-all measurements of deep currents to substantiate this. On the other hand, one of the few direct observations that have been made, that of the southward flow under the Gulf Stream made by Dr. John Swallow, indicates an appreciable speed even close to the bottom in contrast to the indications of the age determinations.

Without a clear picture of how the ocean overturns and with no accurate time scale for interaction with the atmosphere, oceanographers and meteorologists alike are at a loss to explain adequately the general mechanism of the earth's climate. Now man, with his carbon-dioxide-producing industry, has become yet another unknown modifying factor.

The Big Experiment

The influence of this new and geologically unique factor may be operating in any of several directions. It could be tending toward a new ice age or could just as likely be producing another great tropical epoch like that prevailing when coal and oil deposits were laid down. Perhaps its influence is more moderate than such extremes suggest. The interactions are so involved that experts do not yet know how to sort them out. One thing they are sure of—this influence is at work on a scale to dwarf all previous changes man has made in his environment.

To be precise, the carbon dioxide experiment began with the industrial revolution, when men started burning fuels in unprecedented amounts. Since the beginning of that revolution they have produced something like 12 per cent of the total carbon dioxide already present in the air. The capacity of the oceans to absorb this gas is enormous, however. Most of the excess produced in the past century probably has been removed in this way. The next century will be different. Revelle estimates that 1,700 billion tons of carbon dioxide will be produced by man's fires during those hundred years. This is about 70 per cent of the amount of that gas now in the atmosphere. However, no one knows how much of this actually will accumulate.

Dr. Columbus Iselin has outlined a theory which, though it is speculative, at least indicates what might happen. He first points out that oxygen measurements below 800 meters' depth in the Atlantic show less oxygen content than they did 30 years ago, indicating that at least the Atlantic Ocean waters are not being renewed by overturning at the present time. The reason for this, he explains, may be the relatively warm climate of the past few decades. The ocean won't overturn until the climate turns colder. Unless this happens, the polar regions won't be cold enough to produce the cold dense water that sinks and generates bottom currents which, flowing toward the equator, push warmer water to the surface and cause the oceans gradually to overturn. At the same time, he adds, if the ocean doesn't overturn, its ability to exchange heat with the atmosphere will be hampered and its ability to absorb carbon dioxide will be cut down.

These effects would probably have an important but unpredictable influence on the weather. If the ocean's ability to soak up carbon dioxide is reduced, this would increase the greenhouse warming effect as more of that gas accumulated in the atmosphere. Thus there may be a climatic persistence effect due to the oceans which enhances warming after such a trend has started. Once the climate has warmed up to a certain point, the oceans would stop overturning. Because less carbon dioxide would be removed from the atmosphere, this in turn would accentuate the warming trend, which would then tend to persist.

Iselin says that something like this may have happened in climatic regimes in the past. He points out that if oceans don't overturn, the oxygen in deep water is gradually used up. In such oxygen-depleted water, marine life ceases. Organic refuse, formerly eaten or decomposed by deep-water creatures and microorganisms, will accumulate on the ocean bottom as it rains down from the relatively abundant life of the surface waters. These are conditions for forming coal and oil. At the present rate with which deep-water oxygen in the Atlantic seems to be decreasing, Iselin estimates this oxygen-depleted condition would be reached in a thousand years.

Added to any such persistence effect of the oceans is the cumulative influence of the flood of man-made carbon dioxide. "This is the big climatic experiment," Iselin says. "One of its questions asks if we are helping to slow down ocean overturning and its attendant effects on the weather. Are we making a tropical epoch or are we, perhaps, starting another ice age? We don't know enough about the oceans and the weather yet to be sure which way the effect will go."

What is needed are accurate world-wide carbon dioxide measurements. The first really good census of this gas in air and ocean was made during the IGY. With these data, charts are being drawn up indicating sources and sinks of the gas and its movements and accumulation around the world. In other words, they help define the regions where carbon dioxide is being added and, by comparison between charts drawn for different times, aid in estimating how fast it is being added. Likewise, they trace out regions where the gas is absorbed and help fix the rate at which it is removed from the air. This is an important step in determining the carbon dioxide influence on terrestrial heating and on the weather.

But whether or not men are hastening its advent, there is reason to believe that the earth is heading into another ice age. Four times in the past million years the ice sheets have advanced, and four times they have retreated. We now seem to be living in an interregnum between the last advance, which ended 10,700 years ago, and a new glaciation that may come in the millennia ahead. If geophysicists understood the mechanism of the ice ages, they would probably be able to assess the course the carbon dioxide experiment will take.

Frozen Paradox

The earth is by nature a semi-tropical planet. It has been relatively warm and moist throughout much of geological time. For 90 per cent of the past half billion years, the post-Cambrian eras, its average surface temperature has been 72° Fahrenheit in contrast to the present average temperature of 58°. Tropical and subtropical climates prevailed to high northern and southern latitudes. Even the poles were ice-free. For such a dulcet planet, the terms "ice age" and "glacial epoch" seem paradoxical. Yet every so often the heat engine that maintains the climatic balance shifts gears, and ice sheets creep over land and sea.

There have been three of these glacial epochs since Cambrian times and at least five before that. They seem to have come at more or less regular intervals of 250 million years. Each has lasted only a few million years and may have been split into several distinct ice ages when glaciers alternately advanced and retreated. The last glacial epoch had five such advances and retreats. The Quaternary period, which includes the Pleistocene glacial epoch and which began a million years ago, has already had four ice ages. A fifth ice advance may come within the next 75,000 years or so, although the present climate is gradually warming up. Dr. Hurd C. Willett of the Massachusetts Institute of Technology, a meteorologist who has specialized in climate trends, estimates that the world at present has come two thirds of the way between the climatic extreme of an ice age and the warm peak of an interglacial period. What causes the periodic icy departures from the earth's normal climate? Why does the great heat engine shift gears? This is another fundamental question for which geophysicists can only guess at the answer.

There has been a plethora of theories to explain the shifts of climate—far too many to detail them here. Most of them, however, shake down into one of three general types. They either explain climate shifts by astronomical changes in the earth's relation to the sun; by strictly geophysical causes such as migrations of continents and poles, the up-lifting of mountains, or the spreading of volcanic dust; or finally by solar effects—that is, changes in the energy output of the sun. These different types of theories were reviewed in the light of modern knowledge during a two-day conference on climatic change held several years ago by the American Academy of Arts and Sciences. The papers presented there were published in 1954. Although they are five years old at this writing, they still stand as an authoritative review of the field.

The consensus of the conference was that, while many things may influence the earth's climate, variations in the sun's output of radiation seem to be the one principal factor that could account for world-wide climatic changes, especially the major glacial epochs. For example, A. J. J. van Woerkom of Yale University explained how some ice-age theories have been built on the fact that certain slight and well-known variations in the earth's orbit and the orientation of its polar axis change the distance between the planet and sun from one winter (or summer) to the next and slightly alter the angle of incoming sunshine. These things would change the amount and nature of solar heating from one winter (or summer) to the next. There have been a number of theories that suggested these astronomical changes in the earth's relation to the sun could become significant enough to start the icecaps growing. But van Woerkom's calculations show that, while the changes would probably have some effect on climate, they are too small to account for glaciation.

Most geophysicists today do not believe there is enough evidence to support ice-age theories based on such geophysical effects as major shifts of the poles or the drifting about of continents either. But mountain building is something else again. C. E. P. Brooks, the great British climatologist, has noted that, just as the earth's normal climate is warm and moist, its normal geography is one of low-lying continents and widespread seas. And, just as the climate has been periodically interrupted by glacial epochs, the geography has sometimes been drastically altered by epochs of mountain building. Brooks and others have thought the effect of the uplifted land in altering the circulation of air and oceans would be a sufficient cause for glaciation. Critics such as Willett point out, however, that, while there has never been a glacial epoch without continental uplift and mountain building, there have been epochs of uplifting with few or no glaciers. The current view is that, while uplifted land masses are probably a necessary base for the ice sheets, they can't cause glacial epochs by themselves.

Such periods of mountain building could conceivably be accompanied by enough volcanic activity to fill the air with dust that could in turn cut down the sunshine reaching the surface. Dr. Harry Wexler, director of meteorological research for the United States Weather Bureau, has estimated that changes of about twenty degrees Fahrenheit in average surface temperature are involved between glacial and interglacial periods. He notes that blankets of volcanic dust, or even changes in atmospheric carbon dioxide, of reasonable amounts, could contribute significantly to surface temperature changes in this range. Again there is not enough data to support ice-age theories based on these factors alone. The present balance of opinion among ice-age theorists is that uplifted continents, volcanic dust clouds, and other geophysical effects may be contributing factors, but the variability of the sun is the dominant influence.

The question remains: What makes the sun change its energy output? Dr. Ernest J. Öpik of Armagh Observatory in Northern Ireland has made a detailed study of this question. He notes that it would take relatively small variations in solar output to do the job. He estimates that an 8 per cent cutback from the present solar output would be enough to drop the earth's average temperature to the 41° Fahrenheit of the coldest ice ages, while a modest 9 per cent increase in output could raise the temperature to the "normal" 70° average. Öpik has suggested a mechanism that would make the sun behave this way.

The nuclear furnace in the core of the sun "burns" hydrogen as fuel. But the sun is made up of many other materials as well. As the fuel in the core is "burned," fresh hydrogen slowly diffuses in from the surrounding outer layers. As it diffuses, it leaves behind heavier elements which tend to concentrate and, like a cloud of smoke, to block radiation from the core. Because of this, the core heats up and begins to expand. To do this, it has to work against gravity. The net result is that so much energy is spent in the expansion that the sun actually has less heat than usual to send into space. This means that a 10 per cent rise in heat production in the core could, according to Öpik's calculations, cut down the over-all heat output by an equivalent 10 per cent. When this happens, earth's heat engine gets less energy and a new ice age begins.

According to Öpik, this process should occur at intervals of a few hundred million years and should last for a few million years. This would seem to fit the timetable and duration of the major glacial epochs nicely, but it does not explain the alternating advances and retreats of the ice during an individual epoch. Öpik thinks there may be minor variations in solar output, like the flickering of a candle, that might account for the different ice ages within a given glacial epoch.

There are certain similarities between general climate shifts of all types that support this theory. For example, Willett describes all climatic changes, from major glacial epochs to minor fluctuations of a few decades or less duration, as changes of essentially the same nature, changes that tend to run in cycles. The difference between them, he says, is merely one of degree. Also, he points out that all climatic cycles seem to be world-wide. When the weather swings colder in the Northern Hemisphere, it swings colder in the Southern Hemisphere as well, and vice versa. Any glacial theory, he says, has to explain why all climate cycles seem to belong to the same family and why they are always world-wide in scope. As far as he is concerned, variations in solar output seem the most likely explanation.

Whatever the ultimate cause of climate change may be, our present climate is very sensitive to changes in average temperature. A drop of only four degrees might be enough to bring on an ice age. It would mean a climate cool enough so that summer melting might not be able to remove the winter's accumulations of ice and snow and the glaciers would grow and move southward. On the other hand, the British geophysicist Sir George Simpson has dissented from the assumption that the temperature has to drop to start the glaciers growing. Instead, he has argued that the temperature would have to rise. He pointed out over twenty years ago that the chief result of a general cooling might be a drop in the moisture content of the air and a damping down of the atmospheric circulation. This could cut down snow and rainfall so much that ice would be unable to accumulate in spite of the cooler summers. Moreover, the Arctic seas would freeze, cutting down even further the amount of moisture and snowfall in northern latitudes. A general warming would have an opposite effect. Increased evaporation from the oceans would load the air with moisture. Winter snowfalls would be heavy—too heavy for summer melting to keep up with—and glaciers would start to grow. There would be more cloudiness, helping to increase the amount of incoming sunshine reflected back into space. If the warm-up continued strongly, summer melting would, of course, predominate and the ice sheets would again melt. But a slight warming, according to this theory, could conceivably start an ice age. No expert today understands the climate mechanism well enough to confirm or refute this theory. Thus it has remained a possibility that has to be considered in evaluating world climate trends. It is one reason why experts don't know what the carbon dioxide experiment will lead to.

Most glacial theories have not had much to say about the climatic role of the oceans. The action of the thermodynamic flywheel is not understood in any event, while the main job of transferring heat from equatorial to polar regions is generally believed to be carried out by the atmosphere. Thus glacial theorists have tended to study the effect of solar and other possible influences on the atmospheric weather patterns and to assign the oceans a secondary role. Recently, however, a radically new theory has been proposed in which the ocean is the key factor, at least as far as the Quaternary ice ages are concerned.

Atlantic Thermostat

It would seem obvious that during an ice age the polar waters of the Arctic Ocean would be frozen as solidly as everything around them. However, by turning their backs on the obvious and working out what might have happened had this ocean been open during the past four ice ages, two geophysicists have come up with a remarkable theory of climatic change in which the sea acts as a kind of thermostat. They also conclude that the earth is heading inexorably into still another ice age in spite of its present warming trend. The geophysicists are Dr. Maurice Ewing and Dr. William L. Donn, associate professor of geology and meteorology at Brooklyn College. Here is the way they think the ocean thermostat may work.

The Arctic Ocean communicates with the rest of the seas over a narrow sill between Greenland and Norway, most of which is less than 300 feet deep. Its connection through the Bering Strait with the Pacific is too restricted to count. If the waters of the North Atlantic and Arctic oceans could freely interchange over this sill, the latter wouldn't freeze over. This, according to the theory, was the case before and during the past four ice ages of the present epoch. It would have meant a radically different weather pattern in the north than is found there today. The Arctic is cold enough now to form glaciers. But there is so little snowfall that summer melting can more than keep up with the winter accumulation. With an ice-free Arctic Ocean warmer than the surrounding land and moistening the air, the situation would be different. Heavy snowfall would come down and build up into glaciers, changing into steel-hard ice under its own weight. These ice sheets would begin to flow south, bringing severe weather with them, until centuries later they engulfed regions as far south as New York and Paris.

Meanwhile the growing ice sheets would withdraw water from the oceans, lowering sea levels around the world. At some point the water level would drop so low that the interchange across the North Atlantic sill would effectively cease. The Arctic Ocean then would freeze, cutting off the precipitation supply for the glaciers and signaling the end of the ice age.

Donn and Ewing say that something of this sort seems to have happened at the end of the last ice age at least. They have found indications in bottom cores taken in the Atlantic and Caribbean that the waters there may have suddenly warmed significantly about eleven thousand years ago. This sudden widespread warming might be easily explained if the Arctic froze over and stopped exchanging its cold waters with the Atlantic.

Once the Arctic did freeze and cut off the snowfall, summer melting would again have the upper hand. The ice sheets would retreat, giving up their imprisoned waters to the oceans. Sea level now would start to rise, until at some point the warm waters of the Atlantic would thaw out the Arctic and start the ice cycle all over again.

Ewing and Donn have also suggested that the present glacial epoch may itself have started from purely geophysical circumstances. They assume that a million years ago the poles were so situated that the North Pole was in the midst of the Pacific. The poles then migrated to their present positions, setting the Atlantic thermostat into operation and initiating an epoch of ice ages. This does not explain the previous glacial epochs, however, nor why they have occurred so regularly every quarter of a billion years.

Glacial theories based on migrating poles and the drift of major crust elements are scientifically unpopular. John Wolbach of Harvard University summed up the prevailing expert opinion when he told the Academy climate conference that the notion of continental drift "seems an objectional hypothesis, creating more problems than it solves." He added that "a change in the position of the earth's axis of rotation is an even less tenable explanation because such a change could be produced only by the action of enormous forces exterior to the earth." [Remarks made by Bullard, Ewing, Heezen, and others during the International Oceanographic Congress in September 1959, after this chapter had been sent to the editor, indicate the concept of drifting continents may be revived.]

Ewing and Donn avoid such standard objections to polar migration by suggesting that the earth's axis has remained stable and the continents have kept their relative positions while the crust as a whole has moved about. They note that analysis of the alignments of magnetic particles frozen into sedimentary rocks, which are a guide to past geomagnetic conditions, hints that the earth's crust may slide over its interior and bring different geographical areas into true north and south polar positions at different times. This is what they think happened abruptly at the beginning of the Pleistocene. But such crustal slippage is not a widely held theory. Reviewing the state of geomagnetic knowledge, E. H. Vestine of the Rand Corporation and formerly with the Carnegie Institution of Washington, one of the world's leading centers for geomagnetic study, called the magnetic indications of crustal slippage an "interesting inference" that has yet to be checked by other means. The poles are generally believed to have remained more or less where they are geographically for a very long time. Öpik, for example, considers it "proved" that the relative positions of continents and poles haven't changed in 100 million years. Commenting on this aspect of the Ewing-Donn theory in the magazine *Science*, D. A. Livingstone of the Zoology Department at Duke University calls polar migration "difficult to accept in the face of fossil evidence" that indicates the poles have remained where they are for at least the present Cenozoic era, which began sixty to seventy million years ago.

On the other hand, the ocean thermostat presumably could work whether the Pleistocene "refrigerator" were turned on by polar migration, solar fluctuations, or some other factor. It would not account for all climatic cycles, which Willett thinks should have much in common. But it might account for the simultaneous advent of ice ages in both hemispheres. Ewing and Donn estimate that the increased reflecting ability of the Northern Hemisphere as snow and ice fields grew and cloud cover spread could cut down the earth's total heat absorption enough to bring on a general cooling of the whole planet. As in the case of other ice-age theories, however, the available data are inconclusive. The mechanism of the Atlantic thermostat is a novel but unproved speculation.

Meanwhile our own climate at the moment is growing warmer. The polar icecaps are melting, and the sea, currently rising at the rate of two feet a century, is slowly encroaching on the land. This could have serious implications for coastal regions the world over.

The Advancing Sea

During the IGY, scientists scaled mountains to sample glaciers, bored deeply into the Greenland and Antarctic icecaps, and floated about the Arctic Ocean on ice islands. From their varied investigations they brought back a common story—everywhere the ice is melting, but no catastrophic rise in sea level is yet in sight. On the other hand, this may be only the prelude to a thoroughgoing thaw if the present warming trend continues.

According to the latest calculations of the United States Weather Bureau, the rate of warming of the earth's surface right now is something like two or three degrees' rise in average temperature per century. What causes the warming is not known. It may be a solar effect, an already noticeable result of the increase in atmospheric carbon dioxide, or something completely unsuspected. The climate has run to cycles of warming and cooling ever since the last ice age. The over-all result has been a significant warm-up over the past eleven thousand years. The present warming trend, which dates from the turn of the century, appears to be more closely related to one of the short-term cycles of warming and cooling than to the over-all long-term warm-up.

Just before the start of the IGY, Öpik calculated that if the Greenland and Antarctic icecaps were completely melted they would yield 4,860,000 cubic miles of water. Spread over the entire sea, this would amount to a water layer 186 feet thick. When IGY explorers probed the Antarctic icecap, they found so much more ice than had been expected that former estimates of how much ice there is in the world may have to be increased by something like 40 per cent. If the ice of Greenland and Antarctica did melt during the present warming trend, this could add well over 200 feet to world sea levels.

Fortunately the Greenland and Antarctic icecaps, which have most of the world's ice, do not seem to be melting nearly as quickly as the mountain glaciers or the Arctic sea ice. But this is no guarantee for the future. The Arctic sea ice has shrunk 12 per cent in total area in the past 15 years and now averages 6 feet thick. That is about half as thick as it was in the late nineteenth century. It may one day begin breaking up. Since it is already floating in the ocean, its melting will have little effect on sea levels, just as a melting ice cube in a brimming glass of water won't make the glass overflow. On the other hand, with one to two per cent of the world's water locked in their frozen masses, concomitant melting of the icecaps and glaciers of even a few per cent could significantly affect sea levels.

Actually the sea already has risen a good deal since the great thaw set in after the last ice age. At its peak the ice drew the oceans down by perhaps as much as 500 feet, according to maximum estimates. The sea has gained back at least 300 feet of that drop in level and seems to be gaining more all the time. It is not known whether the post-glacial rise came in an initial spurt which has since tapered off or whether the oceans have been steadily rising for the past eleven thousand years. Furthermore, the sea-level picture is complicated by compensating changes in the sea bottom itself.

The rocks below the earth's crust are more rigid than steel to forces that act on them for only a short time. But under prolonged pressure they flow like viscous pitch. If water is added to the oceans above them, they sag under the increased load. The density of this rock magma is about three times that of water, so when extra water is added the sea bottom yields by one third while sea level rises by two thirds of the amount of added water.

What is true for the sea is true for the land, whose relatively light rock masses float in the viscid magma. The burden of the ice sheets, which reached several thousand feet in thickness, depressed the land. When the ice melted, the land floated up again. One can see this happening today. Stockholm, for example, is rising a foot and a half per century, while the north Baltic coast of Sweden, where the ice stayed longer, rises over twice as fast. The general uplifting of Scandinavia indicates a former ice burden of 5,740 feet average thickness.

This "give" under the land and ocean floor is called "isostatic adjustment." It complicates the sea-level picture by dropping ocean bottoms and raising at least some shore lines all at the same time. Moreover, it is a slow process. The delayed adjustments in the earth's crust may take 20,000 to 30,000 years to run their course. Because of this, it is hard to foretell what the melting of today's icecaps would eventually lead to. But this much seems certain: if the warm-up continues over the next century, low-lying coastal areas like those around New York, Los Angeles, or London will be in danger of flooding.

On the other hand, men may not wait for nature to run her course. They may grow impatient for the slow melting of the Arctic to free northern sea routes. They may try to intervene in the workings of the heat engine to adjust climatic trends to their own liking. Weather and climate control is on the horizon. Even though they are aware of their ignorance in this field, men may become impatient to try it.

"Adjusting" the Heat Engine

While any present-day schemes for changing climate are either pipe dreams or precocious visions, experts foresee the day when serious proposals along this line will be advanced. Writing in *Science*, Dr. Harry Wexler notes that "when serious proposals for large scale weather modification are advanced, as they inevitably will be, the full resources of general-circulation knowledge and computational meteorology must be brought to bear in predicting results." In this way, he adds, men can perhaps avoid "the unhappy situation of the cure being worse than the ailment." Scientists will have had to do a good deal of advance research if they are to evaluate such proposals. Some of the weather-modification schemes currently discussed, while impractical today, at least indicate areas in which some of this research will have to be done.

Wexler himself has suggested a way to speed up the melting of the Arctic sea ice. He thinks a few well-placed hydrogen bombs might do the trick. It would take ten bombs of ten megatons each (the equivalent of the explosive energy of ten million tons of TNT). Setting these off under water might throw up enough steam to blanket the Arctic Ocean in an ice fog that would substantially cut down the heat escaping from that region by radiation. This, Wexler says, would speed up the melting tremendously.

Thawing out the Arctic is a favorite project with would-be climate tinkerers. It would pay off immediately in ice-free northern harbors and by shortening the sea journey between Atlantic and Pacific ports by thousands of miles. It could raise the average temperatures at latitudes of London, New York, or Moscow by as much as ten degrees Fahrenheit. Besides Wexler's bombs, other schemes include the spreading of heat-absorbing soot or lampblack over the ice and even damming the Bering Strait and pumping in warm water from the Pacific. All of these schemes, even if they were practical to carry out, have a fatal weakness. As Wexler himself points out, unpredictable side effects could outweigh the supposed benefits. After all, the Ewing-Donn theory suggests that unfreezing the Arctic would start another ice age, while Simpson's theory predicts a similar effect.

A different sort of climate-modification scheme has been suggested by Henry Stommel of Woods Hole to avoid the ice age that may be creeping up on us—suggested, that is, with tongue in cheek, for Stommel thinks present knowledge too scant for such speculation. He would do it by damming the Strait of Gibraltar. This would take only about ten times as much fill as the Fort Peck Dam in Montana and would effectively stop the flood of salty Mediterranean water into the North Atlantic. Over several decades the salinity of the Atlantic would then drop, lowering the general densities of its water to the point where cold Arctic water wouldn't sink at all. If this water couldn't sink below the northward-flowing waters of the Gulf Stream, the latter, which now flow up to the Arctic, would be diverted southward and held in a practically closed system within the North Atlantic. Then the interchange of warm water between Atlantic and Arctic oceans would be checked, and any ice age tending to develop along the lines of the Ewing-Donn theory would be blocked.

Commenting on this in the *Scientific American*, Stommel has neatly summed up the status of such schemes today and the great need for more basic research. "Common sense rebels against such an argument," he wrote. "It is hard to imagine so fantastic an effect from so small an intervention by man. And indeed the argument is loaded with unproved assumptions and tenuous speculations. We could construct an equally plausible argument that the same stratagem might cool rather than warm the earth. I cite this entertaining fantasy only to show that we need a great deal more information before we can begin to talk knowledgeably about altering the climate. All such speculations merely illustrate how little actual knowledge we have and how valuable it would be to develop a better quantitative understanding of the ocean circulation."

EIGHT

Waters of Life

To the multitude of marine organisms, the oceans are literally the waters of life. Except for the bordering shore areas, the rigors of the land—extremes of weather, temperature, and aridity—are unknown in the climatically stable oceans. At the same time, dissolved minerals and the natural aeration of the circulating surface waters make them an ideal growing medium for the plant life that is the basis of all life in the sea. These waters seem in some respects to be almost an extension of the living organisms themselves. They carry food to sedentary and passively floating creatures. They bring together sperm and ova to fertilize the eggs of many animals. They cradle, nourish, and resettle the young of countless species. And in ways biologists are only beginning to understand, they distribute traces of potent chemicals that some organisms make to prepare the water for certain favored succeeding organisms or, conversely, to exclude competitors.

With most of its inhabitants protected from harsh atmospheric extremes and with many of them virtually bathed in their food supply, even a layman can begin to appreciate how the sea supports a rich variety of animal life. That variety can only be suggested here by outlining the basic principles and relationships that underlie this wealth of life and by briefly introducing a few of its interesting representatives.

Perhaps one of the first things one should note is that while the oceans are all interconnected their inhabitants are not everywhere the same. Populations and their characteristic species vary widely from place to place, often with no apparent obstacles to their intermingling. Like the land, the sea has its barriers to animal migration, except that they tend to be more subtle. Most of them are merely differences in such things as temperature or salinity, or are related to the play of the

G

currents. Immersed all their lives in sea water, many marine creatures are attuned to its chemical and physical composition, sensitive to slight variations.

For those animals that live near the bottom, topography can be a barrier too, just as it is on land. The Wyville Thomson Ridge that separates deep-water Arctic and North Atlantic forms in the area northeast of Scotland is a case in point. But for the most part, the lives of the creatures that inhabit the seas are governed by the characteristics of the water. Nowhere is this more evident than in the collective life of that community of assorted floating plants and animals known as the plankton.

The Wanderers

"Plankton," meaning literally "that which is made to wander," is one of the most expressive scientific names that has been borrowed from the Greeks. To wander is exactly what these floating plants and animals are made to do. They are either too small or their swimming powers are too feeble to resist the flow of the currents, and they are carried willy-nilly wherever the waters go.

There are countless billions of microscopic plants and equally countless numbers of tiny animals feeding on them. There are larvae of fish and of many other marine creatures in various stages of develop-

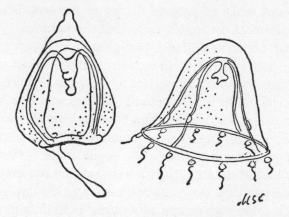

FIG. 35: *Two of the tiny transparent jellyfish (medusae) of the plankton.* Steenstrupia nutans (LEFT) *about 17 times life size;* Phialidium hemisphaericum (RIGHT) *about 10 times life size. Medusae are the larvae of sessile polyps.*

ment. Here and there miniature jellyfish are floating. These are called "medusae" and are the reproductive form of certain sedentary polyps. Tiny arrowworms move about, feeding on fish larvae and similar small prey, while others of the planktonic wanderers feed on them. All told, there are representatives of every major phylum of the animal kingdom, at least in the larval stage. They include one order, the Radiolaria, that is known only in the marine plankton. According to Professor Alister Hardy of Oxford University, one of the world's outstanding authorities on plankton and fisheries, "it is no exaggeration to say that in the plankton we may find an assemblage of animals more diverse and more comprehensive than is to be seen in any other realm of life."

This diverse assortment of organisms is united by two necessities of

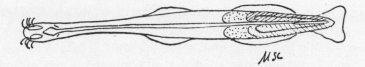

FIG. 36: *An arrowworm, one of the Sagitta.*

their common experience—their status as passive drifters and the need to keep afloat in a fluid medium. The latter is the common environmental influence behind many of the curious shapes the plankters have evolved.

The problem of floatation can be solved in several ways. Planktonic fish eggs, for example, contain small drops of clear oil. When they hatch, the young larvae live for a time on what is left of the yolk carried in an attached sac and are in turn buoyed up by the oil drop. Another way of solving the problem is to increase surface area without appreciably increasing weight. This gives the organism a greater frictional resistance to sinking. Some species have spines. Others have filmy appendages of protoplasm. Still others have various arrangements of fine hairlike projections. They float like thistledown on a summer breeze.

The effectiveness of such floatation devices has been graphically demonstrated by species of an organism called *Ceratium* (a Dinoflagellate), which can adjust the length of its hornlike projections to meet varying conditions of viscosity. Warm water is less viscid than cold, so that an object of given shape and density will sink twice as fast in tropical waters as in polar seas. If these organisms are carried into relatively warm water, they compensate for the loss in viscosity by growing longer horns. If later they re-enter cooler water, they shed the excess length, always adjusting their bodily resistance to the present need.

In one way or another the diverse collection of wanderers called the plankton is the first link of almost all food chains in the sea. Fish ranging from fingerlings to the great basking shark feed directly on the small planktonic animals. Others eat the fish that eat the plankton. Many animals of the shore and shallow-water bottom just say put and strain out whatever planktonic food the water flow brings them. Intermingled with the living plankton is a good deal of dead and decaying organic matter. This detritus also feeds some of the animals and the bacteria found in the plankton itself.

In deeper waters there is a continual rain of detritus and the larger remains of dead and dying organisms from the upper sunlit planktonic zone. This feeds animals at intermediate depths, while a host of hungry mouths are waiting on the bottom. Some bottom animals look like plants, spreading branching, food-gathering arms. There are also shellfish of many types and other creatures, all equipped in one way or another to collect this rain of nutriment. These in turn become food for worms, starfish, sea urchins, crustaceans, and many other roving bottom animals, as well as for bottom-feeding fishes like the cod, haddock, and plaice. The latter, in their turn, become an important element in man's diet.

Whatever escapes larger mouths is attacked by bacteria, which break down the organic materials into basic minerals, phosphates, and nitrates. These are returned to the sea, where in time they may again reach the upper waters and be taken up by plants to enter the food cycle once more. Indeed, this brief sketch of the food economy of the sea should properly start with the plants. With their photosynthetic ability to use sunlight to make organic substance, they are the primary energy source for all the rest of marine life.

The Grass of the Sea

Nobody knows exactly how much plant material is produced annually in the ocean. Its total tonnage must be immense. In a good year the world's fishermen land something like eight to ten thousand million pounds of herring and related fish. Many of these are of small size—sardines, anchovies, pilchards. California pilchards, for example, run five to ten to the pound. The total number of individual fish caught probably runs to tens of thousands of millions. Birds and other fish must catch equally large numbers, while vast numbers aren't caught at all. Then there are the other food fishes caught in large quantities and the multitude of species that are never touched by man. Truly there are inestimable numbers of fish in the sea, let alone other animals. The vegetable production that ultimately feeds these fishes, a production that must be many times their total weight, is at this stage of knowledge beyond precise reckoning. Yet, except for the relatively insignificant amounts of seaweed growing along the shores and the floating weeds of the Sargasso Sea, this great bulk of vegetation consists of minute one-celled plants. The "grass" of the sea has to be harvested with a fine cloth net and studied under the microscope.

This situation reflects a basic factor in the life of plants floating in the ocean; namely, the importance of having a large surface area in ratio to volume. For one thing, the larger this ratio, the more resistance there is to sinking. But even more important, the more area there is in relation to its bulk, the more readily can an individual plant absorb sunlight filtering through the water and take up enough of the nutrient materials, which may be present only in minute amounts, to meet its needs. Here is a decisive evolutionary advantage favoring smallness of size. Plants might evolve other means of buoyancy, such as the bladder floats of many seaweeds. But in the competition for light and food, the ability to absorb these readily is what counts. Hence the rise of the microscopic phytoplankton, as the planktonic plants are called. A cube the size of one of these plants has hundreds of times the surface-to-volume ratio of a cube one inch on a side.

One of the most abundant groups of the phytoplankton are the diatoms. Encased in transparent silica shells, they glisten like jewels in little crystal caskets. Some species have the shape of perfect little pill-boxes. Others are more rectangular or elongated, rodlike and needle-shaped. Every plant is an individual separate cell. Yet many species, as they multiply by dividing in two, remain joined together in long chains. Sometimes these chains look like diamond bracelets. Sometimes they have hairlike appendages that assist their floating, making them look like multi-footed animals.

These little brown-green plants are the only type of alga that forms a siliceous exoskeleton. The skeleton or shell is in two parts called "valves," which are joined by "connecting bands." They can be thought of as fitting together like the top and bottom of a pillbox.

Under an ordinary compound microscope the shells of some species do indeed look like little glass boxes intricately patterned with perforations, pits, and striations which form "designs" characteristic of individual species. The electron microscope, which can magnify images

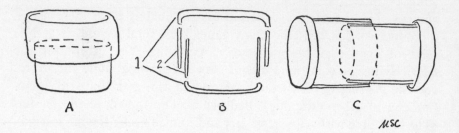

FIG. 37: *Many diatoms are shaped like pillboxes, as in* A. *The closely fitted tops and bottoms are made in several parts, as in* B. *The two end plates are the valves. The vertical sections are the two circular "connecting bands" which help fit the whole together. This is the simplest of the varied and often complex diatom structures. As they grow, the little pillbox diatoms may divide or may become extended cylinders, as in* C. (See also Plates 15–18.)

hundreds of thousands of times, shows even more intricate detail. Some species have several systems of increasingly smaller pits and holes and more than one layer of silica. Others have valves made of little threads woven together like baskets. These intricate structures, coupling strength with lightness, allow the diatom to present a far greater surface area of protoplasm to the water than would be the case if it were merely encased in a neat little box.

When a diatom divides, each of the two new individuals keeps one of the old valves, growing a second one to complete its shell. This process is completed before separation takes place, the new valves being grown within the old and fitting tightly into them to form the bottoms of the "pillboxes." Since the new valves are formed inside the old, one of the individuals so formed will be smaller than the original cell. Thus in a series of such divisions the average size of a population of diatoms will get progressively smaller. This gives a considerable size range to any particular species. Sometimes a given population can be identified and traced in its planktonic wanderings by its regular decrease in average size. But there is a limit to this, for the plants can't go on dividing to the vanishing point. Eventually, after dividing a number of times, a diatom cell discards its valves entirely. New valves, two or three times as large, are then formed inside its swelling protoplasmic mass, which in this form is called an "auxospore." In this way, the original size is recovered.

This sequence of division with occasional regrowth is the only definitely known way in which diatoms multiply. Hardy reports that they may have a sexual phase as well. In some species tiny specks called "microspores" have from time to time been seen forming within the cell wall. These may be gametes (sex cells). But Hardy says this has not yet been established.

Diatoms can also take on a form known as the "resting cell" if living conditions become severe, especially in winter. The old set of valves is again discarded, while the protoplasm concentrates into a tight mass around which a new and differently shaped thick-walled shell is formed. Thus protected, the now-dormant cell sinks into deeper water or even to the bottom to await the spring.

The diatoms share the ocean meadows with a second large group of plants belonging to the assemblage of organisms called "flagellates." These are characterized by one or more whiplike appendages with which they swim or which they can use to create small currents. With the exception of some little-known planktonic bacteria and two or three species of yellow-green algae that grow as large as a millimeter in diameter, the flagellates comprise the rest of the phytoplankton. They are a strangely assorted group. Keeping themselves from sinking out of the sunlit upper water by whipping about their flagella, they live both by photosynthesis and, in some instances, by capturing particles of food like animals. Even the experts aren't sure whether certain species are plant or animal or both. Most of them found in the plankton, however, are definitely plants, living by photosynthesis and in many cases actively seeking the light with the aid of a small red "eye spot." In some species the eye spot has been elaborated into a complex organ with a lens and pigment cup.

The more notable of these curious plants are the Dinoflagellates. Some of these are brilliantly luminescent, making the sea sparkle at night or causing the breaking waves to flash with cold blue-green fire. *Noctiluca* is probably the most brilliant and is also one of the few dinoflagellates that lives more like an animal than a plant. *Ceratium*, mentioned earlier for its ability to regulate its body resistance to sinking, can also give a spectacular performance. When organisms like these abound, nets, fish, oars, and other objects that disturb the water will seem coated with fire as millions of individual Dinoflagellates are set aglow, their light coming from chemical reactions stimulated by the agitation.

Dinoflagellates are distinguished by having two flagella. One runs along a beltlike groove encircling each individual, while the other trails behind like a propeller. Between the two, the little plants waltz round and round as they propel themselves forward through the water. Many species also have distinctive spines, one pointing forward and two pro-

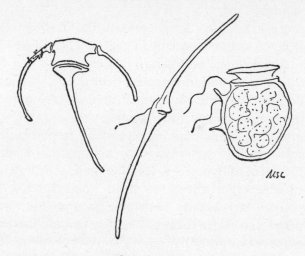

FIG. 38: *A few Dinoflagellates. Two species of* Ceratium (LEFT) *about 200 times life size; and* Dinophysis acuta (RIGHT) *about 400 times life size.*

jecting backward from behind the groove of the transverse flagellum. The bodies of these plants are encased in a cellulose wall of little plates arranged like a mosaic.

By fixing the energy of sunlight in forms that make it available to animals, the microscopic diatoms and flagellates are the basis of almost all the rest of the life of the sea. At the same time, an abundance of oxygen and carbon dioxide dissolved from the air and the nutrient minerals carried in solution make the sea an ideal place in general for these plants to grow. Nevertheless, there are limiting factors. For one thing, plants need light, so they flourish only in what is called the "photic zone." This is the upper few dozen meters of water into which sunlight readily penetrates. Another important factor is the local distribution and availability of the nutrient minerals and other chemicals needed by the plants. If any of these is in short supply, it will limit the plant growth, no matter how plentiful the others may be. The variations of these necessary chemicals, both geographically and seasonally, explain much that would otherwise seem puzzling about the striking variations in abundance of the phytoplankton.

March of the Seasons

One way to illustrate the regulatory influence of these chemicals is to consider the seasons in the temperate waters of the North Atlantic. Here, as the buds begin to swell on land and the crocuses appear, there is a prodigious outburst of plant growth. Within a fortnight the diatoms that have been resting through the winter increase some ten thousand-fold. As the season advances and summer comes, however, the vernal abundance of plants steadily declines, only to be followed by an equally sudden, though shorter and somewhat less intense, outburst in the fall. After that the population again declines to its lowest ebb of the year as the plants wait out the winter. This sequence is readily explained by the distribution of the essential fertilizing nitrates and phosphates.

During the winter the upper waters are thoroughly stirred by wind and storms and by the convection set up as water cooled at the surface becomes relatively dense and sinks. Dissolved minerals are distributed fairly evenly through the upper few hundred feet, and the temperature becomes uniform throughout this depth. As the days lengthen and light intensity grows, there is a moment when conditions again become favorable for plant growth. The necessary nitrates and phosphates being available, the spring outburst commences.

But as the season advances, the uppermost waters are warmed. They become relatively light—light enough to float on the cool denser water below—and a thermocline develops that seals off vertical mixing. The depth of the thermocline includes most if not all of the photic zone, where the plants are living and reproducing. This means that the supply of phosphates and nitrates can't be replenished. These minerals are relatively thinly distributed at any time. Together with iron, strontium, and silicates, they account for only 6 per cent of the salinity of the sea. Thus the minerals in the layer sealed off by the thermocline are thinly spread to begin with and are soon used up, bringing plant activity to a halt. Unable to keep pace with the persistent grazing of animal plankters, the plant population drops sharply through the summer.

In the autumn the cooling air and increasing gales again stir the waters, destroying the thermocline and bringing a new supply of miner-

G*

FIG. 39: *March of the seasons: Winter storms and winds stir the waters deeply, bringing nutrient minerals to the upper layers (1) where, as the light intensity increases during spring, an outburst of planktonic life begins (2). As summer comes, and a thermocline seals off vertical mixing, the minerals are depleted and the plankton declines (3). Then the gales of autumn again stir the waters, bringing fresh minerals up from below and the plankton bursts forth again until the winter light becomes too weak to support photosynthesis (4).*

als from below. The light is still intense enough to encourage growth, and the plants burst out in their second orgy of reproduction. Then their numbers again decline as the light becomes too weak to support active photosynthesis.

These seasonal ups and downs illustrate the crucial role of the fertilizers, a role that affects the geographical abundance of the plants as well. In tropical waters, for example, the light favors plant growth the year round. Yet the more persistent thermocline of these latitudes tends to prevent mixing of the surface waters and the replenishment of the vital minerals. This is why tropical phytoplankton is generally less abundant than that of temperate and polar waters in spite of the greater variety of tropical species. In like manner, wherever upwelling currents bring up the phosphates and nitrates that have been accumulated near the bottom by the action of bacteria, the seas abound in phytoplankton and in the animal life it supports.

But this is not the whole story. There are indications that marine plants and animals are favorably, or in some cases adversely, affected by traces of unknown chemicals. Some of these may act like vitamins in the diet of land animals and seem to be just as essential. Indeed, vitamin B_{12}, Cobalamin, which is present in sea water, is known to be necessary to several of the marine flagellates and at least one of the diatoms.

The late Dr. E. J. Allen of the Plymouth (marine biology) Laboratory in England ran an experiment almost fifty years ago which vividly illustrated the presence of these largely unknown trace chemicals. He tried to grow phytoplankton in artificial sea water that was made up according to a very precise analysis of the real article. But the plants would not grow until about one per cent of natural sea water had been added to the medium.

Certain unknown trace chemicals also seem to be essential to at least some marine animals. Dr. Douglas P. Wilson of the Plymouth Laboratory recently illustrated this by trying to grow fertilized eggs of two types of worms and a sea urchin in two samples of sea water, which, as far as was known, should have made no difference to the test animals. One water sample was characteristic of the English Channel. The other was taken from the Celtic Sea west of the Channel. The larvae grew well in the latter water. But those raised in the Channel water were abnormal and unhealthy. Either some still-unknown substance was lacking or some inimical substance was present in this Channel water that did not show up in the chemical analyses.

Still other biochemical factors are suggested in the succession of plant and animal species that follow one another in the plankton. The seasonal fluctuations of the phytoplankton set a general pattern in temperate waters. But within that pattern various species rise in abundance and then decline, to be replaced by others. It looks as though individual plant or animal species may release something into the water that inhibits their own growth but aids the growth of a successor. Then too, there are the planktonic bacteria which provide food for many tiny animals and may also release chemicals important to planktonic life. The synthesis of growth factors by terrestrial bacteria is well known. It is reasonable to expect marine bacteria to fulfill a similar key function in the biochemistry of the plankton.

Scavengers of the Sea

Bacteria play such an important role in ocean life that they deserve a brief section of their own. They thrive in all parts of the ocean, from the surface to the greatest depths. They can eat organic matter in any state, solid or liquid, suspended or dissolved. Because of this, they are regarded as the principal scavengers in the sea. Moreover, they make such good work of it that, according to Dr. Claude ZoBell of Scripps, one of the few marine biologists in the world studying bacteria today, the ocean can be described as the world's largest and most efficient septic tank. As by-products of this activity, the bacteria produce carbon dioxide and the phosphates, nitrates, and perhaps other chemicals that maintain the fertility of the sea or affect its life cycles.

Although bacteria are found throughout the water, pelagic (free-floating) species are most abundant in the photosynthetic zone at the surface, while the greatest abundance of all marine bacteria is at the bottom. There these tiny organisms build up reserves of fertilizing minerals and serve as an important food supply for bottom-grazing animals such as protozoans, worms, sponges, mud eaters, and the like. In shallower parts of the ocean there is a good deal of solid organic matter raining down to sustain bacteria. In the abyss, where such material is scarce, the bacteria probably feed on dissolved matter carried to great depths by currents.

The full story of the marine bacteria has yet to be understood. The subject is vast and the workers are few even for oceanography. Yet the unanswered questions have a practical bearing on such things as prospecting for oil and learning to farm the sea. ZoBell points out that bacteria are instrumental in making oil. He estimates that oil is being formed in sediments right now at a rate comparable to that of the present recovery of oil. The new oil is too diffusely spread to be recovered itself. Nevertheless, a knowledge of the conditions under which bacteria help make oil now would aid prospectors in looking for geological signs of where such conditions prevailed in oil-making epochs of the past.

Even more important, ZoBell says, is the need to understand the role of bacteria in the food cycles of the sea. How fast and by what chemical processes do they produce the nitrates and phosphates? To what extent are the bacteria themselves a food supply for other organisms, especially in the photosynthetic zone? What other chemical roles do the bacteria play? ZoBell thinks that there may be nitrogen-fixing bacteria in the sea that play a role comparable to that of nitrogen-fixing plants on land. If these can be identified, one of the key elements in maintaining fertility of the water, so important for any future scheme for ocean farming, will have been found.

ZoBell also points out that the antibiotic activity of bacteria may turn out to be a major factor in ocean life. On land many bacteria are known to produce chemicals that exclude or kill off other bacterial species. Some of these chemicals, the antibiotic drugs, are used to treat human diseases. As many antibiotics have been found in the sea as on land, although none of the former have yet been found useful as a drug. On the other hand and in view of the diversity of the sea, there may be more and better antibiotics eventually found there. In any event, antibiotics appear to be important in the marine life cycles themselves, although their role has only begun to be explored.

The sea is like a great chemical vat teeming with life. The water in that vat is a fairly good solvent. It facilitates a complex chemical interaction between the bacteria, plants, and animals of the plankton, to say nothing of higher forms, that is only dimly sensed today. This is a challenging area for research that will have to be explored if men are ever to farm the sea; that is, to regulate its ecology to grow food crops, as they now do that of the land.

To return to the marine food system itself and to the little floating plants that are its basis, it is obvious that these plants can pass on the energy of sunshine only if they are first converted into a form that higher animals can eat. This is the role of the grazers, the so-called "key industry animals." These are the marine analogue of the field mice and the deer, the cattle, sheep, and other vegetarians that turn the grasses of the land into animal protein that meat eaters can consume.

The Grazers

The grazers of the sea are almost as small as the microscopic "grass" they feed upon. They are all part of the drifting animal plankton—little crustaceans, small larvae, and many other forms, collectively called the "zooplankton." This is the term biologists use to distinguish these drifters from the more powerful animals, such as the fishes, whales, or squids, which can swim in any direction they please. The latter are known as the "nekton." There is still another specific name for bottom dwellers. These are called the "benthos."

The most prominent of the grazers, and indeed of the whole zoo-plankton, belong to the class Crustacea, and of these the members of the subclass Copepoda are overwhelmingly the most numerous. Copepods, the "oar-footed"—so named because of two long appendages at the head that wave about like oars—swarm the seas in countless numbers. Like all grazing animals, they are less numerous than the plants on which they feed. Where these latter are numbered in millions, the former are numbered in thousands or tens of thousands only. Yet

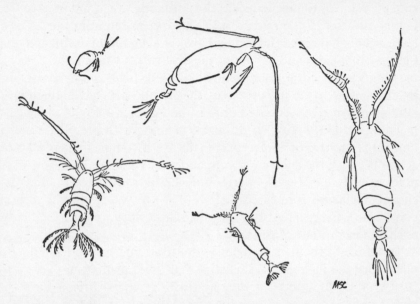

FIG. 40: A *selection of Copepods:* Temora longicornis (UPPER LEFT); Arietellus insignis (LOWER LEFT); Gaetanus pileatus (UPPER MIDDLE); Anomalocera patersoni, *female* (LOWER MIDDLE)—*preceding all about 3 times life size;* Anomalocera patersoni, *male* (RIGHT) *about 8 times life size.*

Hardy thinks it no exaggeration to state that there are more copepods in the world than all other multicellular animals combined, including the insects.

The planktonic copepods are generally small—about the size of a pin-head or, at most, a grain of rice. They are the main link between the microscopic energy-fixing plants and the flesh-eating consumers of the sea. These little crustaceans reproduce profusely and rapidly. Ten days is enough to cover the life cycles of some species. Thus they can quickly increase their numbers to exploit a bloom of diatoms or flagellate plants. This in turn makes the vegetable abundance available to other animals so that, in the general economy of the sea, a wealth of phytoplankton is usually reflected in a wealth of animal life.

There isn't space to list the other considerably less numerous grazing animals here. However, one curious creature should be described, for his amazing filtering apparatus first revealed the existence of exceedingly tiny flagellate plants that escaped the meshes of the finest tow nets. These minute flagellates, which are very numerous, now can be cultured in the laboratory. But their existence was first discovered toward the end of the last century when the German planktologist Dr. H. Lohmann began studying the filtering mechanisms of a class of animals called Larvacea, whose most prominent members in the plankton belong to the genus *Oikopleura*.

Oikopleura has a small body with an undulating tail that is about four times as long, the whole measuring something less than an inch. It secretes an elaborate "house" made of thin, transparent, gelatinous material. This first appears as an elastic envelope which the animal

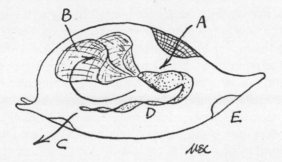

FIG. 41: Oikopleura *in its wonderful house:* A—*water entry gate;* B—*filters leading to mouth;* C—*water exit;* D—Oikopleura; E—*emergency exit.*

separates from its body with flicks of its tail. Then, undulating this tail to create a flow of water, it inflates this fragile envelope around itself like a balloon. And what a marvelous balloon it is! It has a grille that prevents all but the finest particles from entering with the currents created by its tail. Once inside, these particles are sieved out by a pair of conical nets leading to the owner's mouth. Lohmann found that these nets, with meshes closer than the finest man-made gauze, trap flagellates measuring only one or two thousandths of a millimeter in diameter. One can only marvel at the evolutionary processes that have produced so efficient and intricate a mechanism.

The history of the Larvacea is something of an evolutionary wonder too. They belong to the phylum of the tunicates, many of which are sedentary animals called ascidians. *Oikopleura* and other Larvacea are transformed larvae of ancient bottom-living animals similar to ascidians. Through accelerated development of their reproductive organs, the larvae became sexually mature while still in the free swimming state and have dropped the immobile adulthood of their ancestors. This remarkable transformation was pointed out by the late Professor Walter Garstang (1868–1949) of the University of Leeds. It was part of his larger theory of the evolution of animal forms through modification of the young, the most important biological principle to come from studies of the plankton.

"Larval Forms"

When Garstang began his researches, one of the widely held biological theories was the so-called "biogenetic law" associated with the name of the nineteenth-century German zoologist Ernst Haeckel. "Ontogeny recapitulates Phylogeny," said this "law." In layman's language this means that the development of the young of any species (ontogeny) is a synopsis of the evolutionary history of the adults of its type (phylogeny). Thus the metamorphosis of tadpole into frog was supposed to be a key to the amphibian's evolution, while the gill pouches of the human embryo bore mute testimony of ancient aquatic ancestors. Garstang rejected this view and replaced it with a dynamic principle of his own. "Ontogeny does not recapitulate Phylogeny," he told the Linnean Society of London in 1921, "it creates it."

Believers in Haeckel's law thought of evolution as proceeding through gradual changes in adult forms. Garstang, who was intimately acquainted with the host of larvae that drift with the plankton, knew that evolutionary forces were a potent influence in the life of the young larvae as well. Far from being a mirror of adult evolution in the past, the development of larval forms is a field of evolutionary change in its own right. Here, he surmised, was a route by which the gradual molding of evolution could make drastic changes almost at one sudden jump.

Many of the planktonic larvae come from sedentary bottom-living or shore-dwelling animals. By drifting with the water they spread their otherwise immobile species like the wandering seeds or fruits of rooted plants. Garstang realized that, instead of representing a primitive adult stage long discarded, planktonic larvae often showed remarkable adaptation to their mode of existence.

Natural selection tends to favor two major characteristics of these larvae. On the one hand, there are advantages in modifications that enable them to remain floating and drifting as long as possible, thus spreading their kind widely. Yet there are competing advantages in changes that facilitate their maturing quickly to give birth to offspring before falling prey to an enemy. Garstang showed how the forms of many planktonic larvae compromise and adjust between these two rival needs. Here was evolution acting directly on the young in an unmistakable manner. He called this process of evolutionary development through modification of the young "paedomorphosis."

Within the framework of this general process, it is easy to see how forms like the Larvacea have originated. As previously mentioned, there is an advantage in the rapid onset of maturity so that the animal can get on with the main business of propagating its kind. This is offset against the competing advantages of being able to float with the plankton as long as possible to achieve maximum distribution. These factors favor an accelerated development of the reproductive organs in relation to the rest of the body—a phenomenon called "neoteny." Thus the Larvacea have dispensed entirely with the bottom-living adult form and have become true planktonic animals, maturing and reproducing as they drift along. In their case, the change-over seems to have been made in two stages. They have directly evolved from larvae of a creature called *Doliolum*, which had already become "pelagic"—that is, an inhabitant of the open sea.

Garstang's ideas have spread slowly among biologists. He never got around to writing a comprehensive statement. Instead, his ideas were presented between 1921 and 1949 in four serious scientific papers and in a number of informal verses which seem to be his natural mode of expression. The latter are colorful and engaging statements of many of his central ideas and have been published posthumously in a little book appropriately entitled *Larval Forms*. The following, entitled "Oikopleura, Jelly Builder," is both typical and to the point:

> Oikopleura, masquerading as a larval Ascidian,
> Spins a jelly-bubble-house about his meridian:
> His tail, doubled under, creates a good draught,
> That drives water forward and sucks it in aft.
>
> A filter in front collects all the fine particles—
> Micro-flagellates and similar articles—

Which pour in a stream through a jelly-built tunnel
Into his mouth and its mucilage funnel.

The funnel begins with his endostyle gland,
Which flicks mucus up to his circular band:
The stream through his mouth trails it out into threads,
And the whole is rotated as fast as it spreads.

In effect this rotator's a neat centrifuge
That lets out the water and keeps in the ooze:
The water's sucked outwards by paired water-wheels,
The residue serves him with plentiful meals.

Now although Oikopleura sits by himself
In the midst of his house on a jelly-built shelf,
He's firmly attached in front by his snout,
And never lets go till his house wears out.

But his body behind is completely free
And bathed by the water that comes from the sea
Through two lattice-windows let into the walls,
Which limit the size of incoming hauls.

Into this water-space the effluents flow
That start from the spiracles' outward throw:
And lest water-pressure the bubble should burst,
A tubular valve in front blows first.

What shall we say of this marvellous creature
Who breaks all the rules by his composite nature?
The puzzle increases the more it's observed
How far from the track of his fellows he's swerved.

When his jelly-house starts as a lump on his back,
His tail is the finger that stretches it slack:
He probes with its tip between body and test
And loosens the parts which too closely are pressed.

Then, after windows and traps are all ready,
The tail pops inside and, with motions more steady,
Sets the pump working, the water streams in,
The jelly-house swells, and the fishings begin.

We believe we can satisfy any scrutator
That anatomy, house, and pharyngeal rotator
Are pure Doliolid in all their relations,
With highly original specialisations.

His tail is the problem and also the base,
For nothing will work if this you erase:
It seems that, from lack of metamorphosis,
He's larva and adult in half and half doses.

Like Haeckel's biogenetic law, most of Garstang's ideas were speculation. They deal with subjects that are difficult if not impossible of
experimental proof. On the other hand, his concept of paedomorphosis
changed biologists' outlook on the processes of evolution. It once was
thought that when evolutionary lines became too highly specialized
they were doomed, like the dinosaurs, to extinction. Now, while this
remains a possibility, it no longer is thought inevitable. However
specialized the adults of a particular line may become, their younger
stages still are capable of change and adaptation. Then, by the process
of neoteny, they can produce a new evolutionary line to become perhaps
a whole new order, class, or even a phylum. In this way, Garstang
speculated, the vertebrate line which led to man himself once arose
from the paedomorphic transformation of the larvae of sessile bottom-
dwelling animals.

"This is the major contribution that Garstang made to zoological
thought: to have first shown that such a possibility is not unreasonable,"
comments Alister Hardy in the introduction to *Larval Forms*. He
adds, "I, for one, am confident that the coming generations of zoologists will judge it to be among the more fundamental conceptions
given to our science in this century."

To return to the planktonic animals, there is one more feature that
should be outlined, for it is probably the most puzzling and at the same
time the most widespread characteristic of these wandering creatures.
This is their habit of daily commuting over vertical distances that may
amount to several hundred feet.

The "Commuters"

Every day as the light waxes and wanes the animals of the plankton
undergo a curious vertical migration. At night they climb upward toward the darkened surface, only to sink downward again with the rise
of the sun. Some species regularly travel 200 to 300 feet up and down.
This is a considerable effort for these weakly swimming animals. Yet
it must have a profound significance in their lives, for the migratory
habit has been evolved independently by almost every major group of

the zooplankton. Moreover, it has been found in deep-water planktonic animals as well as those drifting within a few hundred feet of the surface. Nobody knows just what the mechanism or significance of this strenuous migration is. It may be connected with feeding and, even more importantly, it may to some extent release the tiny drifting animals from their bondage to the currents.

The problem is far too complicated to go into its details. Many investigations have been carried out by a number of marine biologists over the past half century, each of which has only added to the complexity of the picture. However, one can outline that picture roughly by noting that, as far as operating factors are concerned, the movement up and down of particular intensities of light appears to be one of the most important influences. Many animals seem to prefer a particular light intensity, and they tend to follow the zone of this intensity up and down in the water as the daylight comes and goes. For example, Dr. George L. Clarke of Woods Hole and Harvard University has found that the vertical migrations of certain copepods correlate more closely with the movements of light intensity than with any other factor in their environment. But at the same time he found a great variability in behavior. Other factors, perhaps the varying constitution of the water or of the food supply, also seemed to be operating. This is typical of such studies. Sometimes animals that usually stay below in the daytime are found in abundance in sunlit surface waters. There are also indications that hunger may help set the pattern of reaction to light. Certain animals tend to seek the light when hungry, presumably in order to feed on the plant life in the upper waters, and to retreat from it when sated.

Whatever the factors that control the vertical migrations, there is the correlative question of what advantage these migrations are to the animals themselves. Hardy has suggested that this may be a way by which the drifting animals use their weak swimming powers to gain a limited freedom of movement. In the ocean, where water masses tend to sort themselves into layers, conditions change much more markedly in a vertical direction than they do horizontally. Swimming a few hundred feet left or right would usually make little difference to a tiny plankter. But a few hundred feet change of level would probably bring it into an entirely different water mass, often into an oppositely flowing current.

The animal is like a balloonist who can control only his vertical movements, spilling some ballast to go up or valving out a little gas to go

down. If the balloonist wants to change his speed or direction, he has
to go up or down until he finds a favorable wind. There is often a
velocity difference of one or two miles per day between the surface currents and those a dozen or so fathoms down in the ocean. Trying to
swim along itself, a planktonic animal would get practically nowhere
in relation to its water mass. By dropping down a hundred feet in the
morning and rising to the surface again in the evening, an underwater
"balloonist" may well travel a mile or more in relation to the surface.

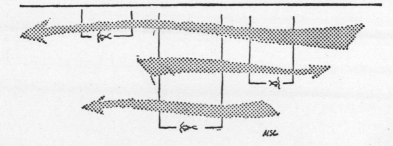

FIG. 42: *Although planktonic animals are poor swimmers, vertical migration
helps them travel. By dropping down or rising a few dozen feet a plankter may
enter a current that carries it several miles horizontally in a day to a new feeding
ground.*

In this way, the little animals can move fairly quickly. If food is short
in one place, the next evening may find them in a richer area. Usually
the surface waters are moving faster than those deeper down, so that
the animal actually is left behind when it drops out of the surface
waters. Nevertheless, it is traveling relative to those waters. The animal
itself probably knows nothing of this. It is merely responding to whatever mechanism induces its daily up-and-down migrations. Yet the
practical effect is that the animal continuously samples a new environment. This also gives the weakly swimming animals some power of
choice. If an environment is uncongenial, they can swim down out of
it and move on. Conversely, if they find themselves climbing into unfavorable water at nightfall, they can hold back as the current carries
them along.

Thus Hardy's suggestion points up a major advantage of the otherwise mystifying habit of vertical migration. A given assemblage of
plants and animals are not condemned indefinitely to travel along together. The drifting of the animals is not quite so passive as it once
appeared, for they can, in a sense, hunt about for new environments

and new food supplies. It is little wonder that this migratory habit has become almost universal among the zooplankton.

This chapter has been devoted largely to the plankton because it is believed to be the base, the ultimate food source, of all other life in the sea. This life, however, in one form or another, has spread to every part of the ocean. That is the subject of the following chapter.

NINE

The Range of Ocean Life

Wherever oceanographers have looked, from the abyssal depths of Pacific trenches to the half-land, half-water world of the shore, they have found living creatures. An impartial observer from another planet would probably quickly grasp a fact that has only begun to be apparent to land-oriented man—the most characteristic life forms of the earth are the marine organisms. In some form they inhabit over 70.8 per cent of the earth's surface throughout all levels of a water envelope many times thicker than the thin zone of life on land. It would take a book in itself to describe this vast and, to the landsman, alien biosphere. The interested reader should consult one or more of the excellent books on the subject listed in the Bibliography. However, the range and variety of this marine life can at least be indicated by highlighting certain of its aspects, such as the life of the shore. This is by far the most challenging environment into which marine life has extended.

The Rigors of the Shore

From the viewpoint of a marine organism, the shore of the ocean is the threshold of outer space. Except for the lowest reaches of the lowest tides, the protective stability of the water is gone. At least part of the time the shore-dwelling organisms have to endure the harsh extremes of the weather, drying in the air or flooding with fresh-water rains, freezing in the winter and baking in the summer. Like the first spacemen who will circle the earth in satellites, shore creatures live on the fringes of a hostile alien environment. Unlike man, however, they have had many hundreds of millions of years to adapt to this rugged existence. The results of this adaptation are evident to any visitor to a rocky shore, where the fairly well defined life zones on the rocks tell a similar story of adaptation to varying degrees of exposure along all the temperate coasts of the world.

Biologists distinguish between several zones of differing degrees of exposure. These are usually named for one of their typical organisms. Thus the zone farthest from the water, where the exposure is greatest, is sometimes called the "Littorina zone" after the hardy little snails

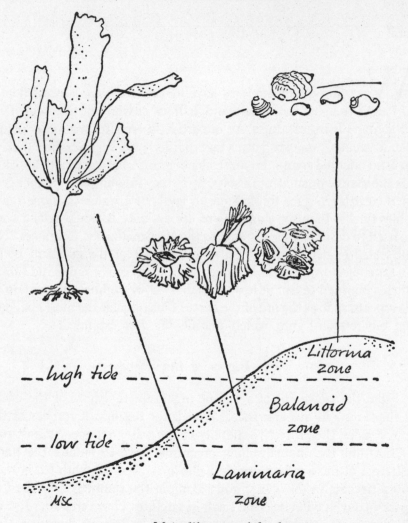

FIG. 43: *Major life zones of the shore.*

that live there. The middle and lower levels, which are covered by water for at least a short time every day, may be called the "Balanoid zone" after its characteristic barnacles. Similarly, the region below low tide to the seaward edge of the underwater seaweed forest is often called the "Laminaria zone," using the Latin name for the kelps that grow there. These are the typical major zones for a temperate rocky shore, although experts may make many finer distinctions.

As far as the shore dwellers are concerned, the boundary between land and sea is usually marked by a black zone of blue-green algae. There may also be a few lichens and some green algae. But the dark plants predominate at the extremity of the ocean world, only occasionally wetted by the spray from breaking waves or by the highest high tides.

The shore below is an area of evolutionary transition between sea and land. Although all of its creatures are tied to the ocean, some of them have gone far in making the slow change-over that will enable them to cross the algal border to a terrestrial mode of life. Consider the snails, for example. The ancestors of all land snails once came from the sea. Today one can see others of these mollusks at evolutionary way stations along the rocky shore.

In a zone extending from above the highest high tides down to where there is about 50 per cent exposure to air, the rough periwinkle (*Littorina rudis*) is found. It is most likely to be seen in cracks and crevices of the rock, browsing on the algae. This particular snail has all but broken its ties with the sea. It has a gill cavity equipped with blood vessels to "breathe" oxygen from the air almost like a lung and can go a month without contact with the water. But more significantly, it has broken one of the strongest ties of all those that bind an animal to the water—the need to use the sea for reproduction and dispersal of its species. The rough periwinkle has become viviparous, bearing its young within its own body until they are ready to be born as tiny snails, miniature replicas of the adult form.

However, no one factor such as ability to withstand exposure to air or breaking of the reproductive tie with the water constitutes the crucial break with the sea. It is the combination of such factors that enables a one-time marine animal to cross the border to the land. In these terms, the rough periwinkle is farther along the evolutionary road to terrestrial living than is its companion in the dry upper zone, the tiny snail *Littorina neritoides*. *Neritoides* can stand even drier conditions than can *rudis*, venturing high up and even a little beyond the algal threshold. But like many another sea creature, it sheds its eggs directly into the water, in this case during the highest of the spring tides.

Farther down the slope, in a zone from 65 per cent or more exposure to air down to the low-water level, the common periwinkle (*Littorina littorea*) abounds. It often lives at the upper reaches of its range, where it is covered only briefly during high tides, showing it is well adapted to cope with exposure. Yet it too sheds its eggs into the sea and so has much farther to go toward adapting to land conditions than its viviparous cousin. The smooth periwinkle (*Littorina obtusuta*) also lives in this lower zone with a range comparable to that of *littorea*. It can stand only brief exposure and is usually found only where seaweeds afford protection against drying as well as a handy food supply. But, while *obtusuta* cannot venture very far into the drier zones, it has already significantly reduced its reproductive dependence on the sea, for it lays its eggs in moist gelatinous masses attached to the seaweeds on which it lives.

In these and other ways some of the snails mark a road of transition between marine life and that of the land. On the other hand, others of the shore dwellers, such as the mussels and the ubiquitous barnacles, are totally water creatures. Even though some species have adapted to living in the drier zones, there is no suggestion of evolving toward a terrestrial life. They are entirely dependent on the ocean. They strain out the food particles the water brings them and in season commit their larvae directly into the sea. (See Plates 13 & 14.)

This is a quite different mode of life from that of the browsing snails. Exposed to waves and surf, these sedentary filter feeders have to be securely anchored. Mussels literally tie themselves to the rock with many tough threads. Barnacles are even more firmly attached. When a barnacle larva is ready to leave the drifting life of the plankton and settle down as an adult, it cements itself to a firm substratum, if it is fortunate enough to find one. Then it quickly builds up its characteristic lime cone. The animal itself is encased in a shell of chitin, the same material that covers many insects. But its main protection is the lime "house." This consists of six closely fitted plates which form what looks like a miniature volcanic cone. The top is closed by a door of four plates which opens when the animal is feeding and closes when the tide is out. These stout little houses withstand the heaviest waves, although the grinding of winter ice may scrape a barnacle-covered rock clean.

Like the snails, different species of barnacles show a preference for different zones of dryness. One species with a difficult Latin name,

Chthalamus stellatus, is generally found high up among the hardier snails, where it is wet by only the highest water of the highest tides, although it ranges in decreasing numbers down to the 10 per cent exposure zone. Thanks to its small size and very firm attachment, this rugged little animal is able to thrive on wave-beaten rocks where even the larger barnacles seem unable to establish a hold.

Just below the dry upper zone is the beginning of the preferred region of the common acorn barnacle (*Balanus balanoides*), which ranges over the middle part of the shore. At the lower part of its range, extending almost to the low-tide level, is found a still larger barnacle, *Balanus perforatus.* As with many other shore animals, this latter barnacle may be found well up in the dry regions. But it seems to prefer the lower, wetter zone. Thus the preferred range of the different species reflects their individual abilities to cope with exposure.

Exposure of greater or lesser extent is of course a constant, perhaps the dominant, fact of life to all of these shore creatures at whatever level they are found. To return to the analogy of the space traveler, for these creatures the threat of exposure to air is comparable to the threat to man of exposure to the harsh conditions of space. And, like the space traveler of tomorrow, many of them have solved the problem by keeping a little bit of their natural environment about them. They have protective shells into which they withdraw when the tide flows out. Barnacles close their doors and mussels shut their bivalves. Some of the snails also secrete mucus films to seal off the opening of their shells. Others of the snails, like the dog whelks and limpets, press the openings tightly against the rock.

Limpets are especially well adapted to do this. Instead of the usual spiral snail shell, a limpet has a single flattened lime cone about the size of a thumbnail. It looks somewhat like the upper half of a small turtle shell. Each limpet seems to have its particular "home" on the rock, where the surface has been gouged to fit its shell exactly. When the tide is in, a limpet ranges over a small area of rock, feeding on larvae that settle on its territory. But with the ebb of the water, it returns to its particular home. There it remains tightly pressed against the rock. Waves that may roll its spiraled cousins about slide harmlessly over its streamlined surface. Some of the sea water is held in a groove running around the inside of the shell, so that the limpet keeps its native moisture securely locked within.

On rock faces beaten by waves and vigorous surf, only the hardier of the animals abound. Whatever seaweeds do manage a foothold are sparse and stunted. In quieter areas, however, the rocks will be covered with a heavy growth of weeds whose species, like those of many animals, show a zonation according to their ability to survive exposure. All of these shore plants are members of the algae. As already mentioned, those found farthest from low water are microscopic plants clinging to the rock as a film. They furnish food for some of the snails that live along the border with the land.

Farther down the shore, where the degree of daily exposure is less, the algae grow bigger. To give a quick listing of typical species, the hardiest of these rockweeds in its ability to endure exposure and the one found highest is the channeled wrack (*Pelvetia canaliculata*). It is out of the water 90 per cent of the time. Some days it is not wet at all at the upper edge of its zone. Just below is the preferred range of the related and almost as hardy spiral wrack (*Fucus spiralis*), which flourishes from levels of about 80 to 60 per cent exposure. The channeled wrack is a European plant, so that on a North American rocky shore the typical downward sequence of the rockweeds begins with *spiralis*. (See Plates 11 & 12.)

The bulk of the shore area, from levels of 50 per cent or so exposure down to 15 per cent, is populated by the bladder and knotted wracks (*Fucus vesiculosis* and *Ascophyllum nodosum*). Of the two, the knotted wracks predominate wherever there is adequate protection from pounding waves. Below all of these and beginning just beyond the lowest of the low-water levels is the Laminaria zone of the kelps. These great broad-fronded plants grow upward from 10 fathoms or more of water to become the largest of the seaweeds.

As in the case of the animals, this is not an exhaustive list of the seaweeds, nor will the species mentioned be found in all places. But it is typical of the algal forests along temperate shores. Compared to land vegetation, the seaweeds are simple plants. They have no need of roots, for when the tide is in they are bathed in a solution of all the minerals and water they need. A grasping organ or "holdfast" provides for attachment to the rock. There is no need for supporting trunks and stems, either, for the water supplies all the support that is needed. Gas-filled swellings on some of the seaweeds help them rise in the water.

At high tide the swaying fronds of these various algae make a weirdly animated forest in which and on which a host of sea animals live and feed. When the tide is out, much of this once-lively forest lies limp over the rock. Then it offers shelter to many animals from the eyes of enemies and from the drying action of the air. Because of this, the life of the shore tends to be richest where the rockweed forests grow.

There are other sheltered places among the rocks that moderate the harsh shore environment too. Tide pools provide a refuge for many animals ordinarily seen only below low-water level. They make handy aquaria where one can watch starfishes, sea urchins, snails, fishes, crabs, anemones, sponges, and many other creatures. Individual rocks also provide shelter beneath them. Here one can often find a host of small animals such as crabs and various worms.

Because of its variety of sanctuaries, a rocky shore supports a richer marine life than does sand or mud. With the latter there is no firm substratum on which to hold against the pounding of waves and surf. What animals do live there are usually buried in the mud and sand. Worms, snails, bivalves, crabs, shrimps, and other burrowers can make a go of it. There are even some plants, microscopic diatoms, living among the sand grains in the wetter zone. But unless one is willing to dig and sift, sand and mud are not as easy an environment in which to observe the life of the shore as are the rocks and tide pools.

This brief outline scarcely begins to sketch the broad picture of shore life. Again the interested reader is referred to one of the pertinent books in the bibliography. However, it does indicate something of the nature of the most rugged environment into which marine life has extended itself. The second most rugged ocean environment lies at the opposite extremity of the marine world in the cold and unilluminated depths of the abyss.

The Great Life Zone

The largest single biological habitat on the earth is found in the deeper waters of the ocean. One doesn't usually think of the ocean depths in this perspective. For most of us they are far removed from the land and shallow-water world we know. Yet something like 60.8 per cent of the earth's surface, 86 per cent of the area covered by ocean, lies a mile or more under water. Except for sealed-off basins such as those of the Arctic Ocean or the Mediterranean or Caribbean seas, these deep waters are interconnecting. The only topographic barriers are those surrounding holes and troughs of exceptionally great depth. These are indeed isolated from one another and are comparable, in their way, to mountaintops on land. Yet even in the deepest trenches, wherever oceanographers have specifically investigated, they have found living organisms. Thus the deep-ocean basins can be thought of as one continuous zone of life. Except for those creatures living near the surface, it is a world monotonously characterized by cold calm water, chronic food shortages, and perpetual darkness broken only by the ghostly lights of its many luminescent organisms.

One way briefly to consider this vast deep-sea realm and its host of strange creatures is in terms of some of the broad characteristics of its life patterns. In this connection the terrific pressures that in Forbes's day were thought to preclude life at any great depth seem to be far less critical in setting these patterns than are such things as light, temperature, the calmness of the water, and the food supply.

Many of the deep-sea organisms are what biologists call "pelagic"— that is, they live swimming or drifting in the water. Organisms that need light live in the sunlit wave-tossed upper waters, the so-called "epipelagic" region. The creatures considered here prefer twilight or utter darkness. They live in the "bathypelagic" region from the limits of light penetration down to the bottom. Many live principally in the dusk of the upper bathypelagic waters, often migrating into the food-rich surface waters at night.

The diminished light intensity has a marked influence on the coloring of these animals. Where there is plenty of daylight many of the planktonic creatures are transparent. Other animals, too thick to see through, are camouflaged to merge into their surroundings. Fish often have dark blue-green backs that blend with the color of the depths when seen from above. Seen from their own level or from below, their silvery sides and bellies reflect the color of their surroundings. But in the dusk and darkness of the deep, protective coloring means the ability to melt into the perpetual night. The characteristic pigments are black, dark brown, red, and orange. Colored with the latter two, some of the most brightly hued animals in the sea live in this bathypelagic world. They are as invisible there as their drably colored companions, for the long red rays of sunlight are the first to be absorbed in the water. Red light virtually disappears after about 300 feet even in the clearest water and on the brightest days. Beyond that, blue rays penetrate deeper than green. By 5,000 feet, virtually all traces of daylight vanish. The bright colors that would be such a disadvantage in the well-lighted surface waters are as effective as the blacks and browns in matching the surroundings a few hundred feet down. It is no accident that the most characteristic deep-water crustaceans are large scarlet prawns.

As the light disappears with increasing depth, one might expect the faculty of vision to become less useful and, as in the case of cave animals, to disappear. There is some tendency for eyes to diminish in size with depth, and blind fishes are well known. On the other hand, it is impossible to generalize about the role of vision in deep-water life. There are some large and very well developed eyes on animals that dwell in the perpetual night. Some deep-living fishes even have telescopic eyes. These protrude from their heads, often fixed in an upward direction, with parallel lines of vision. Do these help their owners see falling food outlined against the lighter background above? Do they and other eyes of deep-water animals serve to pick up the flashes of luminescence that are the only light in the depths? No one knows. While luminous flashes of other animals may be an object of vision, for some of these fish the most highly developed light organs are found on species that live around 1,600 feet, in the twilight zone rather than in complete darkness. As with bioluminescence itself, which will be considered farther on (page 231), marine biologists don't yet understand completely the significance of light and vision in bathypelagic life.

Temperature is another important life factor. Indeed, with some animals it seems to be temperature rather than light conditions that keeps them at intermediate depths. These animals collect in large numbers around well-developed thermoclines which in the tropics and subtropics may lie at depths of 800 to 1,700 feet. This in turn makes the upper bathypelagic levels a good feeding ground, attracting such swift predators as prawns, fish, and squid. Thus temperature conditions as well as those of light seem to pattern life at intermediate depths.

There is a violent reaction to temperature change when animals caught in biologists' tow nets in deep waters are hauled to the surface. They almost always arrive on deck in a moribund state. For fishes with swim bladders the disaster may be due to pressure. A swim bladder is essentially an elastic chamber, a "balloon," inside the fish which is filled with gas and with which the fish regulates its buoyancy. Adjustments in gas pressure are slow, so that a fish is helplessly bloated if raised from the depths too quickly. But many deep-sea fish have no swim bladder. For them it is the temperature shock that is fatal.

Adapted as they are to cold water, some bathypelagic animals are found much higher in cold polar waters than anywhere else in the ocean. This is the key to what was once a biological conundrum. Identical species of certain planktonic animals have been found in both Arctic and Antarctic surface waters but nowhere in the immense stretches of ocean surface in between. Biologists were unable to explain this anomalous bi-polar distribution until it was recognized that the cold water at deep levels provides an unobstructed channel. Pressure is no barrier to the distribution of these animals, but warm surface temperatures are, driving them into the depths of temperate and tropical seas.

Yet another factor affecting the life and form of deep-water animals is the relative calm of the water. Remote from even the wildest storms, the deep-water movements are gentle compared to the waves and agitation of the surface. Animals are able to develop delicate structures under these undisturbed conditions. Their bodies are sometimes so flimsy, they don't survive a net haul to the surface.

Some of the fishes and squid, for example, have bodies encased in thick gelatinous sheaths like the substance of a jellyfish that are quite fragile and yet have a practical advantage in the undisturbed water. Such

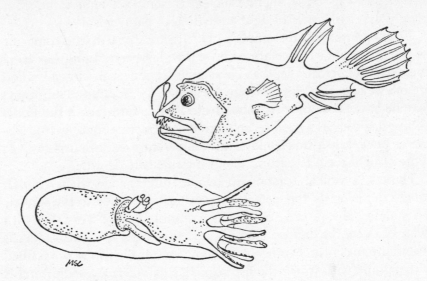

FIG. 44: *Some deep-sea animals are encased in gelatinous sheaths whose water-saturated substance has almost the same density as sea water, making them neutrally buoyant. The octopus* Amphitretus pelagicus (LEFT); *one of the* Haplophryne *angler fishes* (RIGHT). *Both two to three times life size.*

water-saturated tissues have almost the same density as the surrounding sea water. They are more or less neutrally buoyant, enabling an animal to maintain its level in the water with a minimum of effort. This in

10. This sculptured cliff face illustrates the erosive power of waves and spray.

Robert C. & Mary S. Co

11 & 12. The rockweed "forest" (*above*) and some of its denizens (*below*). This is one of the shore's most populous habitats.

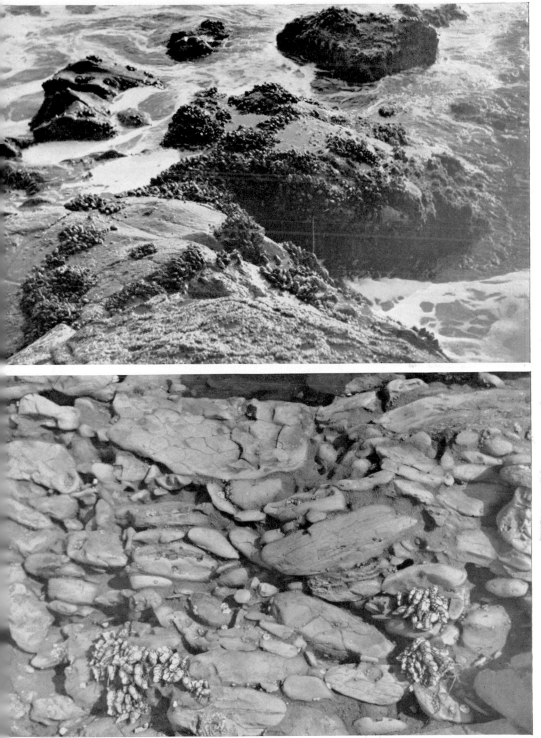

Robert C. & Mary S. Cowen

13 & 14. Shore creatures must endure pounding surf and desiccating exposure. (*Above*) Mussels on rocks; (*below*) barnacles on a cliff face.

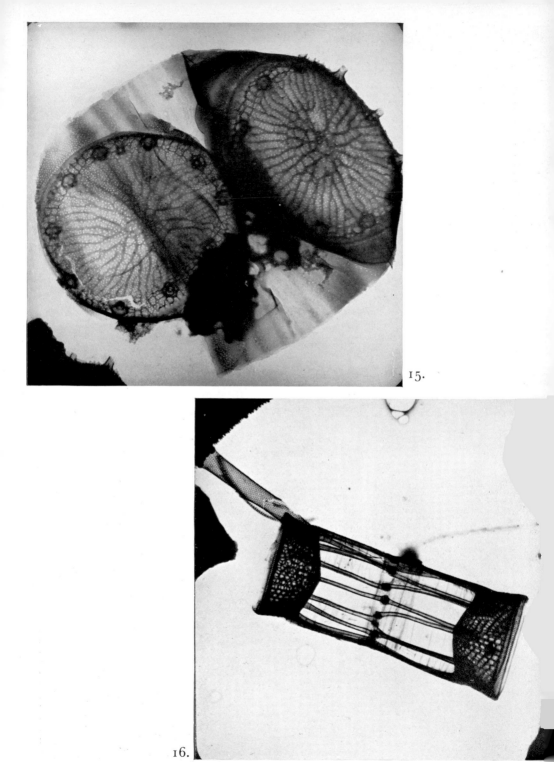

15.

16.

Microphotos from R. R. Guillard,
Woods Hole Oceanographic Institutio

Diatoms as seen through electron microscope. (*Above*) Unknown species
of *Detonula*, slightly crushed; (*below*) *Skeletonema costatum*, valves of
two individuals joined by spines.

17.

18.

Two unknown species of *Thalassiosira*. Both photos show a valve and connecting band. Magnifications range from about 5,000 to 9,000 times for the four plates.

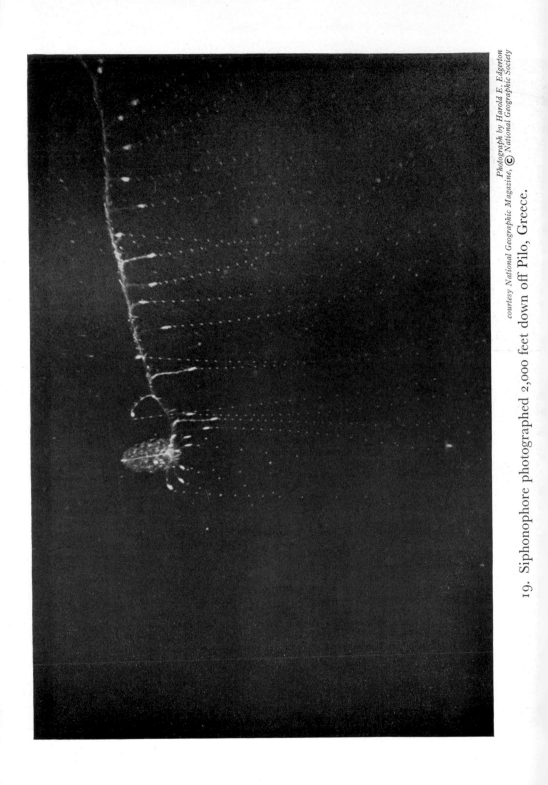

Photograph by Harold E. Edgerton
courtesy National Geographic Magazine, © National Geographic Society

19. Siphonophore photographed 2,000 feet down off Pilo, Greece.

Photograph by Harold E. Edgerton
courtesy National Geographic Magazine, © *National Geographic Society*

20. Deepest photograph at time of publication, taken about 25,000 feet down in Romanche Trench. Note animals circled.

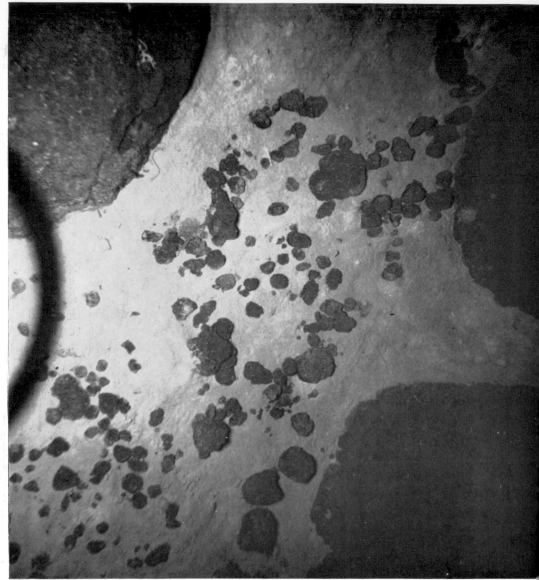

Official, U.S. Navy—Carl Si

21. Manganese nodules in the Pacific, 14,000 feet down.

turn has the further advantage of helping an animal conserve its strength in a region where food is scarce.

Of all the factors listed at the beginning of this section, the distribution of food is probably the most important. It is food, or rather the lack of it, that makes the deeper parts of the ocean such a difficult place to live. The creatures there are at the slim end of the food chains that start in the rich phytoplankton of the surface. As far as is known today and except for those organisms that feed directly on plants, grazers, and other creatures near the surface, life in the depths depends on the sinking of dead or dying organisms or on animals that make regular extensive vertical migrations. Even though some of the deep-water animals don't eat the falling material themselves, the animals they prey upon do. In this way the general food distribution is downward from the primary phytoplankton producers to the ultimate consumers in the abyss.

This downward distribution of food with an attendant thinning out in deeper waters of the amount of life it can support is the scheme that has been generally sketched by marine biologists. However, neither this scheme nor the utter dependence on the surface phytoplankton that it implies is a foregone conclusion. It is based mainly on a century of research from ships floating on the surface. But a few observations that have been made by men who have actually gone into the depths themselves suggest a different picture. One of these men, Captain Jacques-Yves Cousteau, outlined this possible new viewpoint after diving some 4,000 feet to the floor of the Mediterranean in the French Navy's bathyscaphe *F.N.R.S. 3* in December 1953.

The "Living Soup"

Cousteau was interested, among other things, in the deep scattering layer (DSL). This is a puzzling sound-reflecting layer that echo sounders have recorded at moderate depths all over the ocean, often at about 250 fathoms. Rising at night and sinking by day, the DSL seems to be some sort of biological phenomenon. The echo trace left on the recording chart by the DSL is not as hard and distinct as that left by a shoal of herring or larger fish. On the other hand, its smudgy trace often stretches unbroken for hundreds of miles, showing that whatever is making it is spread densely and in wide patches. Perhaps it is due to small planktonic animals. Perhaps it is caused by millions of the small

H

bathypelagic fish that make extensive vertical migrations and have well-developed swim bladders that would reflect sound. These are two of the possible explanations marine biologists have considered. Nobody yet knows just what causes the DSL.

Cousteau had hoped to find this out when he dived in the bathyscaphe. But when he passed through the level where the DSL should have been he found no exceptional concentration of animals. Instead it appeared that there was a steadily increasing concentration of small living organisms the deeper he went. The two French naval officers, Commander Georges Houot and Lieutenant Pierre Willm, who have operated the French bathyscaphe to depths of up to two and a half miles and more have observed this phenomenon too. It also tallies with the few observations made in the early 1930's by William Beebe and Otis Barton in their bathysphere. This was a steel observation chamber suspended from a surface ship by cable which reached depths of several thousand feet.

Cousteau described his observations in *The National Geographic Magazine* as follows:

Houot and I agree that bathyscaphe dives upset some traditional ideas of the sea. For us, at least, the problem of the deep scattering layer is now restated in entirely new terms. So far as we can see, there is, biologically speaking, no DSL, but rather a great bowl of living soup extending on down and growing thicker the deeper into the "tureen" we go. Both Beebe and Barton, the two men who have previously looked out into the deeps, have reported that the density of organisms seems to increase with depth; but so far little attention has been paid to their statement.

The cycle of marine animal life is supposed to depend directly on phytoplankton . . . This [photosynthetic] activity can take place only in the layer penetrated by sunlight, usually to a depth of 600 feet, often not more than 200 feet.

Below this life-giving realm of the sun, says classic theory, the animal population thins out in the dark and the cold, where living creatures are supposed to depend on the plant life at the top, in a vastly complicated web of existence. Yet against this notion are ranged the direct observations of five men who have been to the depths—Beebe, Barton, Houot, Willm, and myself. I cannot propose an explanation of why reality does not match the simple, attractive theory. But there must be somewhere an unsuspected link in the cycle of marine life yet to be discovered.

Here in a few sentences are summed up what may turn out to be one of the most striking discoveries in marine biology. Not only does it put the puzzle of the deep scattering layer into a new perspective, but it calls one of the basic theories of ocean life into question. Perhaps there is a simple explanation that does not involve any radical shift in basic thinking. Hardy suggests that Cousteau's "soup" may consist largely of dead rather than living material. Some of it may be the slowly sinking shells of dead planktonic organisms. The greater part, Hardy thinks, may be the cast-off skins of planktonic crustaceans which periodically throw off their chitinous coverings as they grow, just as snakes cast off skins that have become too tight. On the other hand, there have not been enough firsthand studies to settle the question.

The viewpoint adopted in this chapter is that of the classical theory concerning the food cycles and distribution of life in the sea. This is the firmest basis from which to write, given the state of marine knowledge today. But Cousteau's speculations should be borne in mind. As more and more firsthand studies are made in the deep sea it is not unlikely that traditional concepts based on remote studies from surface ships will undergo radical change.

This leaves the question of why the bathyscaphers have not seen the deep scattering layer; that is, if one does not accept Cousteau's suggestion that it may be the diffuse echo returned by the steady downward thickening of the "soup." It is quite possible that there is a concentration of animals that produces the DSL trace on the echo-sounder records but that they scatter whenever anything big and strange like a bathyscaphe or a camera assemblage comes at them. This would explain why they have not yet been directly observed.

Dr. Harold Edgerton of the Massachusetts Institute of Technology, who has taken many thousands of deep-sea photographs and who has worked closely with Cousteau, thinks this may be the case. One can sometimes see the DSL apparently scatter as a camera reaches it, only to re-form when the camera has passed below that level or been withdrawn to the surface. Edgerton has designed photographic equipment that can be towed or raised and lowered rapidly. In this way he hopes to bring the camera into the DSL so quickly that its animals will be caught off guard and photographed before they can scatter. But this has not as yet been extensively tried. At this writing, the DSL is still without a generally accepted explanation.

To return to the food distribution, as it is conceived today, the downward-raining particles are thought to become both scarcer and larger the deeper one goes. Small bits of refuse are eaten in the higher waters or disintegrate more rapidly than the larger ones. Also, the latter have less surface in relation to their volume and sink more quickly. Thus the animals sustained by the sinking particles tend to become fewer and to some extent larger too. Planktonic animals, for example, are found at all depths. But, as far as the evidence of biologists' tow nets has shown, they tend to be both sparser and larger in the depths than at the surface. The largest copepods are bathypelagic animals. In like manner, the largest representatives of many other animal types known at the surface are found in the depths.

On the other hand, and again so far as is known from what biologists have caught with their nets, there is a limit set to size by the scarcity of food. Deep-living animals are not thought to attain whale-like dimensions. The conditions of deep life seem to be such that food comes in relatively big meals at long and irregular intervals. Many of the animals have adapted to these conditions by evolving enormous mouths, extensible stomachs, and other devices for preying on creatures as big or bigger than themselves, while their over-all bodies have become relatively slight.

The Weirdest Fish in the Sea

The bathypelagic fishes can be truly grotesque. It is impossible to convey their weird appearance in words. The accompanying sketches of a few species illustrate the strange forms that have evolved in the depths—forms that are closely related to species well known in shallow waters.

Most of these fishes are dark-colored—black, dark brown, or blackish violet. They have little luster and in some cases have no scales. Their bodies are generally loose and flabby, with poorly developed bones and muscles. This doesn't seem to be a disadvantage, for, as pointed out previously, the calm water enables such flimsy body structures to survive.

The most striking common feature of these fishes is their enormous mouths. Consider the Stomiatoids, for example. This suborder is one of the largest groups of deep-living fishes. They generally have extended bodies ranging from a few inches to over six feet in length, with rows of light organs arranged like portholes along their sides. They have well-developed eyes below which are red and green light organs. Luminous filaments hang from the chin or throat of many species, occasionally

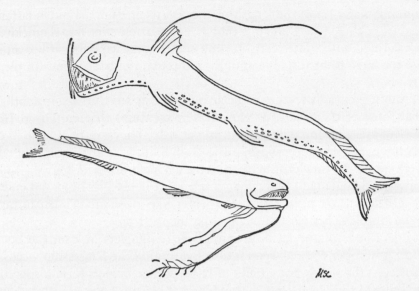

FIG. 45: *Two Stomiatoids:* Chauliodus sloanei, *viper fish* (ABOVE), 1½ *times life size;* Flagellostomias boureei (BELOW), *roughly life size.*

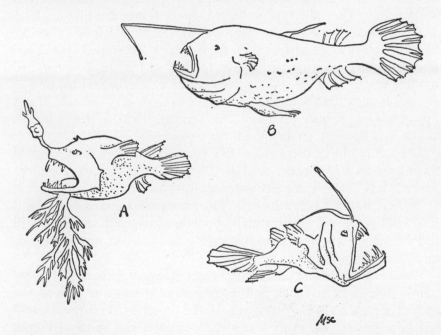

FIG. 46: *Some angler fishes:* A—Linophryne arborifer; B—Ceratias holbölli *with male attached;* C—Melanocoetus cirrifer. ⅓ *to* ½ *natural size.*

running many times the length of the fish itself. But the outstanding feature of these fishes, and one that gives a fearsome look, is their huge jaws armed with great teeth. In one species—the viperfish—the teeth are too large to fit inside its mouth and remain outside when its jaws are shut.

Another curious feature of bathypelagic fish are the "fishing rods" that some of them have developed. The creatures that employ these devices are appropriately named angler fish. They are related to the common angler or "devilfish," a bottom-living shallow-water animal well known to trawler fishermen. The devilfish lies half buried, "angling" with a filament that emerges from just behind its head and ends in a little tuft. It plays this in the water like a fisherman's fly, luring quite sizable fishes close enough to be snapped up.

Like the common devilfish, some deep-sea anglers lurk on the bottom. A number of small species also live among the Sargassum weeds. However, the nearly 100 species of bathypelagic anglers form a special suborder of their own, the Ceratioidea, that live most abundantly below 6,000 feet. These grotesque little fish show their deep-water character in their enormous mouths, very extensible stomachs, and relatively small bodies. They often are globular-shaped, as broad as they are long, with the head accounting for nearly a third of their length. They are generally black and scaleless, with small, poorly developed eyes. Their jaws are armed with long spike-like teeth that fold back when their mouths are closed. These folding teeth make it easy for prey to enter an angler's mouth. But once the teeth have caught, it is difficult, if not impossible, to get back out again. One wonders what happens when an angler fixes its teeth on an animal that is too strong for it.

Although some of these angler fish grow to be a yard long, most of them are only a few inches over all. They are poor swimmers and apparently lurk in the dark quiet water, waiting for a meal to come along. Some have luminous chin barbels. Their most characteristic feature is their angling device, which usually ends in some kind of light organ and probably resembles a tempting crustacean or other morsel that attracts unsuspecting prey.

These angling devices are an interesting example of the evolutionary transformation of an organ and its migration to another part of the body. They are really the first fin ray of the dorsal fin. This ray is modified in some way on many fishes—into a poisonous spine, a tactile filament, or an adornment for courtship display. But in these angler fish not only has it been transformed into an angling device and provided with a light organ, it has migrated from the back to the very tip of the head. Biologists are certain of this migration because, upon dissecting one of these fish, they can trace the motor nerve controlling the angling device back to a segmental nerve that emerges from the spinal cord at the point where the ancestral fin ray once stood.

The angler fish are remarkable in still another way and one which illustrates a crucial problem for animals living in the darkness; namely, that of finding mates. Wide-ranging swimmers probably meet other members of their species often enough in their wanderings for this not to be too great a difficulty. Distinctive light organs may help in mutual recognition. But for poor swimmers like the anglers that lurk about waiting for prey to come to them, it would be fatal to rely on such chance contacts. They have a unique solution. The males of their species have become parasites and live permanently attached to the females.

Since the young of species are more numerous than the adults, young males as a group are much more likely to meet up with females than are older fish. Thus, in the angler fish, evolutionary forces have favored an early union of the sexes that links male and female even before the males are sexually mature. The result is a strange parasitic relationship. The relatively small male bites into the female at almost any part of her body. Their tissues fuse and their bloodstreams form one circulatory system. Permanently attached to and nourished by the female, the male then becomes sexually mature, ready to fertilize the female's eggs whenever necessary. Sometimes two or more males are found attached to one female.

The anglers just described are all bathypelagic. However, one of the strangest of the deep-living anglers is a bottom fish. It was discovered in the course of the Danish deep-sea expedition made in the research ship *Galathea* (1950–52). It represents a new genus and species and has been appropriately named *Galatheathauma axeli* after the chairman of the expedition's committee, H.R.H. Prince Axel. This angler has its lure inside of its mouth. It is a large forked light organ suspended from the roof of the mouth. The fish apparently lies on the bottom with its mouth open, enticing its meals with its glowing lure.

Cold Light

The ability to produce light is widespread among marine creatures. The glows and flashes of luminescent organisms pattern the eternal

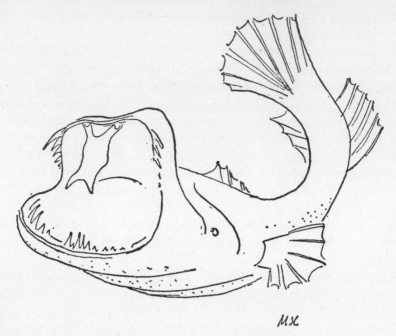

FIG. 47: *Bottom-dwelling angler* Galatheathauma axeli: *Caught by the* Galathea *expedition, it was named for the expedition's chairman, Prince Axel. Note forked light organ in mouth.*

night of the depths just as they often do the nighttime surface of the sea. Dr. George Clarke, who has made extensive studies of marine luminescence, reports that numerous and brilliant light flashes have been detected at great depths by deep-water photometers. In *Oceanus,* the Woods Hole magazine, he says that "since our records at a depth of one mile show flashes occurring as frequently as five or more per second, we now know that the deep sea is not continuously enveloped in inky blackness but at times, at least, must present the appearance of the night sky on the Fourth of July." In some cases, such as lures of angler fish or the protective luminous clouds of deep-water squid and crustaceans, the purpose of the light seems obvious. But in many other cases, biologists do not yet know what significance the lights have for their owners.

The luminous animals are the most efficient light producers on the earth. If human engineers could do anywhere near as well in turning energy into useful light, the lighting portion of our electric bills would be substantially reduced. An electric lamp gets hot because much of the energy it consumes is lost as heat. But as little as one per cent of the energy animals use to make light is lost this way. Theirs is the coldest light known, produced by a chemical process that has been evolved by at least some marine representatives of almost every major group in the animal kingdom.

In some cases, the ability to produce light is merely the ability to discharge a luminous slime. In others, specific organs called "photophores" are involved. They are wonderfully efficient little lanterns with a lens and a concave reflector and can be turned on or off at will. Hardy describes them as being "as good a parallel to the bull's-eye lantern as the camera is to the eye."

In still other cases, marine animals that have not developed light organs of their own have made a home for luminous bacteria on certain areas of their surface. One fish, *Photoblepharon,* has a patch of these bacteria below each of its eyes. When the fish wants to turn off its lights, it draws a fold of skin over the luminous patches.

The really remarkable thing about all these luminous devices is that they have been evolved so widely among marine creatures. Even the intricate little photophore lanterns have arisen independently and with quite similar designs in a number of different types of animals, such as fishes, prawns, squid. To appreciate why this is so remarkable, one needs to understand how slow and bumbling the processes of evolution generally are.

Biologists think of the mechanism of evolution as a blind, haphazard process rather than a purposeful striving on the part of an organism to develop in this or that particular direction. From time to time and in the normal course of events, slight inheritable changes arise in any type of creature. These changes, "mutations," are then passed on to offspring. If a change confers some advantage, it will tend to be preserved and spread through the species over a number of generations. If it is a disadvantage, however, so that the animals affected are handicapped, perhaps in the competition for food or for mates, the mutation usually dies out. Then too, there are many changes that are merely indifferent. These may or may not be preserved.

In the case of the well "designed" photophores, there must have been a series of changes in the organs involved, each conferring some advantage on its possessor, which led finally to the structure of lens, reflector, and nerve-controlled light-producing mechanism. Whatever the advantage or advantages are, they must have a fundamental significance in ocean life. The apparently haphazard process has led to similar results

H*

in too many animals for it to be otherwise. But what can that significance be?

Some animals quite obviously use their light to see by. Certain squid and fish, for example, have luminous organs so placed in relation to their eyes that the field of view is illuminated at least for short distances. One stomiatoid is able to throw a beam of strong blue light in front of itself for some two feet. Yet the most characteristic arrangement of photophores is along the under sides of animals whose eyes look in different, even opposite, directions. Perhaps the lights form distinctive patterns by which members of a species recognize one another. This would be useful both for mating purposes and to avoid eating one's own kind. But then what is the advantage of the brilliant fireworks produced at the surface by tiny organisms such as certain Dinoflagellates? These little organisms don't have vision. Indeed, one would think that their luminescence, stimulated by any agitation of the water, would make them more easily spotted by creatures that eat them. Here the luminescence may be just a by-product of reactions to the agitation of the water. Then there are defensive uses for luminescence. As previously mentioned, many deep-water prawns and squid eject luminous clouds. These serve the same purpose of covering the animal's retreat as do the ink clouds of shallow-living squids and octopi.

In the cases cited here and in many others, the usefulness of light to certain animals is obvious. There are mechanisms for luring prey, for defense, for seeing in the bathypelagic night, and so forth. Yet none of these uses is really of fundamental importance to wide areas of marine life. None can account for the frequent occurrence of the photophores. Even the crustaceans and squids that use luminous "ink" for defense also often have patterns of photophores whose use is anything but obvious. Here again, in some species they may serve as recognition patterns. On the other hand, and in spite of a number of studies by various biologists, the use of these lights for recognition has never been established as a general rule.

In fact, the only general observation one can make about the occurrence of photophores or of the ability to produce light in any fashion was first made by Johan Hjort in *The Depths of the Ocean,* a book published in 1912 which he co-authored with John Murray. Hjort noted that among pelagic animals bioluminescence is as widespread as vertical migration. Moreover, taking the pelagic animals as a whole, there is a correlation between the habit of migration and the ability to produce light.

This suggests that the light itself may be of only secondary importance. It may be the by-product of a chemical process that helps these animals in their migrations, that enables them to endure the drastic change of environment between the surface waters and the depths. Even the photophore lanterns with their lenses and reflectors might be accounted for in this way. The chemical process may be reversible, like that of a storage battery. The photophores, in this case, may be generators. In the darkness they give off light, while the chemical process runs in one direction, producing whatever beneficial effect this has for the animal. Then in the daylight they reverse the process, soaking up the light, with the chemical reactions running in the other direction, just as a storage battery soaks up electricity as its chemical process reverses itself during charging. The animals in question are among the large group that live during the day in the twilight of intermediate depths. It is possible that the lenses and reflectors of their photophores concentrate the dim light and facilitate the recharging process. But this is only speculation. Except for the cases where a specific use is obvious, the function of cold light remains one of the unsolved puzzles of the sea.

The Deepest Life

Another unanswered general question about deep-water life is when and how the depths were populated. It once was thought that the deep basins had remained undisturbed since the remotest era, providing a refuge where ancient animal types could go on living even though surface conditions had changed. Yet most abyssal animals seem clearly related to modern shallow-water forms. There are indications that sweeping changes may have taken place in the deep sea itself. If this is true, when did they take place, how did they affect life? Biologists do not know. Whatever happened, that life today has extended itself to the remotest ocean depths.

At whatever depth marine biologists have looked they have found life. Even on the floor of deep Pacific trenches, there seems to be enough food and oxygen to support bacteria and a sparse population of higher forms. Yet when a new record depth is dredged, there is excitement on deck. As in the explorations of the *Challenger*, there is still the thrill of probing the unknown, the same wonder as to whether anything living will be brought up, the hope that some new and strange creature will be found. One of the deepest trenches so dredged, although not the deepest one sounded, is the Philippine Trench, where the *Galathea* expedition fished up bottom-living animals from a depth far greater than they had been found before. Here is expedition leader Dr. Anton Bruun's description of that record haul:

There, deep down in the clear water, was the faint outline of the large triangular bag of the sledge-trawl. It was pitch-black night, but the quarter-deck lay bathed in the beams of our spotlights. Standing by the trawl gallows, watching the trawl breaking surface, was the fishmaster, his arm waving in a slow circle.

At the winch all eyes were intently following the motions of his arm, as they slowed down and then came to a stop, the hand raised as a signal to stop hauling in. It all went with the fine rhythm of experienced teamwork, but the occasion was a special one: it was the first time that the indicator had stood at zero after reaching 12,163 metres [39,907 feet], the full length of our wire.

During the work of taking in the trawl and the two small dredges that had been fixed to the trawl frame (it took a few minutes but felt like an eternity), we prepared for the disappointment of seeing a bag without any bottom animals in it; for a failure, in short. We comforted ourselves with the thought that it was the first attempt with the full length of our new wire, that everything had gone like clockwork all night, that the wire was safely home and we should be able to make a fresh attempt . . . Then the facts came out in rapid succession. "There's clay on the frame!" somebody cried. "It's been on the bottom!" And then: "There are stones in the bag!" Everybody on board who could leave his job gathered around the big dishes while nervous fingers unloosed the cords so that the contents could be carefully removed. We hardly noticed the red prawns, luminescent euphausids, or black fishes; we all knew these to be pelagic animals, caught on the way up through the free water masses. But there, on a rather large stone, were some small whitish growths—sea-anemones! Even if no more animals had been found, this would still be the outstanding haul of the expedition. It was proof that higher animals can live deeper than 10,000 meters [actually 10,190 meters or 33,433 feet]. Is it surprising that all were overjoyed? And that pleasure became excitement when out of the greyish clay with gravel and stones we picked altogether 25 sea-anemones, about 75 sea-cucumbers, five bivalves, one amphipod, and one bristle-worm? It was an unexpectedly rich variety of bottom-dwelling animals. . . .

. . . We [eventually] found a whole little animal community. All the large groups of invertebrates were represented—polyps, worms, echinoderms, molluscs, and crustaceans. The known depth limit of life had been pushed some 2.5 kilometers lower down; and whereas it might have been doubted whether we should find anything in the Philippine Trench, there is now no reasonable ground for supposing that life cannot also penetrate the few hundred meters further down to the new record depth . . . in the Mariana Trench . . . [Life was found January 23, 1960. See page 280.]

One of the hopes that has gone with fishing the deeps has been that of finding survivors from a remote geological age. The dinosaurs died out on land. Perhaps, it was suggested, the calm and supposedly unchanging waters of the abyss had provided a refuge for survivors from past eras in the sea. Yet except for a few rarities like Neopilina, an ancestor of the snails which has been found in the Pacific, and the coelacanth, the search for "living fossils" has been disappointing. And even the celebrated coelacanth suggests that the search has been in vain.

This strange fish had been thought to be extinct for fifty million years until a specimen was found off South Africa in December 1938 and identified by the South African ichthyologist J. L. B. Smith. Several others have been found since then. At the time, it was widely assumed that the fish was a true "living fossil." In their heyday, three hundred million to fifty million years ago, the coelacanths were a widespread animal group that inhabited fresh water as well as salt. Their characteristic form, with short stubby fins that look more like paddles than true fish fins, hardly changed during that long period, nor indeed in the fifty millions years since then. When the first modern coelacanth was found it seemed obvious that, as surface conditions changed unfavorably, the remnants of the coelacanth line had retreated to the depths.

But Smith himself does not think this was the case. For one thing, he says that the specimens caught have been too well built and vigorous to be true deep-water creatures. Most abyssal animals are dead on arrival or die shortly after being hauled aboard. Moreover, when the first

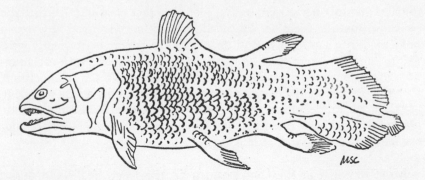

FIG. 48: *Coelacanth.*

coelacanth was caught, the haul included several tons of sharks. Even among shallow-water fishes, only the hardiest can survive the crush of such a netful. The fall in being dumped on deck and the pressure of the heap usually finish off the rest except for an occasional tough shark. The coelacanth, 5 feet long and weighing 127 pounds, was on the bottom of the heap. Yet it snapped viciously when approached and lived out of water for several hours. "No deep-sea creature could have endured all that and lived," says Smith.

Then too, the modern coelacanth doesn't look like a deep dweller. It is blue in color, which suggests shallow water. Also, it is well armored with scales and ruggedly built. Smith thinks it may live in rocky areas, perhaps among reefs below the main action of waves and surf. Far from being a "living fossil," a degenerate form that evolution has passed by and which has taken up shelter in the depths, the coelacanth seems to have become well adapted to modern marine life without the need for the drastic evolutionary changes that so many other animal lines have undergone.

In recent years marine biologists have begun seriously to question whether the depths are really as good a haven for evolutionary refugees as they were once supposed to be. The animals generally found there are directly related to well-known shallow-water forms. Also, there are indications that the abyssal environment itself has undergone more sweeping changes than had been believed. In his book on the coelacanth, *The Search beneath the Sea*, Smith writes:

It is by no means certain and not even likely that the fishes that live in the depths, or their ancestors, went there to escape competition with other fishes. My work has repeatedly shown the enormous stretches that even feeble fishes have colonized, and all the evidence indicates that fishes tend to move and seek new places to live, just like other creatures. All the types we know from the deeps are derived from ancestors who lived in waters of ordinary depth, and though most deep-sea fishes are of course greatly modified to suit the special conditions, all are clearly related to surface forms, none of which are any markedly better equipped to withstand "competition" than the ancestors of the deep-sea forms. In the depths bodies are soft, bones are light, eyes are enormous or have become obsolete, and huge jaws are filled with long fangs, often barbed. There is no valid evidence to support the idea that any of them retired to the depths to escape competition.

More recently, at the "Symposium on the Deep Sea" held during the 1959 annual meeting of the (American) National Academy of Sciences, Robert J. Menzies of Lamont reported that, geologically speaking, deep-living species seem to be surprisingly young. Menzies is studying the smaller organisms, some of which are microscopic. These are much more abundant than the larger animals, making it easier to get a statistically valid and representative picture of their populations.

"With each cruise," Menzies said, "was the hope that the presumed constant deep-sea environment would yield its trilobite, possibly only a millimeter in length. Each trawl sample, however, showed this not to be the case—that is, even the little fellows of the fauna were morphologically like the big ones; namely, closely related to shallow-water genera and species."

Except for bottom-living Foraminifera, whose forms can be traced back to the Paleozoic era, Menzies found that the average geological age of the deep-sea organisms decreases with increasing depth. Even the Foraminifera don't upset this general rule. Menzies thinks that their apparent great age may be due solely to their simple structure. In other words, the forms now living in the deep may be of recent origin. But because they are so simple, they differ little from the Foraminifera of past eras.

Menzies suggests three possibilities to account for the apparent youth of the deep-sea fauna. First, there may have been no deep sea prior to the Mesozoic era, which began some 195 million years ago. This echoes the theories of geologists who think the bulk of the ocean water is of recent origin. Although he suggests this as a possibility, Menzies himself thinks it unlikely.

A second possibility is that there actually was a Paleozoic deep sea but that its animals were killed off by changes in circulation, sedimentation, and food supply. As still another possibility and one which he favors, Menzies suggests that there has always been a deep-sea fauna which has suffered repeated extinctions and repopulations, so that the animals now living there originated from shallow-water forms within the past seventy million years.

If this latter proposition is correct, then the deep-water environment has been far from stable throughout geological time. The temperature record of the oxygen thermometer as read by Emiliani indicates that this may have been the case, for it shows temperatures of the deep-sea bottom to have been eight to ten degrees Centigrade higher in the Eocene, forty to sixty million years ago, than they are today. In this connection, Menzies notes that most deep-living animals now are cold-water creatures. Except for a rare form like Neopilina, the few relatively warm-water animals among them may be the only kind of "living fossils" one will find—not ancient forms that found sanctuary in a changeless environment, but survivors of a geologically recent and uniformly much warmer deep sea.

At this writing, the question of when and how the depths were populated is an open one. A significant number of ancient forms may yet be discovered in the abyss. Perhaps geological research will trace more certainly the history of the ocean environment, confirming or disproving that substantial changes have taken place within its deep waters.

It is interesting that this fundamental question in marine biology is tied to the equally basic question in marine geology of when and how the oceans originated. And, as in the case of geology, the recent evidence argues against the long-held notion that the ocean basins have been stable throughout geological time. Future research in marine biology and geology thus have a fundamental question in common. To quote Menzies once more: ". . . the present day composition of the abyssal fauna seems to require one or several major ecological changes affecting the whole of the deep oceans. The determination of the magnitude of the changes rests mainly with future deep sea geological and zoological work. On such a framework we can adequately build a fund of information which will tell us more about the origin and evolution of life on our earth."

TEN

The Promise of Plenty

THE ocean is like a grab bag stuffed with riches out of which man has been taking only those few packages he can lay hands on easily, often by blindly groping. There are living riches that represent a large and relatively untapped food resource. There are mineral riches spread thinly throughout the water or scattered about the sea bed. One of the bright promises of oceanography is that an increase in scientific knowledge of the sea will help man systematically to exploit the resources of the marine grab bag.

Probably the most dramatic and far-reaching aspect of that promise is the prospect of substantially increasing the world's food supply. There is no need to emphasize here the widely reported statistics on humanity's burgeoning population growth. Mankind faces the bleak outlook of continuing chronic hunger for a majority of the earth's people unless food supplies can be multiplied. Seen in this light, the ocean presents an opportunity and a challenge that man can no longer afford to ignore. Taking food from the sea today is largely a matter of hunting. With research and capital investment, the yields of fishermen could be increased. But however productive it may be in its own terms, hunting is a most inefficient way to exploit a food resource. Today aquaculture, the farming of the sea, is largely a scientist's dream, but when fully developed it will be as revolutionary an advance over fishing as agriculture has been over hunting on the land.

Here is a fact of tremendous significance for a hungry world. A few rough figures will indicate how well filled this potential oceanic food basket really is. Each year the world's fishing fleets bring in something on the order of 20 million tons of edible fish. This is supplemented by a smaller but significant harvest of shellfish, a minor amount of whale and seal meat, and in some areas by a harvest of seaweed. All told, the present world production of sea foods is something like 29 million tons a year. Although this annual catch is impressive, it represents just a drop from the oceanic horn of plenty.

For one thing, the food animals themselves are only the end product of food chains that start with the plankton, the primary food source in the sea. With the present state of knowledge, it is difficult to estimate the total plankton resources of the oceans. However, their vastness is hinted by the fact that the waters of the Gulf of Maine in late summer may contain as much as 10 million tons of planktonic material. This is half of the weight of the world's annual catch of fish from the entire ocean. To look at it another way, it has been estimated that a typical plankton-producing area of the sea may yield 4,000 tons of vegetable matter per square mile per year. This compares with 600 or 700 tons a year for a square mile of good Kansas wheat land.

Plankton yields vary from place to place and from season to season. The seas' total productivity is still unknown, so that it is difficult to draw meaningful over-all comparisons between the food potential of the world's continents and its oceans. Nevertheless, the few figures cited here indicate that the ocean's primary food resource, the plankton, is truly prodigious. Higher organisms that feed on the plankton and that can, in turn, be eaten by man must also be abundant. That is why many oceanographers look to the sea to meet the increasingly pressing food needs of mankind. The question is how best to develop and use the ocean's food resources. It is a question to which experts can give only tentative and incomplete answers today. The immediate need is for extensive research both to determine the nature and extent of these food resources and the principles men need to know to manage them efficiently. The first thing to consider is how the present means of exploitation, fishing, can be significantly improved.

Improving the Fisheries

According to the Committee on Oceanography of the National Academy of Sciences, the Brown committee, "Sea food is more expensive than it needs to be." The reason, the committee explained, is that "one of the most important factors that limit production of sea food is the inefficiency of fishing. With few exceptions, the philosophy of exploiting fish and shellfish has not advanced much beyond the primitive level of food hunting and gathering. There is a good deal of passiveness, of fatalism about many fisheries. The determination of where and when to fish is often influenced by a mixture of tradition, personal experience and superstition. The apparatus and techniques in common use are the products of slow advances by trial and error."

Thus whether or not men learn to take more food from the sea is largely a matter of how badly they want to do it, of how much money and effort they are willing to devote to the job, and of how willing they are to break with long-established traditions. In a recent and thorough survey of the oceans' living resources, Dr. Lionel Walford, chief of the branch of fishery biology of the United States Fish and Wildlife Service, estimates that, given today's knowledge, techniques, and traditions, the best that could be hoped for would be to increase the world catch by something less than a factor of two.

This is a pessimistic statement with which to start. Yet it should be emphasized at the outset, for it is the essence of the problem. Dr. Walford made his estimate by limiting himself to present conceptions of the seas' productivity and present knowledge of marine resources. He also limited himself to present philosophies of exploiting these resources, to existing uses of marine plants and animals and to the species now used, to known kinds of techniques and equipment and to parts of the world where they can economically be used. To overcome any one of these limitations calls for specific research and development on a scale never before attempted.

That is asking a good deal. From the viewpoint of the fisherman, fishing is a risky business. His capital includes his boat, gear, and, in the case of large integrated enterprises, shore facilities. These all represent expensive fixed costs. Yet, like a hunter's rifle, they carry no guarantee of a profitable return. The fisherman takes his chances with the vagaries of the sea. The fish he exploits vary widely in abundance. He can never be sure of getting a good haul. Even when he is successful he can't be certain of finding high enough market prices to return him even a slim profit.

Fishermen can't afford to support extensive research or to carry on experimental operations at a financial loss. There is a strong economic incentive to stick with what has worked in the past and to fish only for those animals that have proved their market value. This is reinforced by traditions that fishermen as a whole are loath to break. That is why it will take conscious determined effort, probably by government agencies, to carry out research and to develop the techniques and equipment needed to increase significantly the yields of fishing. After that will come the task of persuading fishermen to use them and of inducing the public to accept new and perhaps strange-looking animals as part of their sea-food supply.

Granted the effort, what might be done to improve the present situation? Oceanographers have some ideas, but it will take a series of research projects to outline the answer. For example, even though a modern fishing fleet is equipped with electronic navigation devices and with echo sounders and search aircraft to locate schools of fish, its fishing apparatus of nets, lines, and trawls is basically the same as fishermen have used since primitive times. It is possible that radically new and more efficient methods could be developed if the reactions of fish to different chemical, sound, or electric influences were understood. In the Caspian Sea, certain fishes have been caught by attracting them with electric lights and scooping them up with a suction pump. Perhaps this sort of thing could be developed into a new and widely practical form of fishing. The only way to find out is through research.

Electricity offers other possibilities. It has already been used fairly extensively in fresh water to attract and repel, to guide and stun fish. If it could similarly be used in the sea, it could become a powerful tool both for today's fishermen-hunters and tomorrow's sea farmers. But here there is a serious technical problem to be overcome. Sea water is a much better conductor of electricity than fresh water. Also, there are no natural boundaries in the open ocean comparable to riverbanks or shallow lake beds which confine an electric field generated in fresh water. Because of these two factors it would appear from theoretical considerations to require a great deal more power to produce an electric field that would control the movements of fish in the ocean than to produce it in a restricted body of fresh water. On the face of it, this would make electric fishing techniques too expensive to be practical. However, research could very likely find a way around this difficulty. It is possible that a low-power electric field, too weak to guide the motion of fish in a given direction, might still be able to upset their normal escape reactions so that it would be easier to net them. This could be particularly helpful in mid-water trawling, where it is easy for strong swimmers to avoid the trawl.

In West Germany, the International Electronics Laboratories of Hamburg have developed an electrical fishing system that solves the power problem by using pulses, rather than a continuous flow, of current. Although these pulses may run to several thousand amperes, power needs are cut from several thousand kilowatts to as low as ten kilowatts. The system consists basically of a three-foot diameter flexible tube with a positive electrode and a light at its underwater end. A negative electrode is suspended a few feet from this end. Fish, attracted by the light, are directed toward the tube's mouth by the current pulses. A pump sucks the fish up the tube and into the trawler's hold. Although the system is not yet ready for large-scale use, it reportedly has worked well during a number of sea trials.

Otis Smith, a Delaware fishing-fleet owner who is not averse to experimenting, also has been using electricity in fishing for menhaden. He has developed a process using relatively small amounts of power that generates a strong enough electric field to guide the menhaden. after they have been trapped in the usual way with a net. The fish are pumped on board through a hose which has a bell-shaped end made of copper that acts as an electrode. When the current is turned on, the fish rise in the net and are attracted to the copper opening of the hose. This has turned out to be a profitable technique, and Smith is using it throughout his fleet. He is continuing his research in the hope of being able to abandon the net altogether, using electricity alone to capture the menhaden. This is an encouraging indication of what might develop if the possibilities of electric fishing are thoroughly explored.

Fishermen spend much of their effort just looking for something to fish. Even with the help of echo sounders and search aircraft this is an inefficient and often discouraging task. The Brown committee notes that "one of the most effective means of reducing present fishing costs . . . would be to improve methods of predicting the times and places where fish will concentrate." To be able to do this, oceanographers will have to make extensive studies of the life cycles of fishes. They will have to trace the relations between food fish and their environment and to understand how changes in that environment affect the fish. They will have to find out the roles of food, predators, disease, and other factors affecting the fish.

These things are important to know from the viewpoint of conservation too. Without this knowledge it will be impossible intelligently to manage fisheries to make the most of them. Experts simply don't know all the relevant factors. Obvious restrictive measures such as regulating the size of the catch of adult fish are not necessarily the answer. For many fish it is not the number of fish left to spawn that determines

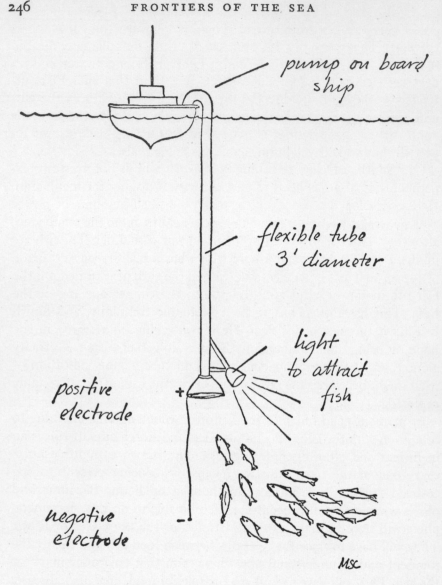

pump on board ship

flexible tube 3' diameter

light to attract fish

positive electrode

+

negative electrode

−

MSC

FIG. 49: *Electric fishing (schematic): With this system, developed in West Germany, fish are attracted by a light, and guided by an electric field toward a tube through which they are pumped into the trawler's hold.*

the size of the future population. There are many and largely unknown influences affecting the survival rate of infant fish that seem in combination to be the crucial factor. Man's fishing is only one of these. Unless a particular stock is being quite obviously overfished, there is no guarantee that leaving more adults in the water will increase the stock of young fish.

Consider the mackerel, for example. Every year these important food fish lay eggs by the billions. A relatively few adult fish would be enough to keep the species abundant if most of their offspring reached maturity. However, the mortality rate by the time the young fish reach a two-inch growth has been estimated at as much as 99.9996 per cent. The great mackerel fisheries may depend on the survival of a few ten thousandths of one per cent of the annual spawning. What is more, the difference between good and bad years as far as mackerel fishing is concerned may be a difference of only one or two ten thousandths of one per cent in that survival rate.

What determines survival? It probably is a variety of combinations of water conditions, availability of planktonic food, currents, occurrence of predators, and the like. An understanding of the life cycle and ecology of fish such as the mackerel would probably suggest a number of ways to increase survival to help achieve good fisheries year after year as well as aiding in predicting their occurrence.

Some studies of this kind have already been made, but there is as yet no comprehensive picture to guide the fisheries' biologists. There are many gaps to be filled. Until they are filled, it will be hard to predict where one should fish and even harder to outline the most efficient long-term fishing practices.

Still another area where research could help the fisherman is the identification of presently unfished useful species—a kind of biological census of the seas. Today only a handful of the hundreds of thousands of species of marine plants and animals are being used. There may be many for which it would not prove to be worthwhile fishing. Others not valuable today, could become so in the future as population grows and pressure on food resources increases. Indeed, in large areas of the world today, especially off the coasts of Asia, such a census is badly needed. In those areas the resources of even recognized food fish have not been assessed.

Along with such assessments, oceanographers point out that one needs to take a broad view of possible uses. Already other products besides human food are coming from the sea. There are fish meals for animals and a variety of special chemicals and fertilizers. These were only a token of what might be extracted if specific research efforts are made along these lines. Commenting on this, the Brown committee observes:

A number of invertebrate animals and also algae have been found to possess particularly interesting properties. Many absorb trace elements from the water and concentrate them in their tissues; some organisms are poisonous, some give off substances which repel or attract other species. These properties suggest that systematic biochemical studies may lead to the discovery of new marine products, such as insecticides, herbicides, soil conditioners, fertilizers, and medicinals including antibiotics.

None of the products of the sea will be of much use, however, unless they can be delivered to consumers at a price they can afford and in a form which they can conveniently use. This is a problem for the technologist rather than the oceanographer. But it needs to be mentioned, for, unless it is solved, it will do little good to increase the exploitation of the sea. In many maritime countries today, countries which have dense populations and chronic food shortages, only those people who live near the sea can benefit from its produce. Modern methods of preservation are too expensive for the inland population to afford. Other cheaper methods of preservation must be found if the people who need it most are to benefit from increasing the production of food from the sea. The present situation in Thailand is an example.

The Problem of Preservation

In Thailand no one needs to go hungry. This is one Asian country that historically has been noted for having an abundance of food. Yet many of the Thai people are undernourished. Their diet is long on rice and short on animal protein. The problem is largely one of distribution, of a lack of inexpensive yet effective ways of keeping food fit for eating while it is being transported in Thailand's heat. There is plenty of animal protein available, especially from the rich fishing grounds off the Thailand coast. In a large coastal city such as Bangkok, one can readily get fish and other forms of meat. Here the average diet is only about 60 per cent rice. Away from the cities, however, Thailanders may get as much as 90 per cent of their food calories from rice. The result is widespread chronic malnutrition. If a way could be found to keep fish or fish products edible for just a few days—a way that is practical and economical under Thai conditions—it would revolutionize the food situation there.

Dr. Pradisth Cheosakul of the Department of Science of the Thai

Atomic Energy Commission for Peace, is one of the research workers looking into this possibility. He points out that, as in all hot countries, the rate of spoilage of fish is appalling. Fishing boats spend a minimum of time on the fishing grounds. They try to bring their loads quickly to shore as soon as they are caught. Yet spoilage is considerable even during the few hours' journey to shore. More spoilage takes place during transportation to nearby markets. Once there, the fish must be sold within a day or it has to be thrown out for fertilizer. There is no question of transporting it to the protein-hungry inland regions.

Ice is of some help. However, Cheosakul says it melts so fast in the heat that it is no solution to the problem. Also, it is a costly product, since fuel and power are exorbitant in Thailand. Canning is no answer either. A canning industry is starting up, but it will take a long time to reach the point where cheap wholesome canned goods are available in quantity.

From purely technical considerations, Cheosakul says that refrigeration and freezing would be the best solutions. Indeed, this is what was recommended by a study team from the United Nations Food and Agricultural Organization (FAO). But after considering it thoroughly, the Thai National FAO decided that this wouldn't be feasible under present conditions. Rough roads would soon wreck transportation equipment. High capital costs would make it difficult to sell the products at an economical price or to build a refrigerated fishing fleet with a big enough capacity to do any good. Then too, what good would it do to deliver fish by refrigerated cars if there were no facilities for storing them on the receiving end? These latter facilities are too expensive to be built at this time. Thus fish brought in by refrigerated transportation would quickly rot if not sold immediately.

Under these circumstances, Cheosakul and his fellow researchers are thinking in terms of new kinds of fish products and of cheap preservation methods. Fish meal may be the answer. This type of fish product is made in many countries, although it has not yet been developed for human consumption. The meal is usually made from scraps, from whole undressed fish, and from so-called "trash" species. A meal that is both acceptable and wholesome needs to be developed for the dinner table. Cheosakul says that in his country such a meal can be made by grinding up small sardine-like fish which are already sold in the markets. These would be ground whole. Dressed sharks or mackerels could also be used.

There is still the problem of preservation. Fish oil in the meal quickly turns rancid and insects make serious infestations. Cheosakul is experimenting with heat processing. He is also looking to the possibility of irradiation. Radiation, either from radioactive materials or from atomic reactors and radiation-producing machines, can destroy insect pests and inhibit rotting. It remains to be seen whether or not it would affect the food value of the fish meal itself.

Would Thailanders eat the meal even if it can be preserved and distributed economically? Cheosakul thinks that they would, although gaining acceptance of a new food product can sometimes be quite difficult. He explains that the Thai people like spicy sauces with their rice. The fish meal could be added to these sauces, where it would enrich the protein-short rice diet. Another way of using it would be in a curry, a favorite Thai dish. Even in remote areas, small bits of fresh fish are often available locally from streams or fresh-water fishponds. With a little fresh fish to give flavor, one could thicken curry sauce substantially with fish meal and again have a nutritious rice dish.

Still another way of using the meal that would fit into traditional Thai menus would be in a kind of fish cake or paste that now is made from dried fish. Cheosakul says that although Thailanders do not generally like salty foods there is a certain dried salt fish that is considered a delicacy when baked and pounded into what amounts to a meal. It is mixed with browned garlic, sugar, and salt to give a delicate taste balance of sweet and salt. This mixture, which is often eaten with watermelon, is widely savored by rich and poor alike. It should be an easy matter to introduce fish meal in place of the baked and pounded dried fish.

The situation in Thailand is typical of that in many countries throughout the world, especially in tropical and subtropical regions. Although specific circumstances may differ from place to place, the example of Thailand illustrates how important a complement to man's efforts to increase his production of sea foods is the development of new products and of economical processing and preservation techniques.

Even in highly industrialized countries, the technology of processing can make the difference between a profitable and an uneconomical fishery. Off the northwest Pacific coast of the United States and Canada, for example, there occurs a small shrimp that formerly had not been considered especially valuable. Then machinery for peeling these little shrimp was developed and introduced. The result was a spectacular growth of a new shrimp fishery. In 1957 the states of Washington and Oregon produced two million pounds of these shrimp. Their production in 1958 was around ten million pounds. This is the kind of engineering research that will have to be undertaken to back up the work of the oceanographers if their search for new ways to exploit the ocean's living resources is to pay off at the dinner table.

To return to that search itself, it is often pointed out that when fishermen catch fish and other common forms of sea food they are harvesting the ocean's food resources several steps up the food chains. This has given rise to the recurrent question: Can the harvest be made closer to the base of the food chains? Can men profitably fish for plankton?

The Vision of Plankton Fishing

After his trip across the Atlantic on a raft, Dr. Alain Bombard reported in *Life* magazine that the plankton he had eaten "tasted like lobster, at times like shrimp and at times like some vegetable." Thor Heyerdahl, who fished for plankton from his raft *Kon-Tiki,* called it "good eating." However, there is a tremendous difference between survival rations for men adrift on a raft and a plankton fishery that could supply a sizable population regularly. Yet the idea is tantalizing.

Every step up a food chain involves losses. In the food chains of the sea, where there are a number of steps between the plankton and man, these food-energy losses are considerable. At best, there is only 20 per cent efficiency in going from grass to milk on land. But for one of the richest fishing grounds, Georges Bank, it has been estimated that it takes 1,000 pounds of phytoplankton to provide a pound of fish for market. Most of the food the higher marine animals eat goes into activity and maintenance. Only a small percentage is used for body building. In terms of energy and food value, the resources of the sea are most abundant at the level of the plankton. The question is whether, in this form, they are or can be readily available to man.

The present picture is somewhat discouraging. Plankton is very patchy, both in occurrence and in quality. One of the biggest problems would be to find ways of collecting it and concentrating it in useful quantities. In ordinary coastal waters in temperate latitudes, for example, one would have to filter a volume of water equal to something like sixty times the volume of a large living room or high school classroom to get the equivalent of a pound of beans. Then too, one would have to be constantly on guard against poisonous species and other unwanted plankters.

Of course plankton fishermen would be selective in their fisheries. They would hunt out species of high food value that occur in large masses. There is no doubt that such plankters exist. Whales and many fishes, both large and small, feed on them exclusively. Walford reports that one basking shark had a thousand quarts of copepods in its stomach when caught. The great blue whale feeds largely on krill in polar seas. These shrimp-like euphausiids must swarm in huge masses to support such large mammals. To cite a different example; in the heavily fished waters of the North Sea, the standing crop of zooplankton is estimated at over 10 million tons wet weight.

Plankton of a kind that one might consider "good eating" is abundant. But this still does not mean that it would be abundant enough in any one area to be profitably harvested in bulk. Again it is estimated that in a good year North Sea fishermen average something over 58 tons of herring per hundred hours. They would have to strain about 58 million tons of North Sea water to gather an equivalent amount of plankton.

It would take specific detailed research adequately to answer the question of whether men can hope to exploit the plankton—research on plankton itself, on possible fishing methods, and on processing. Yet, based on today's sketchy knowledge, figures like those given here have made experts bearish. When one thinks of all the water that would have to be handled to collect commercially useful amounts of plankton, the fish and other familiar food animals are seen in new perspective. They are a mass of unpaid workers doing the filtering for us, working around the clock and concentrating the planktonic food in a form convenient to man.

The present expert consensus is that the best way to harvest plankton is to let the fish do it for us. But this is not the end of the dream. Kansas wheat is very far removed from the wild grains our ancestors harvested. Likewise, through specific research and through a general understanding of life factors in the sea, it may one day be possible to breed special food crops of plankton which could be grown under controlled conditions in enclosed waters. That would be a sophisticated phase of aquaculture, the farming of the sea, and that is the challenge of the future.

Farming the Seas

If men are to develop sea farming, they will need the equivalent of the land farmer's agricultural experiment stations. These stations, usually run by governments, are the chief agency that has turned scientific knowledge into practical farming techniques. Agriculture has, of course, been developing for thousands of years. But the great advances it has made in recent times have come through the practical application of scientific knowledge. This has been the work of the experiment stations, which carry practical research to the point where it can be turned over to farmers for immediate use. There is no comparable institution for aquacultural research today. Yet such an agency is probably more vital to practical development in this field than it has been in land farming.

Agriculture could and did develop to a fair degree without the aid of science. Man is, after all, a land dweller. His domestic animals and his food crops were selected from wild stocks with which he had long been familiar. When man began developing agriculture he was not working in an unknown alien environment. He had a heritage of practical knowledge to draw upon, knowledge gained through long ages of food gathering, and common sense was at least a workable guide.

How different it is with the ocean. Here the only heritage of common-sense knowledge are the traditions of fishermen and of the few fish farmers or shellfish raisers whose total effort is insignificant compared to the fishing of wild stocks. To develop aquaculture on a scale large enough to make a meaningful contribution to the world's food supplies is a job that requires both a comprehensive and fundamental research effort to understand the alien marine environment and practical research that will turn the new knowledge into workable sea-farming techniques.

The primitive aquaculture practiced today—fish farming, shellfish raising, seaweed cultivation—illustrates this point. This type of marine cultivation generally makes use of protected waters such as bays, estuaries, swamps, brackish-water lagoons, passages protected by barrier islands, and so forth. It is from these easily enclosed areas along the edge of the sea that full-fledged sea farming will likely spread out in the future.

In the simplest operations, the sea farmer corrals marine animals into a diked or fenced enclosure, perhaps by letting them swim in with the tide, and without feeding them or fertilizing the water lets them grow for a suitable period. This at least helps protect the animals from predators and ensures that the farmer knows where they are when he wants them. In more elaborate operations the animals are fed directly or fertilizing materials are added to the water to encourage the growth of natural food organisms while predators are controlled. In some cases, the young fry of fish such as mullet or whitefish are caught in the open sea and raised in an enclosure.

Hundreds of thousands of acres are cultivated in this way throughout the world, largely along the coast lines of Asia. But there are millions of equally suitable acres that are not cultivated. One of the first things that has to come in developing aquaculture is a more general appreciation of the value of these inshore and brackish-water areas. Yet in many places, especially in western maritime countries, these areas are regarded as waste space rather than as a rich resource. They are neglected or polluted by sewage disposal or, if used at all, they are made into dumps or filled in to add a little bit to the land.

The brackish-water zone is especially valuable. Not as salty as the open sea and fed by mineral-rich water from the land, this zone is the habitat of valuable shellfish such as oysters, clams, and mussels. Many food fish also frequent these waters. Walford says that a well-managed brackish-water farm can be "handsomely profitable" even with today's limited aquacultural know-how. For one thing, it is bound to produce more fish per acre than could be caught by ordinary fishing in unfenced water. Moreover. Walford estimates that, by just using whatever animals enter the enclosure naturally and without feeding or fertilizing, over half as much animal protein can be produced as on average farmland. By careful selection of stock, removing predators, and feeding and fertilizing, he estimates that a brackish-water farm can produce more than three times as much flesh, acre for acre, as the land.

However, even the most enlightened sea farming is only a hint of the food-raising potential that has yet to be realized. The Brown committee notes that "where sea farming is practical it has developed as an art rather than as a science . . . and even at its best it is now on a level where agriculture stood around 1700." As has already been pointed out, it has been the combined work of fundamental science and practical research that has accounted for most of the progress in agriculture since that time. It is difficult today to foresee the full sweep of progress that will come in sea farming if and when a similar effort is launched in aquaculture. Nevertheless, some possible lines of development already are indicated.

One of these will be the management and cultivation of wild stocks on their own natural ground. A fairly simple step in this direction would be transplanting food fish from one area to another where conditions are more favorable for their growth. Professor Walter Garstang carried out early experiments along this line when he was director of Great Britain's Lowestoft Laboratory in the first decade of this century.

Following up some earlier Danish experiments in transplanting plaice, he moved young plaice from their normal feeding ground along the coastal banks of Holland to the Dogger Bank in the North Sea. He already knew that the growth rates of these fish varied throughout the North Sea, depending on the local food supply. His experiments showed how to use this fact to advantage. The feeding grounds off Holland, for some reason, were oversaturated with young plaice. They crowded together and competed intensively for the limited food supply. The Dogger Bank, on the other hand, was rich in food but was not heavily populated with young fish. The result was that in a little more than a year the young plaice transplanted to the Dogger area grew three times as much as those left behind.

Years later, in 1930, Garstang gave a series of lectures in which he urged transplanting as a presently practical way to increase the productivity of North Sea fisheries. He reported that "the plaice transplanted grow three, four, and even six times as rapidly as on their native shores." The International Council for the Exploration of the Sea, which represents a number of European countries, including Great Britain, appointed a special committee to investigate the suggestion. The committee estimated it would cost about £3,000 sterling to transplant one million plaice to the Dogger Bank. In two years the yield from these transplants would be anywhere from £7,400 to £10,000, while the plaice left behind would give a yield of about £1,000. Moreover, there would be an inestimable but significant favorable effect on the growth rate on the native feeding grounds, in this case the Horns Reef off Denmark. After considering all contingencies, the committee estimated that the operation would probably net a profit of £3,400 to £6,000. It recommended undertaking a large-scale transplanting experiment as soon as possible.

That was in 1931. Unfortunately the committee's recommendation was not followed up. Large-scale fish transplanting is a development for the future. But its feasibility has at least been indicated. Meanwhile the related technique of introducing valuable species into new habitats has been tried out on a limited scale with mixed results. For example, striped bass, shad, and soft-shell clams have been transplanted from the North American east coast to its Pacific shores. The North American Chinook salmon has been established in New Zealand. This is a promising way to enrich the native stocks of an area deficient in food animals. But it has yet to be perfected. The Brown committee reports that "for the few examples referred to as successes there have been many more failures, owing to a lack of adequate preparatory . . . studies, and even where there have been 'successes,' there have been no follow-up studies to measure the consequences . . ." Again a promising area for practical research has been marked out, but the definitive work has yet to be done.

Another possibility for increasing the supply of food fish, especially in the case of bottom-feeding fish, is cultivation to remove unwanted animals that compete for the food supply. Dr. Gunnar Thorson of the Zoological Museum in Copenhagen estimates that, on the feeding grounds off Denmark, starfish and other invertebrates that feed on the same food animals as do the fish leave the latter only one or two per cent of the available food supply. From man's viewpoint, these invertebrates are like weeds in a garden. If enough of them could be removed to give the fish 20 per cent instead of a mere one or two per cent of the food supply, the yield of fish in a given area could be increased ten times over what it is today.

To do this will take research. It will take fundamental studies to determine which and how many animals can be eliminated from an area without upsetting the necessary balance of life. It will take practical developmental research to produce techniques and machinery to do the weeding. The time will probably come when large areas of the continental shelf will be cultivated, as one now cultivates the land, by dragging some sort of combing or filtering device along the sea bed to weed out unwanted animals or perhaps by using some form of chemical control analogous to selective weed killers.

Still another way man may one day increase sea-food production is through the use of fertilizers to stimulate growth in unproductive areas. It would be expensive to try to add artificial fertilizers to large ocean areas. But oceanographers point out that this won't be necessary. The sea has all the nutrient minerals needed if one can get them into the sunlit zone where the phytoplankton grow. Where there is upwelling, as off the coast of Peru, minerals are constantly brought up from the depths. Plant growth is abundant and the area is rich with fish and other animal life. Oceanographers envision some kind of artificial upwelling in regions that are now deficient in phosphates and nitrates but that otherwise might support a rich population.

One scheme that is being widely and at least half seriously discussed is the so-called salt-water siphon. In most shallow parts of the sea, if a vertical pipe were set up and water started flowing through it, either upward or downward, the flow would continue indefinitely.

Surface water is usually saltier than the deep water. If the two types of water were at the same temperature, the saltier of the two would also be heavier. Surface water stays on top because it is significantly warmer than water deeper down. However, when water flowed through the pipe in either direction, it would tend to be warmed or cooled by the water surrounding the pipe. Thus bottom water started up the pipe would arrive at the surface at more or less the same temperature as the surrounding water. Because it is less salty it would be lighter than the surrounding water, so it would flow out of the top of the pipe. Likewise, surface water flowing down the pipe would be heavier than the surrounding water when it arrived at the bottom and would keep on flowing downward. In either case, once the water has been started on its way, it would keep on flowing. If done on a large scale, this would overturn enough of the water to bring substantial amounts of minerals to the surface. Another way to cause this overturning might be to use a nuclear reactor to heat the bottom water, making it rise by convection.

Schemes such as these sound almost like science fiction. Yet the Brown committee says it considers the idea of artificial upwelling "promising enough to recommend that grants be given, first for feasibility studies, then for detailed engineering development of promising proposals, and finally for pilot scale trial of devices which are developed." It has included this in its proposed ten-year program of intensified oceanographic research in the United States.

Although it could become an important aquacultural technique, artificial upwelling would not always be enough to bring fertility to a given area. As pointed out in a previous chapter, there are trace chemicals in the sea that are as important as the phosphates and nitrates. These unknown substances, which occur in minute amounts, are essential to plant growth and also have a direct effect on animals. These substances must be isolated, identified, and their effects understood if large-scale aquaculture is to be developed on a scientific basis. In some instances it may take only a small injection of one or more of these

I

substances into surface waters to increase substantially their productivity. Then too, there may be bacteria or other organisms whose activity is essential or inimical to the primary plankton growth in which future sea farmers will be interested. These organisms also need to be sought out and, where necessary, controlled or employed.

"Comprehensiveness in marine biological research is not a luxury," writes Lionel Walford in the conclusion of his survey book *Living Resources of the Sea*. He adds:

Our use of the sea as a source of food and other biological raw materials is technologically and philosophically about 200 years behind our use of the land . . . But why put up with such antiquity? Why should not technologies and philosophies advance? If we learned how to use sea resources fully and scientifically, the material rewards should well compensate for all the investment that would be required for the learning. There is no way of evaluating these rewards now. Nor can anyone honestly promise that they will in fact be forthcoming, any more than anyone could have promised the ultimate use of atomic energy. There is no simple, direct short-cut to a full understanding of the proper uses of the sea. The most economical, efficient way to reach that understanding is not to try to do it penuriously. If we really desire to exploit the sea fully, if it is knowledge that we need for that purpose . . . then we had better make the necessary costly investment and put full effort into the job of acquiring that knowledge.

So far the support of this kind of research has indeed been penurious. The regular budgets of marine research institutions have been too taut to support a comprehensive biological research program, while support from governments and the fishing industry has been spotty. The latter has tended to support research only when directly related to specific fisheries' problems and often only when one or another fishery was in trouble. Scientists sometimes were not called in until it was too late for the slow processes of research to be of practical help. However, with the increasing interest now being shown in oceanography in many countries, this situation may change. The ten-year research program suggested by the Brown committee for the United States includes a rounded biological effort. There is no need to detail the various technical recommendations here. It will suffice to report that, if carried out, the recommended program would go a long way toward laying the foundation for the comprehensive knowledge that is needed to develop scientific aquaculture.

With the population of the world rapidly increasing, certainly it would seem that mankind has no choice but to make the effort that will enable it to increase substantially its production of food from the sea. In this connection, Dr. Georg Borgstrom of Michigan State University has made some interesting calculations on the importance of the present harvest from the sea to a protein-hungry world. Borgstrom notes that sea food is sometimes dismissed as insignificant because it represents only a small proportion of the world's food calorie consumption. "What has been forgotten," he says, "is that fish account for 12 per cent of the world's animal protein. They are especially important in a country like Japan, where they make up less than three per cent of the calorie consumption, but 74 per cent of the animal protein."

According to Borgstrom's calculations, the United States would have to increase its dairy farming by 30 per cent to make up for the protein it receives from fish. In Japan, this figure would be 990 per cent; in Portugal, 165 per cent; in Norway, 143 per cent; and in the Philippines, at least 200 per cent. In this broad perspective an increase in sea food production would be much more significant for the world's diet than would an equal increase in the supply of non-protein foods.

Ocean Treasure House

While the world is hungry for protein, it is also hungry for minerals and metals. As the supplies on land are exhausted, men may turn to the sea with its great wealth of dissolved minerals to help meet their needs. Here again a good deal of research will be needed. In this case, it will be more a matter of engineering development than of fundamental oceanographic exploration. As the demand arises, as land supplies peter out, this development will undoubtedly come. At the moment and with a few exceptions, the Brown committee thinks that "the land will continue to be the more economical source of most minerals as far ahead as we can see now." However, when the time to draw upon them does arrive, the mineral resources of the oceans' 328,740,000 cubic miles of water should be virtually inexhaustible.

Taking minerals from the land is like living on one's savings. But mining the ocean is living on income. Every stream and river reaching the sea carries with it dissolved minerals. Some of these are leached from rocks or soil. Some come secondhand from man. Metals corroding in junk yards are slowly converted to other forms through the action of wind, rain, and chemical change. Eventually many of them find their way into the water flowing seaward. Rich phosphate fertilizers, mined from rock once laid down by the sea and spread on farmlands, likewise go through a series of steps to end up in the ocean treasure house. And so it goes. One way or another, the mineral wealth of the land gradually migrates to the sea. That is why men would be able to make large drafts on the ocean mineral bank without drawing down its reserves.

There is some uncertainty as to whether the sea first got its saltiness from these river sources or from volcanic upheavals and other primeval geophysical phenomena. But there is no doubt that the 7,000 cubic miles of water annually carried seaward by the world's rivers is the major source of ocean minerals today. This flow carries, among other things, an estimated 160 million tons of sodium chloride (common salt). Today there are some 166 million tons of dissolved salts in a cubic mile of sea water. Eighty-five per cent of them is common salt. There are also over 26 million tons of magnesium salts, 4 million tons of potassium sulphate, and a variety of other elements such as copper, zinc, tin, and iodine in small traces.

Here, indeed, is a vast supply of minerals for the taking. But this taking is complicated by the extreme dilution in which the materials are found. The ocean's wealth is spread so thinly, it is in no sense a "rich ore." This is compensated to some extent by the ease with which large quantities of water can be handled compared to the handling of solid ores and by the fact that minerals taken from the sea are renewed year by year. These are advantages no land mine can claim.

Many of the ocean's minerals could be extracted today as far as technology is concerned. In general, the economics of doing so are unfavorable. There is the famous example of gold, which is present in sea water to the extent of 25 tons per cubic mile. That is a lot of gold. Yet its concentration is so thin that all processes devised for extracting it have cost more than the recovered metal is worth. But where technology and economics meet, the sea is an inexhaustible mine. For example, the United States now gets all of its magnesium and 80 per cent of its bromine from sea water. Mixtures of sodium and potassium compounds, calcium and magnesium compounds, and common salt are other minerals now produced commercially from the sea. Of all of these, table salt is the one most widely taken from the sea throughout the world. This is not the only source of salt. Nevertheless, world sea-salt production runs to four or five million tons annually.

Salt was also the first mineral to be taken from the ocean. Sea salt is known to have been used by primitive man thousands of years ago. It was extracted, even as it is in many places today, through solar evaporation of sea water in shallow basins. In the past century or so, men also began extracting magnesium, chloride, bromine salts, and potash from sea salts obtained by evaporation. Probably the world's biggest "solar sea-salt plants" are the great natural evaporation basins of the Dead Sea. Here large amounts of potash are produced from the highly saline Dead Sea water. Moreover, it is estimated that with proper capital investment these basins could supply a substantial part of the world's need for potash, magnesium, and bromine at prices competitive on the world market.

However, while solar evaporation uses man's cheapest fuel—sunshine —it is a primitive and inefficient way of extracting sea salts in quantity. Thus industrial producers look to chemical and electrochemical means of extraction that, although they use more expensive fuels, are still economical. In the United States, magnesium and bromine are the principal minerals produced from sea water in this way. Here the Dow Chemical Company has been a world leader in applying modern chemical engineering to this ancient problem. It has been largely through the efforts of Dow that most American magnesium and bromine now come from the sea.

Using chemical means rather than evaporation to mine the sea is essentially the difference between removing large amounts of water from the salts and removing only the materials wanted from large amounts of water. In evaporation, one is in a sense producing quantities of water vapor for the sake of the residue of salts. After the water is evaporated, specific minerals still have to be separated from the mixture of sea salts. The chemical plant, on the other hand, takes only what is wanted out of the water and discards the rest. Large volumes of water can be quickly processed in this way. Dow's plants at Freeport, Texas, use over a million gallons of water per minute for processing and cooling.

Two Dow engineers, W. P. Schambra and Donnell A. Ballard, have used the capacity of these plants to illustrate the difficulty of producing more than the few minerals already mentioned from sea water. They point out that for technical reasons a plant handling something over a million gallons a minute is about as large a plant as can be conveniently operated. A plant this size handles some two million acre-feet of water in a year, where an acre-foot is about 326,000 gallons. Using a plant of this size as a standard production unit—that is, one sea-mineral "factory"—the engineers then estimated how many of these factories it would take to supply United States' needs for critical materials at the 1957 rate of consumption.

One factory would be enough to supply all the magnesium needed. Less than two factories would be necessary for potassium, and less than three for sulphur. But it would take 63 factories to supply fluorine compounds, and even more to produce all other minerals currently listed as critical. Schambra and Ballard noted that 63 factories would be a tremendous undertaking to build, while the numbers of factories needed to produce the remaining critical minerals were out of the question. Nickel, for example, would require 427,000 factories; copper would need 800,000; and iron, the most difficult of all, would need 10 million factories. This is why, with the present state of technology, the only critical materials taken from the sea are magnesium and some potassium. Bromine is not on the critical list.

However, the picture is not quite as bleak as it may seem. There has not yet been enough incentive to spark broad research on ways to extract minerals that are in extreme dilution. The marine plants and animals that do concentrate some of these minerals give encouragement that, if the search is made, the problem of dilution can be overcome. These organisms concentrate elements several hundred- and even several thousandfold. For example, iodine recovered from the ocean is actually extracted from seaweeds. Iodine salts themselves are so diluted in sea water that they scarcely show a trace in a chemical analysis. Yet the algae can concentrate these dilute salts enough to be an economically valuable source of the element.

Also, Schambra and Ballard have pointed out that part of the economic problem in recovering some elements is the fact that the final value of the product is less than the cost of pumping the required sea water more than a few inches high. They suggest that processes may be developed that could operate on the waste water from a bromine or magnesium plant. In that case, the pumping costs would be absorbed by the bromine or magnesium operation which would have to pump the water anyway. In like manner, it may be possible someday to design mineral-extraction plants that could use the waste brines from a distilling plant that produces fresh water from the sea. In any event, this would have to wait until the latter form of water supply is itself made economical.

Meanwhile another type of ocean "treasure" has entered the picture. Scattered about many parts of the sea floor are lumps of material rich in manganese, nickel, and copper. Although they have been known to oceanographers for almost a century, recent dredge hauls from relatively shallow depths have aroused a good deal of interest in the practical possibilities of literally mining these materials from the bottom of the sea.

Mining the Ocean Floor

There's a fortune in valuable metals literally lying about the ocean bottom waiting for someone with the techniques and the capital to come along and pick it up. But the financial risks involved are large and the profits uncertain. Oceanographers have known about these metal deposits since the *Challenger* expedition. Yet only recently has it seemed at all possible to go out and get them. John Mero, a mineral engineer, studied this possibility while he was a graduate student at the Berkeley campus of the University of California. He says it's too early to tell whether men should try to mine the sea bottom, although the indications have been at least mildly encouraging.

The metals in question are manganese, cobalt, nickel, and copper. All of these have strategic and commercial importance. Manganese in particular is vital in making steel. Moreover, many countries like the United States have no high-grade ores and have to import much of their supply. Material containing these metals is lying about many areas of the sea floor in lumps called "nodules." According to Mero's estimates, the areas with minable concentrations add up to something like 14 million square miles and contain hundreds of billions of tons of nodules. On the average, the nodules run to something like 20 per cent manganese, 15 per cent iron (not considered of importance here), and 0.5 per cent each of nickel, cobalt, and copper. Some of the richer deposits may yield as much as 45 per cent manganese, 1 per cent cobalt, 1.4 per cent nickel, and 1.8 per cent copper as an area average.

The nodules are roughly potato-shaped and usually run from about ½ to 10 inches in diameter, with occasional larger ones being found in deep dredge hauls. Mero points out, however, that the dredges used so far will pick up only relatively small objects. There may be many more large nodules than the dredge hauls indicate. It would take a thorough investigation with deep-water cameras to find out.

The manganese comes from several sources. Some of it is leached out of the land and carried to the sea by rivers. Some of it is thrown up by undersea eruptions that pour out volcanic debris into the oceans. Some of it is leached directly out of undersea rocks. Once in the water, the manganese quickly reacts with dissolved oxygen and, as part of the endless chemical activity of the sea, precipitates out as manganese dioxide on anything handy. One can find this deposit all over the ocean bottom. It turns up as small grains in deep-sea oozes and clays. If there is any small object lying about, such as an old shark's tooth, a whale's ear bone, or just a lump of clay, it will precipitate around that and form a nodule. And as the manganese dioxide forms itself into nodules, it carries bits of cobalt, nickel, and copper along with it. In this way the nodules get their mixed cargo of valuable metals.

The nodules will keep on growing as long as there is manganese available and they are in contact with the water. Mero says they would probably grow at an almost "explosive" rate if the sea in their neighborhood were saturated with this metal. But that rarely happens. No one knows how long it has taken the nodules so far examined to grow, although some estimates set the growth rate as slow as one millimeter in a thousand years. They won't grow at all if they're covered by sediments and cut off from the water. This may be a significant factor in their development. Since sediments shift about with ocean currents, some nodules may alternately be exposed and covered. Others may be exposed only briefly when they first start to form, and so forth.

However long it took them to grow, there is a thick peppering of nodules in many places today. They were first discovered during the *Challenger* expedition. About twenty-five years later the United States Bureau of Fisheries' ship *Albatross* also found large amounts of nodules at widely spread locations. If these nodules were lying about the land as they are about the sea floor, they would be a tempting prize for commercial mining companies. But thousands of feet of overlying sea water are a formidable barrier. The discoveries of the *Albatross* and the *Challenger* were all but forgotten until the International Geophysical Year. (See Plate 21.)

In 1957, ships from Scripps Institution of Oceanography again dredged the deep bottom of the Pacific as part of their IGY program and again brought up quantities of nodules. This time the oceanographers were curious as to the possible commercial value of such a seemingly rich prize. They consulted Dr. Herbert E. Hawkes, Professor of mineral exploration at Berkeley, who turned the problem over to Mero.

Basically Mero had to answer two questions: What are the technical and economic prospects for dredging up the nodules? After getting them, what are the prospects for processing and selling the metals at a profit? These are tough questions. Mero notes wryly that the oceanographers asked an engineer to study the problem because they wanted someone who wasn't convinced the job was hopelessly uneconomical to start with. After long months of study he came up with a report in January 1959 that was cautiously optimistic on both counts.

The manganese nodules, which he describes as "dirty-brown to earthy-black, friable, and easily scratched by a knife," can probably be processed by well-known techniques. Getting them up from the sea floor is another matter. Mero suggests two possible methods. First, he points out that the usual deep-sea research technique of dragging a metal dredge over the bottom could be used but might have practical disadvantages, such as low production rate and lack of control of the dredge on the ocean floor. As an alternative he suggests a kind of under-water "vacuum cleaner" that would scoop up the nodules as it runs over the bottom and pump them to a barge on the surface.

This latter sounds like an item out of the property department of a science fiction movie producer. With its suction arms reaching thousands of feet below the sea, it would probably look like one too! While no such machine exists, Mero's suggested model is based on components in industrial use today. For example, some mining operations involve pumping sizable boulders with water. Some oil operations use electric motors submerged in thousands of feet of a fluid more corrosive than sea water.

Here is how the device would work at sea. Most of the weight would be supported by buoyant tanks set a few hundred feet down to avoid the turbulent surface layers of the water. These would house the principal motors as well. Much of the remaining weight would be supported by a second set of floats at the surface. Waves would wash over these floats and they could serve as markers and moorings for the crew at the surface. Suspended from these various floats would be the long pipeline of the hydraulic dredge. This would end in two fanned-out arms that travel over the ocean bed. Only about one per cent of the total weight would bear down on the sea floor as these arms moved about. Thus they could easily ride up over obstacles and would not fall suddenly if they slipped over a cliff. One further advantage of this rig—if a storm came up, the gear could be left floating in the sea. It wouldn't drift far, since most of it would be out of reach of the wind and waves. After the blow passed, it could be located again by radio signal sent out by a robot transmitter.

Mero points out that this and other aspects of his study have to be examined thoroughly and in detail by a sizable research effort before

1*

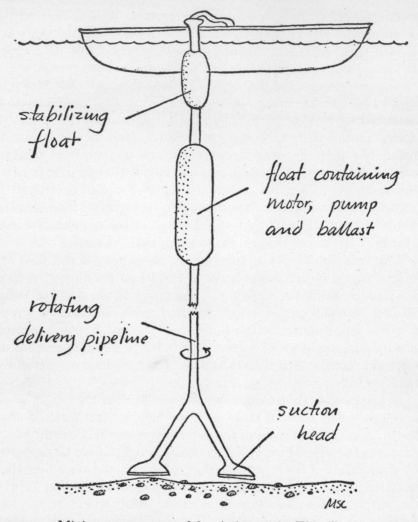

stabilizing
float

float containing
motor, pump
and ballast

rotating
delivery pipeline

suction
head

MSC

FIG. 50: *Mining manganese nodules (schematic): This illustrates one of John Mero's schemes for a deep-water hydraulic dredge.*

one can know if they are workable. The most that his study has done is to indicate enough promise to justify such a larger project. He also cautions that the treasure of the nodules will be costly to acquire. They can be mined economically only from favorable deposits at relatively shallow depths found within a few hundred miles of the coast, at least at first. There are indications that such deposits exist off the east coast of the United States.

He adds that the manganese would not be worth recovering for its own sake at today's prices. But the cobalt and nickel would be profitable, and the manganese could be had as a by-product. On the other hand, the countries now supplying manganese ore are believed to want to do much of the processing themselves in the future so they can have a more valuable product for the world market. Development of the nodule resources would give consumer countries, such as the United States, an alternative source of raw-material supply.

Mero estimates that processing costs of a ton of average-grade nodules might be around $22, while the gross value of the recovered metal products at September 1958 prices would be about $43. Depending on depth and concentration of the deposit, it should cost about $5 a ton to mine the nodules. If the hydraulic dredge proves to be practical, however, he thinks mining costs could be as low as $2 a ton in depths up to 14,000 feet of water. Transportation charges to the processing center could add from $1 to $8 a ton to this cost. It would take $10 million capital investment to set up a 500-ton-of-ore-per-day operation. This would be economically feasible only for high-grade deposits at shallow depths. Mero estimates that an efficient and profitable operation would mine nodules at a rate of 5,000 tons per day. This would take a capital investment of something like $70 million. All of these estimates are tentative, being based on the limited information available today. But, they at least indicate the probable order of magnitude of the costs.

So far American mining and processing companies have been unenthusiastic. In general, they seem to regard the prospect of recovering ore from the bottom of the sea as a highly uncertain business. For example, the Freeport Sulphur Company analyzed some of the nodules and found that they probably could be worked by the same process used with the company's regular Cuban ores. But company spokesmen reportedly have said they have no interest in trying to mine the sea. Similarly an officer of the marine salvage division of the Merritt-Chapman & Scott Corporation said that, at this stage, recovering nodules from the sea bed seemed an impractical proposition. Statements like this reflect the experience of an industry that has to live with economic risks and marginal operations. Future research may confirm these assessments or it may show them to have been overly conservative. In any event, the Brown committee has earmarked $2,600,000 for such research in its recommended ten-year program.

There are also legal difficulties to be resolved. Mero says that it might be wise to call an international conference to lay down the ground rules before any large-scale open-sea mining is attempted. He points out that there is a legal problem here to match that raised by the exploration of space. Who owns the mineral rights under the high seas? Can any one nation or group of nations stake a claim and fend off all comers? Could a mining company be guaranteed any kind of lease, license, or title by its national government? Or will an international agency, perhaps within the United Nations, take over jurisdiction? Similar questions are raised when one thinks in terms of future cultivation and management of marine food resources beyond the territorial waters of any one nation. As men begin more and more to exploit the resources of the sea, the oceans that once were barriers between continents will become a common resource demanding international management.

ELEVEN

The New Oceanography

THE SCIENCE of the sea is now entering a new phase of its century-long development. It is a phase marked by increased research activities throughout the world, by enlarged capabilities for exploration, and especially by the emphasis being placed on international aspects of the science. The oceans belong to no one nation. They are a great resource to be shared by all mankind. The new oceanography is dedicated to developing the principles upon which wise international management of this resource may be based.

History may conveniently date this new phase of oceanography's development from the International Oceanographic Congress held at United Nations headquarters in New York from August 30 to September 11, 1959. It was sponsored by the American Association for the Advancement of Science, the United Nations Educational, Scientific, and Cultural Organization (UNESCO), and the Special Committee on Oceanographic Research (SCOR). There were over a thousand registrants from thirty countries, representing all fields of science associated with the sea. It was the first time in the history of the science that experts in all its phases met to share ideas and discuss common problems. Dr. Roger Revelle, who was president of the congress, remarked that such a comprehensive and internationally representative meeting had been beyond the expectations of oceanographers of his generation.

In many ways, the brightest prospect to come out of this conference was that of increased international co-operation in attacking the research problems of the sea. Such co-operation is much more than an idealistic phrase to oceanographers. They see it as a necessity for achieving their goal of a comprehensive understanding of the oceans. They realize that the earth's water envelope is too big for any one nation to tackle. Moreover, as Revelle pointed out in his opening address, they are aware of their responsibility to provide all mankind with the knowledge needed to exploit the ocean's resources.

The kind of co-operative effort the oceanographers envision was begun during the International Geophysical Year. But the IGY has ended. The question now facing oceanographers is how to put international research on a permanent basis. One mechanism for doing this already exists in the SCOR organization, which was set up to explore ways of continuing co-operative research after the IGY.

The first project being considered is a survey of the Indian Ocean, the least known of all the major seas. No attempt is being made to parcel out specific assignments, for the project is strictly voluntary. However, any country or institution interested in exploring this region is being encouraged to co-ordinate its efforts with those of other investigators to form a meaningful over-all study. The project has, at this writing, been making satisfactory headway, with a number of Indian Ocean expeditions planned for 1960 and beyond by American, British, Indian, Soviet, and other oceanographers.

On the other hand, SCOR has been hampered in its early planning by uncertainty as to where and how it will find money for its projects. Its parent body, the International Council of Scientific Unions, is an organization of scientists with little money of its own. Funds for the IGY came largely from national governments. It is hoped that the various national programs in oceanography will be planned to include participation in SCOR activities. In this connection it should be noted that the special committee on oceanography of the National Academy of Sciences (the Brown committee) has included United States participation in such international research as part of its recommended ten-year oceanographic program.

The expansion of oceanographic exploration is thus taking place within an international context that is at least widely recognized even if it is not yet spelled out in a formal enterprise like the IGY. Let's now consider briefly some of the factors involved in the new oceanography.

The Underwater "Balloon"

Of all the new capabilities envisioned for oceanographic researchers, the most dramatic is the prospect of descending to the remotest depths. The challenge and adventure of exploring the bottom of the sea where until recently the terrific pressures effectively excluded man are the oceanographer's equivalent of a voyage to the moon. Already bathyscaphes have reached a depth of some 6,000 fathoms. These remarkable deep-diving machines are pointing the way to advanced machines with even greater diving capabilities that will enable men to explore virtually all parts of the ocean basins.

To dive to the bottom of the deep sea, man is employing a device that first enabled him to reach the heights of the stratosphere—the free balloon. Indeed, the word "bathyscaphe" itself is a combination of Greek words meaning "depth ship." With a float full of gasoline to provide buoyancy, disposable ballast for controlling ascent and descent, and a pressure-resisting air-conditioned cabin for passengers, the bathyscaphe is very much the undersea analogue of the early stratospheric balloon. What is more, both types of vehicles were introduced by the same man—Professor Auguste Piccard, the famous Swiss scientist-engineer.

One of the earlier-model bathyscaphes, the *F.R.N.S.* 3, has been used for several years by the French Navy. In it Commander Georges Houot and engineer Lieutenant Pierre Willm became the first men to reach the ocean bottom over 2,000 fathoms down when they dived to 13,287 feet off Dakar on February 15, 1954. Piccard's latest bathyscaphe, the *Trieste*, has gone into service with the United States Navy.

The concept of the bathyscaphe began to form in Piccard's thinking when he was a student at the Zurich Polytechnic School. He became intrigued with deep-sea exploration and wondered how a pressure-resistant cabin for human observers could safely be carried to great depths and returned. He says it never occurred to him to suspend the cabin from a surface ship by cable, as William Beebe and Otis Barton suspended their bathysphere. Instead, the principle of the balloon seemed ideal. He envisioned suspending the heavy cabin from a buoyant float. For diving, this would be pulled down by the weight of ballast, which would be jettisoned when one wished to return to the surface. However, high-altitude ballooning was in vogue in those days. Piccard had his first ride in such a pressure-resisting cabin suspended from a buoyant float in 1931, when he made his famous balloon ascents to an altitude of some ten miles to study cosmic rays.

"The evolution of my thought is clear," he says in his book *Earth, Sky, and Sea.* "Far from having come to the idea of a submarine device by transforming the idea of the stratospheric balloon, as everyone thinks, it was, on the contrary, my original conception of the bathyscaphe which gave me the method of exploring the high altitudes. In short, it was a submarine which led me to the stratosphere."

The bathyscaphe did not remain long in the background. In the years before World War II the Swiss inventor made engineering studies of his proposed submersible. They were supported by the Belgian research foundation, Fonds National Belge de la Recherche Scientifique, the same institution that provided funds for the stratospheric balloon, which had been dubbed the F.N.R.S. in appreciation. War intervened. But toward the end of 1945, Professor Piccard was again working on his dream ship with Belgian support. Under his direction the world's first deep-diving submarine took shape—the bathyscaphe F.N.R.S. 2, named in memory of the stratospheric balloon.

In 1948 the F.N.R.S. 2 was tested with the help of the French Navy. It proved the feasibility of the bathyscaphe concept but showed up certain defects in design. For one thing, it couldn't be towed. It was carried to sea in the hold of its mother ship. Observers had to seal themselves into the cast-steel cabin while it was in the hold. Then the bathyscaphe was placed in the water and its float filled with gasoline. Upon their return the observers had to wait until the gasoline had been removed and the bathyscaphe lifted back into the ship's hold. This made for difficult handling, especially when it came to filling and emptying the float in any but relatively calm waters.

Not being designed for towing, the float of the F.N.R.S. 2 was damaged when weather conditions prevented the mother ship from taking her aboard and forced this procedure. The Belgian foundation, this time in co-operation with the French Navy, undertook to build a modified bathyscaphe using the same cabin. This was the F.N.R.S. 3. Piccard was retained as a consultant.

Meanwhile, in the spring of 1952 a group of citizens of the Italian city of Trieste invited the professor to head a project to build a bathyscaphe in their city. He accepted, leaving the F.N.R.S. 3 project. The latter bathyscaphe was then built, tested, and put into operation under the direction of Commander Houot and Lieutenant Willm. Her construction was completed in June 1953. Piccard's *Trieste* was ready for testing in August 1953. Thus the world acquired two submarines capable of carrying men to abyssal depths.

Unlike the original bathyscaphe, the new models could be loaded with gasoline in port and towed to their diving sites. Observers could enter the cabin while it was in the water. A watertight passageway lead-

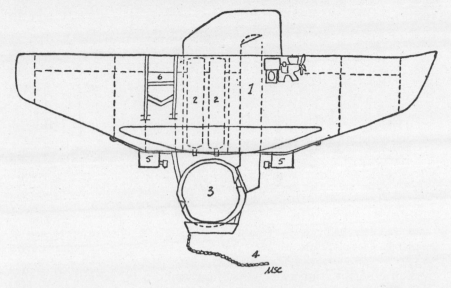

FIG. 51: *The bathyscaphe F.N.R.S. 3: 1—entryway to cabin; 2—shot silos; 3—cabin; 4—guide chain; 5—ballast bunkers; 6—fitting for disposable batteries.*

ing through the float from the upper deck was provided for this purpose. The cabin of the *Trieste* differs from the earlier model in that it is made of forged steel, a stronger form of the metal than a casting. Otherwise, and except for relatively minor technical details, the two submersibles are similar.

To build a bathyscaphe, one has first of all to have a stout cabin, far stronger than needed to ascend into the high atmosphere. Pressures of many tons per square inch have to be withstood in the ocean's depths. The *F.N.R.S. 2* cabin is a sphere 6 feet 7 inches in diameter, with a wall thickness of 3.54 inches, increasing to 5.91 inches around the port-hole and hatch openings. It was made of steel cast in two hemispheres and joined together by a watertight clamping device.

The portholes were a special problem. They have to be both clear and pressure-resistant. Glass was no good. Even quite thick blocks of glass failed under simulated deep-sea pressures. Then someone suggested Plexiglass. Professor Piccard tried it and found it an ideal material. It is clear and strong, yet pliable enough to withstand the required pressures without cracking. The portholes on the *F.N.R.S. 2* cabin are 5.91 inches thick and shaped as frustums of cones with outside diameters of 15.75 inches and inner diameters of 3.94 inches. This

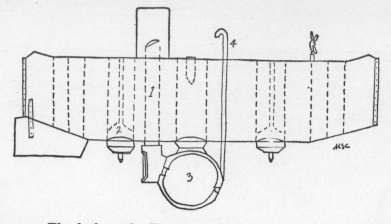

FIG. 52: *The bathyscaphe* Trieste: 1—*entryway*; 2—*shot silos*; 3—*cabin*; 4—*snorkel*. (See also Plate 9.)

gives an observer a far wider view than would a cylindrical peephole with a diameter of 3.94 inches.

Given the cabin, one still has to support it in the sea. The Beebe-Barton bathysphere was suspended from a ship by cable. This has its dangers, for the cable may break, with fatal consequences. Designed along the lines of a balloon, a bathyscaphe tends to bob back to the surface if anything goes wrong with a vital mechanism. The lifting power is provided by a float divided into several compartments filled with gasoline, which is lighter than sea water. Other light and relatively incompressible materials, such as the metal lithium, could be used. Gasoline was chosen because of its relatively low cost, convenience in handling, and availability at the time.

The float is built in such a way that the gasoline is always in communication with the outside sea water. As it sinks, sea water enters the bottom of the float, compressing the gasoline somewhat and ensuring that the pressure inside and outside the float is the same. Thus the float itself can be built of thin sheet metal, saving both money and weight.

The buoyant submersible is made to dive by loading it with ballast. This has to be arranged in such a way that it can readily be dropped. If anything goes wrong with the ballast controls, they must, in engineer's language, "fail safe." Piccard met this requirement by holding the ballast with electromagnets. As long as the current flows through the magnets' circuits, the ballast is held. Should the current fail, ballast is immediately dropped and the bathyscaphe shoots to the surface.

There are several types of ballast. The primary system consists of steel or iron shot contained in cylindrical silos which end in narrow orifices. An electric current magnetizes the shot in these orifices, preventing its falling through. When the current is turned off, the shot pours out freely. This is the system for fine ballasting control. Other forms of ballast, the so-called "safety ballast," are carried to ensure that enough weight can be dropped in an emergency to enable the bathyscaphe to return to the surface. This may be in the form of bunkers filled with lead, scrap iron, or even gravel, whose compartments are held shut by electromagnets. Expendable pieces of heavy equipment may also be held on by electromagnets.

In the bathyscaphe now used by the French Navy—the F.N.R.S. 3— the large batteries that supply most of the power are held on by electromagnets. They can be and have been dropped when the current to their magnets fails, lightening the submersible by some 2,640 pounds. There are also two tons of lead shot carried in two bunkers. The *Trieste* has a simpler ballast arrangement. It carries only nine tons of iron shot in two large silos. However, the silos, which together weigh two tons, can themselves be dropped to provide safety ballast.

Piloting a bathyscaphe is a matter of delicate balance. Fully loaded with ballast and gasoline, the craft barely floats at the surface. Only a slight additional weight is needed to take it down. The F.N.R.S. 2 did not even need this. With observers in the cabin and a full load of gasoline, it slowly sank. Its successors accomplish this maneuver by taking on a slight additional water ballast. In the F.N.R.S. 3, the passage leading from the deck to the cabin is flooded when one is ready to dive. In the *Trieste*, the compartments at either end of the float are used as water-ballast tanks. They are opened in order to begin a dive.

As the bathyscaphe sinks, it picks up speed. There are two reasons for this. First, the gasoline is compressed the deeper it goes, so that the bathyscaphe loses some of its original volume and buoyancy. Indeed, the compressibility of the gasoline is one reason a bathyscaphe carries so much disposable ballast. Jacques Piccard, the professor's son and co-worker, notes that when they dived to over 10,000 feet they had to release over three tons of ballast to compensate for the loss of buoyancy owing to compression of the gasoline. Also, the water generally gets colder as one descends. The attendant cooling of the gasoline causes it to contract. If the pilot does not want to land heavily on the bottom, he jettisons a little ballast every so often to regulate his speed of descent.

On the other hand, he may drop too much ballast and stop dead or even start going back up. In that case, he can siphon off a little gasoline. Again, as he descends he may encounter a much colder layer of water. Until it has cooled, the gasoline will have increased buoyancy in the colder water because this water is more dense than that nearer the surface. The bathyscaphe may be too buoyant to enter this cold layer. In that case, the pilot can either wait for his gasoline to cool or can siphon some of it off.

As he nears the bottom, the pilot jettisons ballast to effect a soft landing or to halt the craft a few feet off the sea floor. Here the guide chain comes into play. It is either a heavy chain or steel rope suspended beneath the hull by an electromagnetic clamp. The end of the chain is the first thing to touch bottom. As the bathyscaphe settles, the weight of the chain is gradually taken up by the bottom. If the bathyscaphe is properly trimmed, it will come to a stop when part of the chain lies on the sea bed. The pilot now can move the bathyscaphe along by means of propellers driven by low-power electric motors or allow it to drift with a current if there is one. In these operations the guide chain helps hold the craft steady. If the bathyscaphe is properly trimmed, the pilot has only to drop the guide chain to begin rising to the surface when it is time to return. If this does not work, he still has many tons of ballast he can jettison.

With its built-in safeguards, the bathyscaphe has proved itself a reliable vehicle. In Piccard's words, it is "a dependable device, in which the father of a family may trust himself without anxiety." Indeed, since a breakdown in the electric controls, even if it is only a burned-out fuse, releases ballast, it can sometimes be more difficult to go down than to come back up.

What is it like to dive in a bathyscaphe? Let's, in imagination, accompany Jacques Piccard to the bottom of the sea as he recounts (in a lecture given at the Massachusetts Institute of Technology) a dive he made with his father to a depth of 10,335 feet:

Now that you have an idea of how the bathyscaphe works, how it may go down to the bed of the ocean and safely rise again, how the cabin is built; if you wish, you may accompany us to the bed of the Mediterranean. The Trieste is waiting for us in the little harbour of Castellammare, near Naples. It is full of gasoline and is floating, like an ordinary submarine, owing to the air-containers placed at the two extremities of the raft. The ballast is already in its place and, in the cabin, all is ready for the submersion. Of course, in order to attain the depth we desire to reach today, it will be necessary for us to be towed on sea-level for a certain distance. Suppose we decide to go to a depth of 10,335 feet, as I did with my father on the 30th September 1953 . . . We leave Castellammare in the evening, in order to arrive in the vicinity of the Island of Ponza in the morning. The greatest difficulty, when the sea is rough, is to embark onto our little submarine. In order to enter into the cabin, it is necessary to climb down the float. For this purpose, there is a five yard ladder, which enables us to reach the cabin.

The first thing we see from the cabin windows is the marvellous blue of the sea-water, but, on account of the waves, the cabin is in continual movement and we have no wish to remain too long in this position. We know that the calm of the descent will begin only when we leave the sea-level behind us. I quickly take the telephone and give the last instructions to our assistants who have remained on sea-level and, at the same time, my father is busy controlling some parts of the apparatus. We must shut the door; fortunately modern technic rapidly advances. William Beebe tells us, in his interesting book, of all the difficulties he encountered in the closing of his bathysphere door; the French bathyscaphe too, using the first cabin built by my father, requires 16 bolts and much time to close them; our present cabin may be closed and made absolutely water-tight, with just one bolt.

At last, we may give the order to open the two taps of the air-container, that is to say the water ballast, and then the bathyscaphe begins to go down. The first impression we have is of the beautiful and complete calm of the water under sea-level. It is somewhat strange to notice that upon leaving humanity one immediately enters into the calm. Little by little, obscurity envelops us. We are now at 150 fathoms and visibility is almost zero, but you must not forget that it is nine o'clock in the morning; if the sun were higher in the heavens, say when it is nearer noon, or during another season of the year, some visibility would be possible up to about 300 fathoms.

Now, in order to see something from the bathyscaphe windows, we must put on the electric light, which we do, and immediately all is fairyland; we have now four searchlights with mercury gas which are working with a 500 volt storage-battery; the water [under the beam of] the electric light again becomes a magnificent blue and to our great surprise we see snow rising all around us. Finally we see with our own eyes the famous plankton that oceanologists have so often spoken about in books; thousands of kinds of jelly-fish of different aspects and thousands of kinds of other sea animals, quite minuscule, all floating in the water reflecting the light from our lamps, which gives us the idea that they are rising; but we are going down.

We could remain for an untold number of hours looking through our windows but, as this is our first submersion at a great depth, we must *continually* control our instruments.

The pressure gauges which tell us the depth we have attained, are continually showing a higher pressure. The red light of our *tachometer* shows us our descending speed (now we are going down at the rate of two feet per second); we hear a little whistle: it is the oxygen leaving the cylinder and entering the cabin—this is necessary to keep us alive, but the most important thing is to absorb the CO_2, which is done through the soda-boxes. With great care we examine to see that no single drop of water has entered the cabin, but all is in order and we continue our downward journey normally.

Twenty minutes have passed since we left the water-level and we are now at a depth of 600 fathoms, the same depth we attained one month previously at Capri.

The *Trieste* now enters a world completely unknown to it, but everything is going normally. For the moment the *snow-planktons* have ceased but we have not yet seen any fish. The immensity of the sea appears completely empty. Seven hundred fifty fathoms, 1,000 fathoms, we then look at the registration manometer and find that our speed is about three feet per second. This is too rapid as we know that we are approaching the bed of the sea and we wish to make a safe and satisfactory landing. In order to reduce the speed of the downward journey we cut the ballast current and, through the window, we see part of the ballast descending to the bed of the sea quicker than we are going and immediately the speed is reduced. After some more minutes we arrive at a depth of 10,000 feet. We know that from one moment to another we shall touch the ground and, in fact, by the light of our projector we are finally able to distinguish the bed of the sea.

10,335 feet below sea-level; that is where we are now and what do we see? Unfortunately our speed was still too great and that day we entered partly into the mud. One of the windows could not then be used for observation but in the meantime we had the good fortune of seeing the underground of the sea, part of the sediment which was formed some hundreds of thousands of years before.

Through the other window we could see the sea water but not the ground. During other submersions and especially in the Gulf of Naples, we saw the bed of the sea quite flat, it may be compared to a desert, it is almost like a vast extent of sand. Near Vesuvius, we found much lava and mud and the water was often of a muddy color but, when we descended farther from the coast and away from the Vesuvius volcano, the water was of a limpid blue. Several times, on the golden sands, we saw numerous small holes, but were not able to distinguish anything in them. Quite near to us we could see small crabs, peacefully walking along the bed of the sea. We distinguished some star-fish and in the water some jelly-fish were often floating, but ordinary fish were seldom seen.

Suddenly, the head of a small fish emerges from one of these numerous sand-holes. It seems to be looking at the bathyscaphe and apparently did not judge it to be too dangerous as it came out of its hole. It was a fish similar in size to a normal sardine, probably it was a kind of *gobbius,* and it began to swim. After one minute many other small fish came out of their holes. In order to make a little survey we put our propellers into action and the bathyscaphe began to move along the bed of the sea. Immediately all the fish disappeared into their sand-holes.

During one of these surveys, we noticed a submarine telephone cable lying on the bed of the sea. We thought of humanity above sea-level, at both ends of this cable; humanity with its troubles and anxieties and of the rapidity of modern life, while we were living momentarily a life of calm and peace.

On another occasion, we landed in the *Trieste* on a sea-weed coral reef, only I must say that the coral was not so beautiful as that which we see in a fashionable jeweller's shop window, there were just small pieces of sea-weed coral here and there . . .

Time passes and we must think of the ascension. For the last time we get rid of some ballast and see the bed of the sea slowly disappear under the bathyscaphe. The journey back to sea-level is made without unforeseen incidents. At 500 fathoms above the sea-bed (at 1,250 fathoms below the level of the water) we could see a phosphorescent fish, about six inches long, but it was too far from us to be well distinguished.

We continue to rise another 500 fathoms and then we see on the pressure gauge that our rising speed is now almost 3 feet per second.

On account of the expansion of the gasoline, our weight is becoming less and less and so our speed will continue to increase. At about 150 fathoms from the surface we again begin to see daylight, at first very faintly, but the intensity quickly increases.

At 100 feet from the surface, the water is almost crystal clear. Suddenly the bathyscaphe commences to roll from side to side and we know that we have returned to sea-level. By our compressed-air system, it is possible to drive away the water from the entrance and exit tube and, this done, we are able to climb up and reach the deck of the bathyscaphe—our deep-sea expedition is now terminated.

My father's principal wish when he constructed his two bathyscaphes was to give oceanographic science a new possibility of research and the first possibility for man to go down, and see with his own eyes, life and conditions on the bed of seas and oceans. This desire has been attained.

With this machine at their disposal oceanographers now can begin to study directly the deep waters and abyssal bottom that they formerly could probe only indirectly from the surface. They will be able to observe deep-water life forms and to study experimentally the properties of the water masses, such as the transmission of sound through them. The latter is one of the principal reasons that the United States Navy is interested in the bathyscaphe. It has bought the *Trieste* and acquired the services of Auguste and Jacques Piccard. The *Trieste* now is based at the Naval Electronics Laboratory in San Diego, California, where Dr. Andreas B. Rechnitzer is oceanographer in charge of her operations.

Both the *F.N.R.S. 3* and the *Trieste* are only the forerunners of the different kinds of vehicles with which men will explore the depths. They both have a limit of about 20,000 feet, set primarily by the strength of their cabins and the capability of their ballasting systems. Stronger bathyscaphes that can reach the bottoms of the deepest trenches are on the way. The French Navy is planning a model that will have this capability. The United States Navy is also interested in reaching such depths. The Soviets are thought to be building a bathyscaphe for extreme depths too. The bathyscaphe has only limited maneuverability, however, being an inherently heavy craft propelled by relatively weak battery-driven motors. Other more versatile devices are on the horizon.

[The depth limits above are estimates which contain large safety factors rather than absolute barriers. Diving tests may show a craft to be able to dive much deeper with safety. Indeed, the U. S. Navy has reported that, on January 7, 1960, Jacques Piccard and Lt. Donald Walsh, took the *Trieste* to what was then the record depth of 24,000 feet in the Marianas Trench. The navy subsequently reported that Piccard and Walsh reached the bottom of the trench at 35,800 feet on January 23, where they saw evidence of life.]

Beyond the Bathyscaphe

The Piccards have for some time been thinking in terms of what they call a mesoscaphe—a "middle-depth ship" to operate down to about 6,000 feet. Where the bathyscaphe is an underwater balloon, the mesoscaphe would be a kind of underwater helicopter. Since it would have to bear only relatively moderate pressures, it could be built of light materials—aluminum, or even Plexiglass for full visibility—and designed to be slightly buoyant. Then by means of an electrically driven propeller it would be made to sink. As in the bathyscaphe, two counter-rotating horizontal propellers would be used to maneuver it horizontally.

If one merely wanted to go down to a specified level and explore horizontally, perhaps in studying the bottom where it is shallower than 6,000 feet, the vertical propeller for up-and-down movements could be dispensed with. Instead, small amounts of ballast could be carried to bring the mesoscaphe to the desired depth. When this level was reached, the pilot could trim his vehicle to float at that depth, perhaps a few feet off the bottom, by dropping the right amount of ballast. Among other things, this would have the advantage of conserving the batteries, since these would not have to drive the vertical propeller. As in the case of the bathyscaphe, the pilot would only have to jettison a little additional ballast to return to the surface.

Meanwhile the quality of high-strength steels has been steadily increasing since Piccard built his bathyscaphe cabins. Dr. W. N. Delenk of the Anderson Nichols Company, the Boston, Massachusetts, firm that built the Texas Tower radar platforms, has investigated some of the latest special-purpose steels with a view to designing improved deep-diving vehicles. He has found steels so strong that he thinks it is now possible to build a sphere 20 feet in diameter with a four-inch-thick shell that would be adequate to depths of 20,000 feet. Moreover, a steel sphere of these dimensions would be self-buoyant to such an extent that the floats of the earlier bathyscaphes could be dispensed with.

If one wished to go below 20,000 feet, then a somewhat thicker and heavier shell would be needed. In this case, some sort of float would have to be attached to give the craft its necessary buoyancy. Here again the materials situation has improved since the original bathyscaphes were built. In those days, the light metal lithium was hard to come by. Now, Delenk says, there is a good enough supply of the metal to consider using it for a bathyscaphe to reach the greatest depths. This metal would have the double advantage over gasoline of compactness and relative incompressibility. However, cost would still be a consideration for lithium is quite expensive.

Still another deep-diving craft is the Aluminaut abyssal submarine being developed at the Southwest Research Institute. The Aluminaut is fulfilling a dream held independently by two men who have joined forces in its development. One of them is Dr. Edward Wenk, Jr., chairman of Southwest's Department of Engineering Mechanics. The other is J. Louis Reynolds, executive vice-president of the Reynolds Metals Company, which is sponsoring the project. Both men have long envisioned developing a true submarine that would reach substantial if

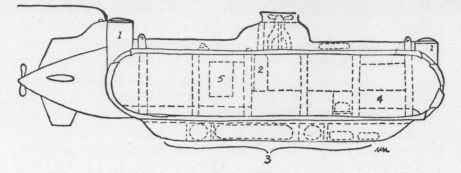

FIG. 53: *The Aluminaut:* 1—*hatches;* 2—*shot ballast;* 3—*droppable keel containing instruments, solid ballast, and submergence tanks;* 4—*two observers;* 5—*pilot.*

not the greatest depths in the sea. This is what the Aluminaut is designed to do.

The machine is being developed with co-operation from the United States Navy and the various American oceanographic establishments. It will be made of aluminum. And, unlike the bathyscaphe, it will be almost as maneuverable as a conventional submarine, although its pressure-resistant hull will enable it to dive many times deeper than present-day fleet submersibles. The model currently being developed will be designed to withstand pressures at 22,500 feet and perhaps deeper. But it will be operated no deeper than 18,000 feet to allow a margin of safety. It should have a range of 100 miles.

The first Aluminaut will be 48 feet in over-all length, with a 30-foot cylindrical pressure hull. The latter will have a 7-foot inside diameter and a shell made of 6-inch aluminum plate. This will be big enough to house a pilot and two observers with as much as 3,400 pounds of associated equipment. The propulsion systems will be battery-operated. The main unit will be mounted astern in an independent capsule filled with oil in communciation with the outside water to ensure equal pressure within and without, as in the case of the bathyscaphe's gasoline-filled float. A second propulsion system with a vertical propeller, as is envisioned for the mesoscaphe, will enable the craft to hover and will aid in descent and ascent.

The Aluminaut, like conventional submarines, will be self-buoyant. It will have water-ballast tanks to enable it to submerge. It will also carry shot ballast, as the bathyscaphes do, while the solid-steel keel can be jettisoned in an emergency.

This first maneuverable abyssal submarine is expected to be ready sometime in the early 1960's. By enabling three men to remain deep beneath the surface for up to 100 hours, it will add greatly to the deep-sea explorer's capabilities, to say nothing of pointing the way to a new kind of military submersible. In this connection it should be noted that Delenk thinks his depth spheres could also be designed into a maneuverable submarine simply by joining several of them together and surrounding the whole assembly with a streamlined skin.

Besides aiding undersea exploration, bathyscaphes and their successors will enable scientists and engineers to supervise operations on the deep-sea bed that are controlled from ships at the surface. This will be a valuable supplement to television monitoring when engineering activities are carried on in deep water where individual divers cannot penetrate. Perhaps the first truly deep-sea engineering venture where this could be helpful is the National Academy of Science's project to drill a hole completely through the earth's crust to the Moho.

The Mohole

There is in the United States a whimsical organization of natural scientists called the American Miscellaneous Society, AMSOC for short. It has no constitution, no officers, and no formal roll of members. It began as a spoof at the scientific organization man. But the spoof has backfired and AMSOC, in spite of itself, has spawned an official committee of the National Academy of Sciences charged with one of the most challenging jobs its members have ever faced—drilling a hole in the bottom of the sea completely through the crust of the earth.

The story begins early in 1957. At that time AMSOC was just a mild satire on alphabetized scientific organizations. Two of its "members," Dr. Walter Munk of Scripps Institution of Oceanography and Dr. Harry Hess of Princeton University, had roughed out a scheme for answering some major scientific questions by drilling through the earth's crust to probe the rock beneath, an idea first suggested before World War II by Dr. Thomas A. Jaggar of the U. S. Geological Survey and National Park Service.

This was an ambitious proposal but quite within the reach of modern technology. AMSOC seemed the ideal outfit to push the project. Other geophysicists became interested, and the scheme was made an "official" AMSOC project during a breakfast at Munk's house in California early in 1957. Gordon Lill, chief of the geophysics branch of the Office of Naval Research, who was present on that occasion, was made chairman of the impromptu AMSOC committee.

Since the crust is up to twenty-five miles and more thick under the continents, it is out of the question to drill there. But under the oceans, where the crust is much thinner, drilling through the Mohorovičić Discontinuity into the top of the mantle is within the realm of feasibility. The proposal was appropriately dubbed "the Mohole."

The drilling could be expected to produce a variety of highly significant data that can be obtained in no other way. First, it would give geophysicists a direct sampling of the mantle and of the material in the Moho. This would shed light on a number of problems, such as radioactivity and heat flow, present geological structure, and the age and geological history of the earth. For the first time, geologists would have samples of various rocks taken in place from the deep crust and the mantle. Instead of studying combinations of minerals put together in the laboratory according to theory, they could work directly with the natural materials. The drilling would also enable them to measure exact thicknesses and to mark the boundaries of various layers within the crust, including the Moho itself. They could then check these against measurements made indirectly with seismic waves from explosions and earthquakes. In addition, the Mohole boring would yield a complete vertical sample of the sediments that are believed to have accumulated in at least some parts of the ocean since the beginning of geological time. It would be an unbroken record of the earth's past.

For reasons such as these, the AMSOC "members" were convinced the Mohole project would be a good thing. Then an element of competition entered the picture. At the September 1957 meeting of the International Union of Geodesy and Geophysics at Toronto, United States representatives introduced a resolution calling on all nations with drilling experience to consider setting up a Mohole project. The resolution was adopted. Soviet experts at the meeting immediately reported that they had the drilling equipment and were willing to tackle the job. Subsequently the Soviet Academy of Sciences announced the appointment of an official group headed by Mikail A. Lavrentyev to handle the project.

The prospect of Soviet competition spurred the AMSOC planners on. Meanwhile they had made a crucial discovery. In order to receive funds to carry out the project, they had to have a formal organizational status. They sought and obtained it from the National Academy of Sciences. Thus it was that the American Miscellaneous Society, founded to poke good-natured fun at organized science, saw its Mohole group transformed into an official organ of the Academy with the nicely alphabetized title of the AMSOC-Mohole Committee. Again, Gordon Lill was named chairman, with Willard Bascom as executive secretary.

With a grant from the National Science Foundation, the committee was authorized to make feasibility studies. The result was a report which called the Mohole project both "feasible and highly desirable." "We find," the report said, "that there are places both in the Atlantic and the Pacific basins where the total distance from the water surface to the mantle is less than 9.5 km. (about 31,000 feet). We also find that leading members of the oil industry believe that 'a 50,000 foot hole would be possible if there were any reason to drill it and if the best drilling equipment and technology were assembled.' [The deepest hole to date is 25,340 feet.]" Encouraged by this, the Council of the National Academy of Sciences—National Research Council subsequently gave the Lill committee full authority to organize and manage all the operations connected with the Mohole project.

Meanwhile Columbia University received $30,000 from the National Science Foundation to seek possible drilling sites. A four-ship expedition led by Columbia's research ship *Vema* has already surveyed a promising 25,000-square-mile area north of Puerto Rico. But there are other places to look at in the Pacific as well as in the Atlantic.

The Moholers are being fussy about selecting a site. Ideally it should be a place where the mantle is within reach and an adequate sediment sample can be obtained; reasonably close to a good port; and with favorable water and weather conditions. In the end, they may have to settle for less than the ideal. But even with all factors in their favor, the drilling job will be difficult. The most that can be said at this writing is that a great deal of practical research lies ahead.

The Mohole project will probably proceed in steps, developing and testing equipment and techniques as it progresses. A number of shallower holes may be drilled before the Mohole itself is tackled. Also, it is possible that different phases of the project will be accomplished at different sites. It may turn out, for example, that the best place to take the sediment core is not the best spot for drilling to the mantle. For the latter operation, the best site would probably be one that is geologically uncomplicated and where the Moho is close to the sea bottom. On the other hand, the sediment sample should be taken at a spot at which it looks as though sediment has collected from earliest times. The two sets of criteria may not be compatible.

All told, the AMSOC committee estimates that the project could be completed in three to four years at an over-all cost of about $15 million. Much of this cost will probably be borne by the federal government, but General Motors has given the project encouragement by offering to lease a million dollars' worth of diesel-electric equipment for one dollar. Lill acknowledges that a good deal of money is involved. But considering the expected scientific return and remembering the vast sums being poured into space research, he does not think this is "an overly ambitious scientific endeavor." After all, he observes, the bottom of the sea is at least as important to us as the far side of the moon.

Atomic Wastes into the Sea

Still another major new research project facing oceanographers is concerned with radioactive substances in the sea. Unlike the urge to explore extreme depths or drill through the ocean's bottom, this research is inspired more by practical necessity than by the drive to increase basic knowledge, although new knowledge will undoubtedly be gained. But radioactive wastes are increasing steadily as more and more nuclear reactors come into operation. In wondering where to dispose of this dangerous waste material, those concerned often look to the sea. But is this a safe place to dump it? Oceanographers are being pressed for an answer.

If releasing vast quantities of carbon dioxide into the atmosphere is man's biggest geophysical experiment, polluting the oceans with radioactive wastes could be his biggest geophysical mistake. Once introduced into the sea, radioactivity will be impossible to take out. If careful research to assess all possible hazards is not completed in advance, unwise practices could create a health hazard far worse than is associated with ordinary sewage disposal, for radioactivity spread by ocean currents would be a global menace. On the other hand, disposal carried out under known and carefully controlled conditions may one day be at least a partial solution to the problem of where and how to dispose of the waste products of the world's steadily growing number of nuclear reactors. But the questions of possible hazards should be asked and answered in the years immediately ahead if the knowledge is to be available when the need for it arises. That is why oceanographers consider the factors relevant to waste disposal to be priority items in their research planning.

Meanwhile there is no hazard foreseen with present dumping practices. As far as is known, all highly radioactive waste products are stored safely on land. Only mildly radioactive liquid wastes are discharged directly into the sea, while solids with relatively low radioactivity are sealed in containers and sunk in deep water. To date the United States has dumped only sealed containers at sea. However, a few European countries do discharge some mildly "hot" liquids. Great Britian probably has had the most experience along this line. The story of the establishment of her first liquid-discharge system at the Windscale plutonium factory near Calder Hall in Cumberland is a good example of the complexities that are involved in handling even very low levels of radioactivity.

Plutonium is an atomic explosive that is made in reactors and extracted from spent fuel elements by a special chemical plant. Windscale processes fuel elements from its own reactors and from other atomic "furnaces" in Britain's growing nuclear program. This activity produces some pretty "hot" waste material, most of which can be concentrated and stored in underground tanks for many years to come. But it also produces wastes with low radioactivity but such a vast bulk that storage would be awkward, if not impossible. These wastes include such things as wash water used to clean garments of atomic workers, the residue from the processing plant after the really "hot" wastes have been removed, and so forth. On the whole, the wastes are not very radioactive, but they do have to be disposed of. Dr. H. J. Dunster was given the job of determining how much of these wastes could safely go into the Irish Sea.

The circulation off the Cumberland coast is such that radioactive effluent (now dumped by pipeline three kilometers beyond the high-water mark) would simply drift back and forth off the coast in tidal currents. It would only slowly diffuse into the rest of the Irish Sea and eventually move out into the Atlantic. This means that any atomic sewage dumped there would stay around awhile, increasing the chances of local contamination. Dunster soon found that there were only three main potential hazards—contamination of food fish, edible seaweeds, and the beaches. These are the principal factors that now set the maximum limits on how much radioactive waste can safely be discharged

As operations have proceeded, Dunster and his associates have found that the sea bottom near the discharge pipe gets fairly "hot." The fish of that area are mainly bottom dwellers, like plaice, and they get some of the radioactive sediment in the digestive tract. But fortunately this

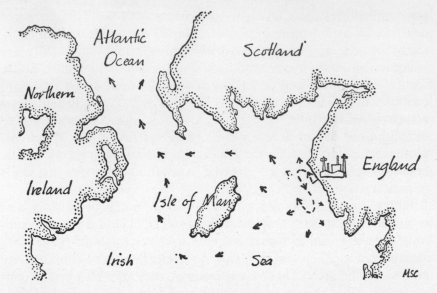

FIG. 54: *Radioactive discharge at Windscale: As indicated by arrows, the effluent tends to circulate back and forth off the Cumberland coast, only gradually dissipating into the North Atlantic.*

is passed out again and the digestive tract itself is removed in normal cleaning of the local catch. On the other hand, continuous monitoring of the commercial catch and of special catches made by Dunster's men themselves has shown a radioactive level well below what is considered safe in the skin and flesh of the fish.

As for the beaches, Dunster found that, while "hot" material does reach the bathing areas, the levels of radiation have stayed well within the conservative limits of safety he has established.

Then there are the seaweeds, specifically *Porphyra umbilicalis*, or purple laver. Commercially unimportant, they led Dunster farther afield than any other single factor. *Porphyra's* lettuce-leaf shape makes it a good collector of radioactivity. If it stayed on the sea bottom and did not pass on its radioactivity to food fishes, the scientists could forget about it. But this particular weed in this particular area is gathered by some of the residents as a secondary source of income. They gather it at the beach and take it by bicycle to the railroad station, where it is sold and shipped to South Wales. There it is eaten raw or cooked into a mash called "laver bread" that looks like very dirty creamed spinach.

Now a little bit of *Porphyra* or the laver bread made from it goes a long way. Most of those who eat it use it only occasionally as a condiment, often to cut the oily taste of fish. But Dunster found two people who ate an average of 75 grams of laver bread a day. If his survey uncovered two such avid seaweed fanciers, there probably are others. So Dunster set and maintains the maximum safe discharge limit at a level such that a person eating 75 grams of seaweed a day will be perfectly safe. Thus, in a sense, two Welshmen with a taste for seaweed set the safety standards for the Windscale discharge. This is a good example of the subtle secondary effects that have to be investigated before dumping atomic wastes into the sea.

As far as the Windscale type of dumping is concerned and under the known circumstances of the waters off Britain, Dunster says that he is satisfied that safe monitoring procedures have been established. Windscale has been discharging its effluent for several years without mishap. Radioactive levels have stayed within safe limits. Other installations in Britain already are or may soon be discharging wastes of their own.

Dunster points out that in setting the safety standards for these discharges he has stern mentors in the independent authorities that must give approval before any discharge can begin. In England these are the Minister of Agriculture, Fisheries, and Food and the Minister of Housing and Local Government. In Scotland it is the Secretary of State for Scotland. This is more than just a matter of the government regulating itself. These authorities are jealous of their prerogatives and motivated by considerations different from those of the atomic energy people. If they are not satisfied as to the safety of what is being done, they can stop or cut down the waste disposal at any time, regardless of how awkward or expensive this would be for the Atomic Energy Authority.

As far as Britain is concerned, this seems a tight system of checks and balances that, coupled with an extensive monitoring program, will keep atomic discharges within safe limits. Dunster readily acknowledges that this only begs the larger question of international regulation as the waste-disposal problem grows.

Britain asked no other nation's leave when it started discharging the Windscale wastes. Since Britain itself would probably be the first to suffer if something went wrong, one can have some confidence in its safety standards at this time. But will this continue to be the case as waste disposal increases over the years? And as more and more countries follow suit, can safety regulation be left to the individual nations?

K

The question stirred wide interest at the United Nations "atoms for peace" conference held at Geneva in 1958. Dutch delegates to the conference formally called on western European nations to set up internationally binding regulations and safety standards in the atomic energy field with special provision for marine disposal. The Dutch are themselves discharging some radioactive effluents into the North Sea. As of this writing, little has come of the Dutch proposal. It is probably only a matter of time, however, before international regulations of some sort are established for ocean disposal of low-level wastes. The need for such regulations is obvious and, even though much specific research remains to be done, there is enough knowledge at hand to begin drafting them.

This is quite separate from the larger question of dumping concentrated "hot" wastes into the deep ocean. Here the need is for more basic scientific knowledge before it will be appropriate to talk about regulation, except perhaps in the form of an interim ban on marine disposal. Some atomic energy experts think the need for such disposal may never arrive. In hearings before the House Merchant Marine and Fisheries Subcommittee in July 1959, United States Atomic Energy Commission representatives said that economic factors are against waste disposal at sea. It is expensive to handle and ship heavily shielded containers of "hot" materials. Storage on land seems to be the most economical method for many years in the future.

On the other hand, it is advisable to be prepared if the need ever should arise. The Brown committee of the National Academy of Sciences notes in this connection that countries with small land areas and large populations may not find land storage such an attractive method, especially if they have ready access to the sea. Also, should a nuclear war ever come, the ocean fisheries may become a major source of uncontaminated food. Fallout from nuclear weapons might be heavy over the land. But in the sea it would tend to be dispersed, while the water would effectively shield organisms from all but the radioactivity in their immediate vicinity. Thus in the event of war it would be important to know just how radioactivity is dispersed in the oceans and how it enters marine food chains. This is an added reason for carrying out the necessary research now.

Since the ocean waters tend to be stratified, some oceanographers think that it would probably be safe to dump properly contained wastes on the ocean floor where it is a mile or more deep. The Brown report notes that vertical and horizontal deep currents are thought to be sluggish, so that it might take decades or even centuries for any escaped

radioactivity to reach the upper water layers where it would be dangerous. But this is only conjecture based on inadequate knowledge. Other
oceanographers are not at all certain that escaped radioactivity would
be confined to deep water. The Soviets in particular vigorously oppose
any suggestion of marine disposal for high-level wastes. They point out
that discoveries such as the countercurrent under the Gulf Stream cast
doubt on the notion that water movements are sluggish. Furthermore,
they say that their own researches indicate significant deep-water movements even at the bottoms of Pacific trenches.

Then too, there are biological factors to consider. Many animals undergo extensive vertical migrations. They might concentrate radioactive substances sufficiently to be a major channel for redistributing
radioactivity released at great depths. This would be an especial hazard
if these animals were part of the food supply for others that in turn
were fished by man. Another unknown but potentially significant factor
is the ability of many marine organisms, including some of those of
interest to man, to concentrate elements that are present in such dilute
form that they are hard to find by chemical analysis of sea water. If
radioactive elements are concentrated in this way, they would be
a hazard even if their concentration in the sea were very slight. Marine
biologists presently have hardly any relevant information with which
to assess these various factors.

These, then, are the kinds of questions the oceanographers are seeking to answer: Where and how fast would radioactivity spread if
introduced into various parts of the sea? How long do various radioactive elements remain in the water before being removed by plants and
animals or by processes that entrap them in the sediments? How would
radioactivity enter the cycles of marine life? It will take many different
lines of research to answer these questions. Perhaps one of the most
direct approaches would be the suggestion of the Brown committee to
introduce substantial, but still safe, amounts of radioactive elements
into the sea and follow their courses around the world.

However it is handled, the research relevant to waste disposal will
have aspects that have to be carried out on an international scale and
will involve investigations that are of fundamental importance to
oceanographic science in general. The Brown committee stresses this
in outlining its proposed ten-year program for oceanographic research
by the United States. Oceanographers of many other countries have
expressed similar views, even though they may not have a definite national research program in hand. Perhaps a United Nations program

will be launched. Research related to waste disposal also has an element of necessity. Because of this and because it raises such broad fundamental questions, the waste-disposal issue is one of the major factors spurring interest in ocean science both on the national and international levels. But this interest must be coupled with a capability among oceanographers to act. This they cannot do until they are adequately equipped with the necessary tools, especially research ships.

The Need for Ships

At present there is only one first-rate oceanographic fleet in the world, that of the Soviet Union. It includes at least seven research ships of from 1,500 to 6,000 tons displacement, two 12,000-ton icebreakers that carry on oceanographic research as a sideline, and a submarine. During the IGY, more than 30 Soviet ships were put on special assignment, of which 14 were large ocean-going vessels that explored the major oceans. This fleet and the large research effort it represents are a challenge to the rest of the world, especially to the United States.

By way of comparison, the Brown committee says that American research ships "are inadequate for the job which must be done. Most of the ships are old and outdated. Many are obsolete and should be replaced by ships of modern design." The United States has at present about 45 research ships. All are small. None even approaches the size of the larger Soviet vessels. Many are reconditioned military ships such as navy tugs. The comparable total of all Soviet research ships, large and small, is probably well over a hundred. As Professor Victor P. Petrov of the U. S. Naval Postgraduate System observes in reviewing Soviet reports of their facilities, "If we do not step up our own efforts in this field, the Soviet Union may soon become the world leader in oceanographic research . . ." Let's take a brief look at some of the Soviet vessels.

The flagship of the Soviet IGY fleet was the 5,500-ton *Vitiaz*. She is a converted diesel-powered freighter that originally had 12 passenger cabins. Now she can accommodate 73 scientists and technicians plus a 64-man crew and has cabins for from one to four persons. The *Vitiaz*, which has been in the research fleet since 1949, can range 11,000 nautical miles, or 66 days at full speed. Her 13 laboratories give ample room for scientists to work during extended expeditions.

Or consider the *Mikhail Lomonosov*, the most modern ship in the world constructed specifically for research. Built in East Germany, she was completed and assigned to the Marine Geophysical Institute in August 1957. This ship has 16 laboratories and can accommodate up to 65 scientists. Such spacious accommodations are an unknown luxury on American research ships. (See Plate 7.)

The Soviets are also operating a research submarine, the *Severianka*. She was overhauled and specially rebuilt for her new duties and transferred from the Soviet Navy to the All-Union Research Institute for the Study of Fisheries and Oceanography at the end of 1958. This remarkable vessel has portholes protected by thick glass, with search-lights so placed that observers at the portholes can switch them on or off at will to watch the scene outside. There are also movie and still cameras by each porthole, enabling the observers to take pictures at will, while a television camera in the bow gives a view ahead. Echo sounders ranging in all directions help locate schools of fish and other objects for study. The *Severianka* can cruise at various depths, observing, measuring, and sampling, or it can lie on or near a relatively shallow bottom to take sediment samples. She often cruises with fishing fleets, observing the behavior of the fish and the operation of the fishing gear. Even though she has been operating only for a short time, the Soviets already credit the *Severianka* with gathering information for the design of improved and more efficient trawls.

One could continue listing components of Russia's scientific fleet, but those already described should suffice to show she has a substantial and vigorous oceanographic program. The United States, says the Brown committee, cannot afford to do less.

The $651,410,000 program recommended by the Brown committee, which at this writing is being seriously considered by Congress, is the minimum it considers necessary to enable the United States to meet the oceanographic challenge of the times. It would be paid for primarily by the Navy and the National Science Foundation, with a few other agencies contributing. Details of the program embrace all aspects of ocean research, but its principal recommendations can be summed up as follows:

First, basic research in oceanography should be at least doubled during the next decade. Because the federal government is by far the largest source of funds, this would mean more than a doubling of government monetary support.

Secondly, such increased basic research should be accompanied by a vigorous program of three-dimensional ocean-wide surveys to at least double the present effort in that field.

K*

Finally, the government should greatly increase its support of applied marine science, especially in military fields, in exploration and exploitation of food and mineral resources, and in aspects related to radioactivity.

Such an expanded program would call for more and better ships. The motley fleet with which American oceanographers have had to "make do" simply is not adequate for the job. Yet research ships are to oceanographers what major tools such as cyclotrons and nuclear reactors are to physicists—expensive items of hardware without which they cannot carry out their researches. To put American oceanographers more effectively in business, the Brown committee has called for increasing the research fleet from its present size of 45 ships to 85 ships. Taking account of ships that will be retired during the next decade, this means building about 70 new vessels of various sizes from 500 to 2,000 tons displacement. The committee emphatically advises against trying to convert ships designed for other purposes and further recommends that steps be taken to ensure that the research vessels are adequately backed up by shore facilities and laboratories to make the most of their findings. Research submarines capable of breaking into and out of Arctic ice, manned ocean-going platforms that could be anchored and stabilized like buoys, and a mother ship for the bathyscaphe *Trieste* are among the other research vehicles suggested.

The cost of this shipbuilding program would be shared by several agencies, including the Navy, Coast and Geodetic Survey, Maritime Administration, National Science Foundation, and the Bureau of Fisheries. For its part, the Navy has already announced a $58,600,000 program to build 18 research ships by mid-1968. Five of these will displace 2,000 to 3,000 tons. This announcement was made in the light of the Brown committee report and is related to its recommended program.

The National Science Foundation has also begun to take action. A grant of $3,000,000 was announced November 25, 1959, to finance a successor to Woods Hole's *Atlantis* (see Plate 8), the only American ship built specifically for oceanographic research, which is being retired. The new ship will have 1,040 ton's displacement, an over-all length of 175 feet, a beam of 36 feet, and an operating range of 7,500 miles at a cruising speed of 12 knots.

With one eye on potential peaceful benefits and the other on military needs, the Brown committee submitted its report with the warning that "action on a scale appreciably less than that recommended will jeopardize the position of oceanography in the United States relative to the position of the science in other nations, thereby accentuating serious military and political dangers and placing the nation at a disadvantage in the future use of the resources of the sea." There is every indication that this warning is being heeded. Thus the spur of cold-war competition has joined with the necessities of the atomic age and a growing awareness of the untapped wealth of the sea to bring about a stronger motivation for public support of oceanographic research than has ever before existed in the United States. This motivation is likely to be felt in other maritime countries as well, bringing about a revitalization of oceanography throughout the world.

Meanwhile there is an aspect of the new oceanography about which men have scarcely begun to think. Yet it could overshadow all other considerations. It is the question of how the ocean's resources are to be distributed among the nations. Dr. Columbus Iselin pointed this out at the close of the International Oceanographic Congress in 1959. After noting that oceanographers can foresee a number of ways in which the oceans will be exploited, especially in the realm of food production, he observed that "it is high time . . . men began to think seriously how the potential vast resources of the ocean can be divided on an equitable basis." This is the same question that was raised at the end of the last chapter in connection with the possibility of mining manganese nodules from the deep-sea bed. In the long run, it is probably the biggest unanswered question raised by oceanographic research today. Iselin said that, in his judgment, economic, social, and political problems involved in serious exploitation of the oceans seem "more formidable than the remaining unsolved scientific problems."

Much of the increasing governmental interest in oceanography may have its roots in the cold war. But the questions raised by oceanographic research transcend national interest. Some are scientific. Others, as Iselin points out, will require the wisdom of statesmen to resolve. It is the special faith of all the oceanographers with whom I have talked in the course of writing this book that the questions will be resolved and that the era of expanded exploration they are entering upon will bring great practical benefits to all mankind.

SUGGESTIONS FOR FURTHER READING

GENERAL OCEANOGRAPHY

Founders of Oceanography and Their Work by Sir William A. Herdman. (London: Edwin Arnold & Co. 1923. 340 pp.)

> A history of oceanography in terms of the lives of the foremost scientists in the field in the nineteenth to early twentieth century.

The Sea around Us by Rachel Carson. (London: Staples Press. 1951. 230 pp.)

> The famous best seller concerning many of the basic questions and theories about the oceans—a literary gem.

The Edge of the Sea by Rachel Carson. (London: Staples Press. 1955. 276 pp.)

> Natural history of the shore line, illustrated by the accurate and beautiful drawings of Bob Hines.

The Sea and Its Mysteries by John S. Colman. (London: G. Bell & Sons,Ltd. 1953. 285 pp.)

> A short account of ocean science for the layman by a leading British oceanographer.

The Sea for Sam by W. Maxwell Reed and Wilfred S. Bronson. (New York: Harcourt, Brace and Company. 1960. 243 pp.)

> A completely revised and updated edition of a classic book on all phases of ocean science for young teenagers.

BIOLOGY

The Life in the Sea by Ralph Buchsbaum. Condon Lectures [July 1955], Oregon State System of Higher Education, Eugene, Oregon. 1958. 101 pp.

> A paperback volume of lectures giving the essential points of natural history in the oceans.

Creatures of the Deep by Klaus Guenther and Kurt Deckert. (London: Allen and Unwin Ltd. 1956. 222 pp.)

A detailed and readable account of the animals of the deep.

The Open Sea—Its Natural History: The World of Plankton by Sir Alister C. Hardy. (London: William Collins and Sons Ltd. 1956. 335 pp.)

The Open Sea—Its Natural History: Fish & Fisheries, Part II (Ibid. 1959. 322 pp.)

The natural history of both fields by the renowned Oxford biologist. His water-colour illustrations add greatly to the reader's enjoyment.

Larval Forms and Other Zoological Verses by Walter Garstang. (Oxford: Basil Blackwell. 1951. 85 pp.)

Mnemonic verse setting forth Garstang's theory of evolution by the young of the species—larval stages—and other subjects.

Old Fourlegs: The Story of the Coelacanth by J. L. B. Smith. (London: Longmans, Green and Co. Ltd. 1956. 260 pp.)

The account of the discovery of the coelacanth and subsequent search for other live specimens.

GEOLOGY

The Earth beneath the Sea by Francis P. Shepard. (London: Oxford University Press. 1960. 275 pp.)

An up-to-date, readable account of marine geology by one of the pioneers in the field. Many lucid illustrations.

TIDES

Ebb and Flow: The Tides of Earth, Air, and Water by Albert Defant. (London: Mayflower Publishing Co. Ltd. 1959. 121 pp.)

A concise semi-popular volume discussing theories and mechanisms of tides.

RESOURCES

The Sun, the Sea, and Tomorrow: Potential Sources of Food, Energy, and Minerals from the Sea by Frederick George Walton Smith. (London. Hurst and Blackett Ltd. 1955. 210 pp.)

A survey of food and mineral resources in the ocean.

EXPLORATION

The Galathea Deep Sea Expedition edited by Anton F. Bruun. (London: George Allen and Unwin Ltd. 1956. 296.pp.)

A collection of articles by members of the Galathea cruise of 1950–52.

Exploring the Deep Pacific by Helen Raitt. (New York: W. W. Norton & Co. 1956. 272 pp.)

A woman's (and layman's) view of an oceanographic voyage, with much pertinent information on theories, instruments, and data gathering at sea.

BATHYSCAPHES

In Balloon and Bathyscaphe by Auguste Piccard. (London: Cassell and Co. Ltd. 1956. 192 pp.)

Piccard's account of the invention and operation of the bathyscaphe. Technical data on the bathyscaphes.

2,000 *Fathoms Down* by Lt. Cmdr. Georges S. Houot and Lt. Pierre Henri Willm. (London: Hamish Hamilton Ltd. and Rupert Hart-Davis Ltd. 1955. 192 pp.)

An account of the *F.N.R.S.* 2 and *F.N.R.S.* 3. Technical data on the bathyscaphes.

Index